Aldehydes—
Photometric Analysis

THE ANALYSIS OF ORGANIC MATERIALS

An International Series of Monographs

edited by R. BELCHER and D. M. W. ANDERSON

Aldehydes — Photometric Analysis

Volume 3

EUGENE SAWICKI
and
CAROLE R. SAWICKI

Raleigh,
North Carolina,
U.S.A.

1976

 Academic Press
London · New York · San Francisco

A Subsidiary of Harcourt Brace Jovanovich, Publishers

ACADEMIC PRESS INC. (LONDON) LTD.
24/28 Oval Road,
London NW1

United States Edition published by
ACADEMIC PRESS INC.
111 Fifth Avenue
New York, New York 10003

Library of Congress Catalog Card Number: 75-11373
ISBN: 0-12-620503-5

Printed in Great Britain by
Page Bros (Norwich) Ltd, Norwich

PREFACE

This is the first of a set of five volumes (volumes 3–7 of the Series "Alde-hydes—Photometric Analysis") which will discuss the many aspects of (a) the photometric analysis of precursors through their derived aldehydes and (b) the formation of aldehydes through a variety of reactions, which in the future could be of increased importance in developing methods of analysis for many aldehyde precursors. The physiological and environmental importance of many of these precursors and of many exogenous and endo-genous aldehyde-forming reactions are discussed in some detail, since this knowledge could be exceedingly useful in developing new methods of analysis and in understanding the rôle that these precursors and their aldehyde-forming reactions play in the environment and in living tissue.

An attempt has been made to cover the literature sufficiently well to give a balanced presentation. Wherever possible, complete references are presented to give credit to the innovators of the many techniques, pro-cedures, ideas, and instruments discussed in these volumes. Since the vast literature is so difficult to cover thoroughly, we recognize that some excellent work may have been omitted inadvertantly. Forgive us for our short-comings in this respect.

Although volumes 3–7 of this Series will be concerned only with the formation and photometric analysis of aldehydes, it should be stressed very strongly that much of the material could be used in the development of useful gas chromatographic, high performance liquid chromatographic, and mass spectrometric methods of analysis.

This volume considers the background and essential practical details of colorimetric, fluorimetric, and phosphorimetric methods of analysis for more than 30 aldehydes, ranging from acetaldehyde through p-anisaldehyde, derived from hundreds of precursors, for which a large number of detailed procedures have been given.

Raleigh, N.C.   EUGENE SAWICKI
December 1974   CAROLE·R. SAWICKI

ACKNOWLEDGEMENTS

We wish to thank the following editors and authors for permission to use the following illustrations which previously appeared in print: Editor, *Analytical Chemistry*, Aliphatic Aldehydes, Figs 11 (107), 12 (54), 16 (67), 18 (146), 20 (72); Total Aldehydes, Fig. 35 (14); Cinnamaldehyde, Fig. 48 (10); Furfural, Fig. 6 (79); Glyoxal, Fig. 14 (4); and 5-Hydroxymethylfurfural, Fig. 36 (3); Editor, *Journal of Agricultural and Food Chemistry*, Furfural, Fig. 2, (95); Malonaldehyde, Figs 46 and 47 (4); Editor, *Journal of the Association of Official Agricultural Chemists*, Pyridoxal, Fig. 81 (73); Editor, *Journal of the Chemical Society of Japan*, Malonaldehyde, Figs 44 and 45 (2); Editor, *Journal of Vitaminology*, Pyridoxal, Fig. 80 (32); Editor, *Analytical Biochemistry*, Glyoxylate, Figs 29 (29), 32 (33), and 33 (34); Pyridoxal-5-phosphate, Figs 83 (29), 84 and 85 (36), and 86 (43); Streptomycin, Fig. 97 (9); National Research Council of Canada, 4-Dimethylaminobenzaldehyde, Fig. 51 (1); Editor, *Applied Microbiology*, Formaldehyde, Fig. 61 (92); Editor, *Journal of the American Oil Chemists Society* Aliphatic Aldehydes, Fig. 25 (231); Editor, *Journal of Pharmaceutical Sciences*, Chloral, Fig. 47 (13); Editor, *Enzymologia*, Pyridoxal phosphate, Figs 87 and 88 (41); Editor, *Chemische Berichte*, 5-Hydroxymethylfurfural, Fig. 38 (53); Editor, *Journal of the American Chemical Society*, Pyridoxal, Fig. 72 (1); Editor, *Histochemistry and Cytochemistry*, Glutaraldehyde, Fig. 7 (1); Editor, *Acta Endocrinology*, Aldosterone, Fig. 43 (37); Editor, *The Analyst*, Pyridoxal, Fig. 73 (2); Editor, *Microchemical Journal*, Glyoxal, Fig. 16 (26), and Glyoxals, Figs 23 and 34 (3); Elsevier Scientific Publishing Company, *Analytica Chimica Acta*, 5-Hydroxymethylfurfural, Figs 37 (71) and 40 (54); *Journal of Chromatography*, Aliphatic Aldehydes, Fig. 17 (69); Oxybenzaldehydes, Fig. 55 (37); Editor, *Spectrochimica Acta*, Aliphatic Aldehydes, Fig. 15 (100); Editor, *Photochemistry and Photobiology*, Retinal, Figs 91 (23) and 92 (45); and The American Society of Biological Chemists, Inc., *Journal of Biological Chemistry*, Total Aldehydes, Figs 36, 37 and 38 (40), and Glyoxylate, Fig. 27 (8).

CONTENTS

A*

To my parents with love:
When I read and hear of the injustice, crime, corruption, lies, atrocities, greed, hazardous chemicals and death which appear to engulf us, I despair. But then I think of your lifetime wholeheartedly spent in love, loyalty, honesty, decency, and beauty, life becomes something extraordinarily beautiful, worthwhile and meaningful enough to pass on to the little ones.

1. ACETALDEHYDE, PRECURSORS

I. INTRODUCTION

Since sensitive methods of analysis are available for the determination of acetaldehyde, the obvious procedure is to apply these to the analysis of compounds from which acetaldehyde can be derived directly from the test substance or indirectly from the reagent. We will be concerned mainly with the former type, as shown by numerous examples in Table 1.[1-153] This table lists a large variety of compounds from which acetaldehyde can be derived. Most of the basic precursor structures are shown in Table 2.

As shown in Table 1, the formation of acetaldehyde involves the following reactions: decarboxylation, dehydration, disproportionation, hydrolysis, Lossen rearrangement, oxidation, oxidative dealkylation, oxidative de-amination, reduction and tautomerism. Examples are: (a) the decarboxylation of pyruvate to acetaldehyde with the help of pyruvate decarboxylase,[128] (b) the dehydration of ethyleneglycol to acetaldehyde, e.g.

$$HO-CH_2-CH_2OH \xrightarrow{H^+} CH_2{=}CHOH \rightarrow CH_3CHO,$$

(c) the disproportionation of 1-nitroethanol to the aldehyde and nitrite[113] or of β-hydroxyethylamines to the aldehyde,[73, 74] e.g.

$$R_2NCH_2CH_2OH + ClCH_2COONa$$

$$\Delta \left\downarrow\right. MeOCH_2CH_2OMe$$

$$R_2N^+(CH_2CH_2OH)CH_2COO^- + NaCl$$

$$\left\downarrow\right. \Delta$$

$$R_2N^+HCH_2COO^- + CH_3CHO,$$

1

Table 1. Formation of acetaldehyde from precursors

Precursor	Reagent[a]	Reactions[b]	Ref.
Acetal	Acid	H during detn	1
Acetoin	Periodate	(O)	2
Acetoin	hv	IMR	3
Acetylcholine	KBH_4 → Alcohol dehydrogenase	(H) → (O)	4–9
Alanine	Ninhydrin	OD → DC	10–15
Alanine	Nitrite → Permanganate	OD → DC	16
Alanine	Nitrite → Lead tetracetate	OD → DC	17
Alanine	Nitrite → Ceric sulphate	OD → DC	18–19
Alanine	Nitrite → H_2SO_4	OD → DC	20
Alanine	Hypochlorite	OD → DC	21
Alanine	Isatin	OD → DC	22
Aliphatic aldehydes	Ozone	β-cleavage	23–25
2-Alkenes	10% aq H_2SO_4	(O)	26
Alkyl vinyl ethers	NH_2OH → DNF → OH^- → H^+	H	27
Aspartyl residues in gelatin		Oxim. → DNP → LR → H → DC[c]	
Azoethane	10% aq H_2SO_4	Taut → H[d]	28
Bis-(α-chloroethyl)ether	Water	H	29
2,3-Butanediol	Periodate	(O)	30, 31
trans-2-Butene	Ozone	(O)	32, 33
Citral	OH^-	H[e]	34
Cysteine	Ninhydrin	Aq. soln boiled[f]	35
6-Deoxyhexoses[g]	Periodate	(O)	36–40
2-Deoxy-D-ribose-5-phosphate	Deoxyriboaldolase[h]	DP	41, 42
Diethylamine	$K_3Fe(CN)_6$ and $Na_2Fe(CN)_5NO$	(O)	43
1,1-Diethylhydrazine	$HgSO_4$ + aq H_2SO_4	(ODk)	44
1,2-Diethylhydrazine	$HgSO_4$ + aq H_2SO_4	(O) → Taut → H[d]	28
Di-isobutylacetal	aq H_2SO_4	H	26
Ephedrine	Periodate	(O)	45–48

Ephedrine	Bismuthate	(O)	49
Ethanol	NAD + Alcohol dehydrogenase	(O)	50–55
Ethanol	NADP + Alcohol dehydrogenase	(O)	56, 57
Ethanol	AAD + Alcohol dehydrogenase	(O)	58
Ethanol	Ferrous sulphate + H_2O_2	(O)	59
Ethanol	Chromate	(O)	60–61
Ethanol	Permanganate	(O)	62
Ethanol	Ruthenium tetroxide	(O)	63
Ethoxy compounds	Chromate	(O)	64
Ethylamines	Benzoyl peroxide	DH	64
Ethylene derivatives	$ZnCl_2$ at 230–250°	IMR	65
Ethylene oxide	R_3N		66
Ethylidene cyclohexane	Ozone → heat	(O)	67
Fructose diphosphate	Aldolase → H_2SO_4 [i]	DP → (O) → DC	68
Fucose [j]	Periodate	(O)	36–40, 69–71
1,2-Heptadiene	Ozone	(O)	72
all-trans-2,4-Hexadiene	Ozone	(O)	72
1,2-Hexadiene	Ozone	(O)	72
β-Hydroxyethylamines	Sodium chloroacetate	DP	73, 74
Lactic acid	Periodate		18
Lactic acid	Hot H_2SO_4	(O) → DC	75–79
Lactic acid	Permanganate	(O) → DC	13, 80–86
Lactic acid	Ceric sulphate	(O) → DC	17, 87–93
Lactic acid	Ceric sulphate, $CuSO_4$ + H_2SO_4	(O) → DC	94
Lactic acid	$CuSO_4$ + H_2SO_4	(O) → DC	95–109
2-Methyl-1,3-dioxolane	H^+	H	110
Muramic acid [k]	$CuSO_4$ + H_2SO_4	H → (O) → DC	106, 111
Nitroethane	OH^- → H_2SO_4	Taut → H	112
1-Nitroethanol	OH^-	DP	113
trans-2-Octene	Ozone	(O)	72
Paraldehyde	Acid	DP	114, 115
1,2-Pentadiene	Ozone	(O)	72
2-Pentyne	Ozone	(O)	72

Table 1—*continued*

Precursor	Reagent[a]	Reactions[b]	Ref.
1-Phenyl-3,3-diethyltriazene	10% aq. H_2SO_4 + Heat	(O) → H	116
Polyoxyethylene compounds	H_3PO_4 + Heat	H → DH	117
Pregnanetriol[l]	Periodate	(O)	118
1,2-Propanediol	Periodate[m]	(O)	36, 119–123
1,2-Propanediol	Enzyme	(O)	124
Propenyl compounds	Benzoyl peroxide	(O)	125
Propylenediamines	Persulphate	(O)	126
1-(3-Pyridyl)-3,3-diethyltriazene	10% aq. H_2SO_4 + Heat	(O)	116
Pyruvic acid	Zn—Cu → H_2SO_4	(H) → (O)	127
Pyruvic acid	Pyruvate decarboxylase	DC	31, 128
Pyruvic acid	Acid	DP	129, 130
Sesamex	H^+	H[n]	26
Steroids, C(OH)—CHOH—CH_3 type[o]	Periodate[p]	(O)	118, 131–135
Steroids, C(OH)—CO—CH_3 type[q]	KBH_4 → Periodate	(H) → (O)	135–136
Steroid glucuronides	Glucuronidase → (KBH_4) → Periodate	H → [(H)] → (O)	137, 138
Tetrahydrofuran	hv	DP	139
Threonine	Permanganate[r]	(O)	40
Threonine	Lead tetracetate[n]	(O)	140
Threonine	Threonine aldolase	DP	141, 142
Threonine	Periodate	(O)	5, 143–150
Triose phosphates	H_2SO_4 and heat[n]	(O)	151
Vinyl acetate	OH^-[s]	H → Taut	152
Vinyl oleate	OH^-[s]	H → Taut	153

[a] DNF = 2,4-dinitrofluorobenzene, OH^- = alkali, H^+ = aqueous acid, hν = irradiation.

[b] H = hydrolysis, (O) = oxidation, (H) = reduction, OD = oxidative deamination, D = deamination, Oxim = oximation, DNP = 2,4-dinitrophenylation, LR = Lossen rearrangement, DC = decarboxylation, Taut = tautomerism, DP = disproportionation, DH = dehydration, ODk = oxidative dealkylation, IMR = intramolecular rearrangement.

[c] MBTH used to determine acetaldehyde.

[d] 100% yield of acetaldehyde.

[e] Poor yield of acetaldehyde.

[f] H_2S and mercaptoacetaldehyde also produced.

[g] Various analogous CH_3CHOH-compounds which were determined similarly include fucose, rhamnose, D-fucosamine, L-fuculose *o*-nitrophenylhydrazone, colitose or 3-deoxy-2-fucose and 3-O-methyl-L-fucose.

[h] 2-Deoxy-D-ribose-5-phosphate acetaldehyde lyase, 4.1.2.4.

[i] 4-Phenylphenol used to determine acetaldehyde.

[j] See 6-deoxyhexoses.

[k] 3-O-(Carboxymethyl)-D-glucosamine.

[l] See Steroids in this Table.

[m] Determined as iodoform at 347 nm after reaction of acetaldehyde with alkaline iodine[119] and as acetaldehyde after distillation at 277 nm.[120]

[n] Followed by determination with 4-phenylphenol.

[o] 21-Deoxy-20,17-diol steroids which give acetaldehyde include 3-keto-Δ^4-pregnene-17α,20β-diol,[133] 3-keto-Δ^4-pregnene-16α,17α,20β-triol,[133] 5β-pregnane-3α, 11β,17α,20α-tetrol,[134] 3α,17α,20α-trihydroxy-5β-pregnan-11-one and its 20β-analog[132, 134] 5β-pregn-5-ene-3β,17α,20α-triol and its 3α-analog,[134] and 5α-pregnane-3α,17α,20α-triol and its 5β-analog.[132, 134]

[p] In some cases followed by characterization with sodium nitroprusside and piperidine[133] or estimation with 4-phenylphenol[132] on paper chromatograms.

[q] 21-Deoxy-20,17-ketols which give positive results include 17α-hydroxyprogesterone, and 16α,17α-dihydroxyprogesterone.

[r] Followed by determination with semicarbazide.

[s] Followed by determination with N-hydroxybenzenesulfonamide and Fe^{3+} at 470 nm.

Table 2. Basic acetaldehyde precursor structures

$$CH_3CH\begin{matrix} \diagup X \\ \diagdown X \end{matrix} ,$$

where X can be any combination of O, S, or N.

$CH_3—CH(OH)—X$,
    where X = H, CH(OH)R, CO—R, CH(NHR)R′, COOH, NO_2.

$CH_3CH(NHR)X$,
    where R = H, alkyl or aryl and X = H, CH(OH)R″, CH(NHR″) R‴, COR″, COOH.

$CH_3CH{=}X$,
    where X = NR, CR_2.

$CH{=}CH_2—OX$
    where X = acyl, alkyl, or aryl groups.

$CH_3CH_2—X$,
    where X = NH_2, NHEt, NO_2, OR.

$XOCH_2CH_2OX$,
    where X = H or alkyl.

$CH_3C{\equiv}C—X$,
    where X = H, alkyl, or aryl.

$CH_3CH_2—N{=}N—X$,
    where X = alkyl.

$CH_3CH_2—NX—NH_2$,
    where X = alkyl, especially ethyl.

$CH_3CH_2—NH—NH—X$,
    where X = alkyl, especially ethyl.

$Ar—N{=}N—NEt_2$,
    where Ar = aryl or hetero aryl.

$XCH_2COCOOH$,
    where X = H or COOH.

(d) the hydrolysis of acetal to the aldehyde and alcohol,[26] (e) the Lossen rearrangement of aspartyl residues in protein,[27] e.g.

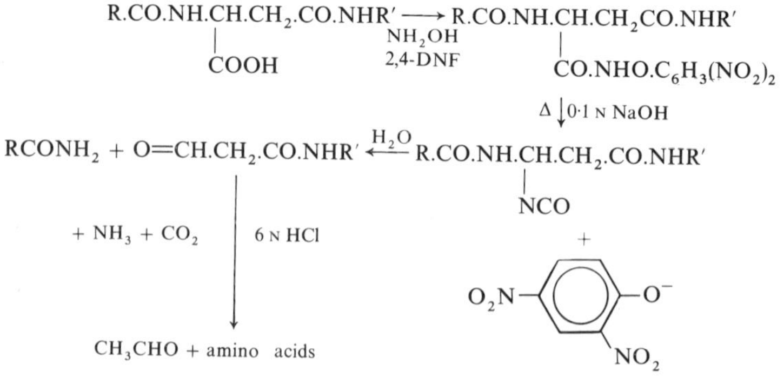

$$R.CO.NH.CH.CH_2.CO.NHR' \xrightarrow[\substack{NH_2OH \\ 2,4\text{-}DNF}]{} R.CO.NH.CH.CH_2.CO.NHR'$$

with COOH on the first structure and $CO.NHO.C_6H_3(NO_2)_2$ on the second.

$$\Delta \downarrow \text{0·1 N NaOH}$$

$$RCONH_2 + O{=}CH.CH_2.CO.NHR' \xleftarrow{H_2O} R.CO.NH.CH.CH_2.CO.NHR'$$

with NCO on the structure.

+ NH_3 + CO_2 | 6 N HCl

CH_3CHO + amino acids

$$O_2N{-}\langle\bigcirc\rangle{-}O^-$$
with + above and NO_2 below.

(f) the oxidation of fucose to acetaldehyde,[36-40, 69-71] (g) oxidative dealkylation of 1,1-diethylhydrazine[44] which involves oxidation by mercuric sulphate followed by tautomerism and then hydrolysis to the aldehyde e.g.

$$CH_3.CH_2 \diagdown N-N^+H_3 \xrightarrow{(O)} CH_3.CH_2 \diagdown N^+=NH$$
$$CH_3.CH_2 \diagup \qquad\qquad CH_3.CH_2 \diagup$$

$$\downarrow$$

$$CH_3.CH_2 \diagdown N-NH_2 \xleftarrow{H_2O} CH_3.CH_2 \diagdown N^+-NH_2$$
$$H \diagup \qquad\qquad CH_3.CH \diagup\!\!\!/$$

$$+$$

$$CH_3CHO,$$

(h) the oxidative deamination of alanine to the aldehyde,[16-20] e.g.,

$$CH_3.CH(NH_2).COOH \xrightarrow{NO_2^-} CH_3.CH(OH).COOH$$
$$\downarrow (O)$$
$$CH_3CHO + CO_2 \leftarrow CH_3.CO.COOH,$$

(i) reduction (followed by decarboxylation) of pyruvic acid,[127] (j) the tautomerism of azoethane followed by its hydrolysis to the aldehyde,[28] e.g.,

$$CH_3CH_2-N=N-CH_2CH_3 \xrightarrow{H^+} CH_3CH_2-\overset{H}{N}-N=CH-CH_3$$
$$\downarrow H_2O$$
$$CH_3CHO + \qquad CH_3CH_2NH-NH_2$$

and (k) the irradiation of aliphatic aldehydes,[22] e.g.

$$RCH_2CH_2CH_2CHO \xrightarrow{h\nu} RCH=CH_2 + CH_3CHO + \quad \square$$

Bis (α-chloroethyl)ether, which has tumor-initiating activity and causes a significant number of sarcomas at the injection site into mice, is readily hydrolysed,[29] e.g.

$$(CH_3CHCl)_2O \xrightarrow{H_2O} 2\,CH_3CHO + 2\,HCl$$

II. ALCOHOL

Alcohol (ethanol) is probably the most important factor in the deaths of more than half the 55 000 traffic fatalities each year. More than half of all the violent deaths in New York City are believed to involve alcohol as one of the factors. The blood alcohol concentration (BAC) is the percentage in hundredths of one percent of alcohol in the blood and is a measurement of human intoxication. With two ounces of 80-proof liquor, a person weighing 160 lb reaches a level of 0·05 BAC in 1 hour. At this level mental sharpness is lost and driving ability is impaired; at 0·08% nearly everyone is too drunk to drive. However, a New York study showed that nearly half of all drivers in fatal crashes had BAC levels of 0·25% or higher.

Chemical tests for drunkenness include on-the-spot breath tests for immediate screening purposes and subsequent laboratory tests for quantitative measurement. Breath tests are believed to be reliable when performed by well-trained competent operators. They have the disadvantages of possible unreliability in the first 20 min following imbibement, a necessity for cooperation of the subject to yield alveolar air (the last puff of expired breath), and their sensitivity to regurgitated, belched, or other mouth alcohol. The breath alcohol concentration can be extrapolated to the blood alcohol concentration. Approximately 2100 ml of alveolar air contains the same quantity of alcohol as 1 ml of blood.

The biological aspects of alcohol metabolism, especially in the formation and reactions of the highly reactive acetaldehyde have been studied in terms of the aberrant metabolism of biogenic amines,[154] reactions of catecholamines with acetaldehyde to form possibly addictive tetrahydroisoquinolines,[155] the role of acetaldehyde in the interactions of ethanol with neuroamines,[156] and the blood acetaldehyde levels after alcohol consumption by alcoholic and non-alcoholic subjects.[157]

Blood alcohol can be determined either through the derived acetaldehyde, through the formed NADH or through a dye formed by reaction of a dye precursor with NADH.

Ethanol can be determined with the help of alcohol dehydrogenase, e.g.

$$C_2H_5OH + NAD^+ = CH_3CHO + NADH + H^+$$

Analysis is made at 340 nm, the wavelength maximum of NADH, but the acetaldehyde could also be determined with MBTH. NADH could also be determined fluorimetrically at $F350/450$ as has been done by an automated method for ethanol.[54] Some 0·02 ml of fingertip blood can be assayed fluorimetrically in this fashion.[55]

Various oxidizing agents, as shown in Table 1, can be used to oxidize ethanol to acetaldehyde. The mechanism proposed for the oxidation with ferrous ion includes the following series of reactions[59]

$$Fe^{2+} + H_2O_2 \rightarrow Fe^{3+} + OH^- + HO^{\cdot}$$

$$HO^{\cdot} + CH_3CH_2OH \rightarrow CH_3\overset{.}{C}HOH + H_2O$$

$$CH_3\overset{.}{C}HOH + Fe^{3+} \rightarrow CH_3CHO + H^+ + Fe^{2+}$$

In the determination of ethanol enzymatically with NADH and alcohol dehydrogenase the presence of acetone in oxidized pyridine nucleotides may be a problem.[56] Thus, in the presence of acetone the semicarbazide reaction coupled with spectrophotometry cannot be used to measure the formation of acetaldehyde from ethanol because acetone semicarbazone gives an absorption spectrum similar to acetaldehyde semicarbazone. In addition the presence of acetone in NADP may help explain the difficulty of demonstrating alcohol dehydrogenase activity (ethanol to acetaldehyde measured by NADH formation) in crude tissue homogenates with NADP as the cofactor since alcohol dehydrogenase can oxidize NADPH with acetone. Finally, acetone contamination of NAD may help to explain the low activity of alcohol dehydrogenase (ethanol to acetaldehyde measured by NADH formation) at pH 7·4 and 23° because alcohol dehydrogenase can oxidize NADH with acetone.

Colorimetry can also be used in the determination of alcohol.[158] 2-(p-Iodophenyl)-3-(p-nitrophenyl)-5-phenyltetrazolium chloride (INT), I, is used as the formazan dye precursor.

I

The colorimetric method is specific, accurate and reproducible in the range of clinical interest, 0·05–0·4% ethanol. There is no interference by methanol, glycerol, or acetone, but since propanol, butanol and formaldehyde react at reduced rates, contamination by these substances should be avoided. The enzymes ADH and diaphorase are used. The formazan absorbs at

Table 3. Determination of acetaldehyde precursors

Precursor	Reagent	λ_{max} (mε) or $f_{exc/em}$	Beer's law range (μg)	Analysis time (min)	Interferences, etc.	Ref.
Acetal	MBTH	602 (40·5)[a]	1·5–20[b]	27	CH_2O, RCHO	3
Acetylcholine	NAD	340/460	0·1–0·8	100	Acylcholines, air, EtOH	5
Alanine	4-Phenylphenol	—	20–80	240	Leucine	26
Alkyl vinyl ethers[c]	4-Phenylphenol	572 (~59·0)	2·3–30	160	CH_3CHO + precursors	26
Azoethane	4-Phenylphenol	570	8–100	70	Acetaldehyde	28
6-Deoxyhexoses	Semicarbazide	224 (8·25)[d]	1·6–82[e]	126	f	40
1,1-Diethylhydrazine	4-Phenylphenol	570	9–180	100	Acetaldehyde	44
1,2-Diethylhydrazine	4-Phenylphenol	570	9–180	100	Acetaldehyde	28
Di-isobutylacetal	4-Phenylphenol	572 (~59)	3–30	160	CH_3CHO + precursors	26
Ephedrine	MBTH	625	0·4–4	123	CH_2O + RCHO	45
Ephedrine	4-Phenylphenol	575[g]	40–150	270	CH_2O + RCHO	47
Ethanol	NAD + ADH	340 (6·2)	25–500[b]	45	RCH_2OH	50, 51
Ethanol	NAD + ADH	340 (6·2)	38–760	h	RCH_2OH	53
Ethanol	MBTH	660 (20)	3·2–60[b]	42	RCH_2OH, RCHO	63
Lactic acid	4-Phenylphenol	570[i]	1–20	120	CH_2O, RCHO, CH_3—COOH	101
Lactic acid	1-Naphthol[j]	430	9–140	26[k]	Propylene glycol[l]	105
Muramic acid	4-Phenylphenol	570	10–30	25	m	106, 111
1-Phenyl-3,3-diethyl-triazene	4-Phenylphenol	570	1·8–18	~40	CH_3CHO	128
Steroids, CH_3CHOH—C(OH)	4-Phenylphenol	565	2–20	140[n]	6-deoxyhexoses	132
Threonine	4-Phenylphenol	570	2–10	130	CH_3CHO, 6-deoxy-hexoses	146
Threonine	MBTH	629 (64)	0·17–3·4	37	CH_2O, RCHO + precursors	145
Threonine	ADH + NADH	340 (6·2)	2·2–11	12	6-deoxyhexoses	143

[a] Also band at λ 675, mε 30·8. See procedure and also Ref. 30.

[b] At absorbance = 0·10.

[c] Where alkyl is 2-butoxyethyl, n-butyl, isobutyl, 2-ethylhexyl, ethyl and 2-methoxyethyl. Approx. 100% recovery of acetaldehyde.

[d] For fucose. In absence of glycine, mε = 8·9. Pure acetaldehyde semicarbazone gives λ_{max} 224 nm mε 12·5.

[e] At A = 0·1 range is 5·3–270 μg.

[f] Glycine added to reaction mixture trapped the formaldehyde and thus erased its potential interference.

[g] Color stable for more than 20 h.

[h] Automatic reaction rate method with precision and accuracy of about 2%.

[i] Colour stable for 1 h.

[j] In H_2SO_4. Heat necessary for reaction.

[k] Ten determinations in 40 min.

[l] Maleic and malic acids give 21 and 14% of colour of lactic acid.

[m] No colour given by D-glycosamine or D-galactosamine.

[n] After enzymatic hydrolysis and paper chromatography.

500 nm. Since the NAD^+ is recycled a lower concentration of ethanol can be assayed, e.g.

$$C_2H_5OH + NAD^+ \xrightarrow{\text{ADH}} CH_3CHO + NADH + H^+$$

$$INT^+ + NADH \xrightarrow{\text{diaphorase}} \text{Formazan} + NAD^+$$

III. REAGENTS

The reagents which have been used in the analysis of various precursors are given in Table 3. The most popular reagents are 4-phenylphenol, 3-methyl-2-benzothiazolinone hydrazone (MBTH), and reduced nicotin-amide adenine dinucleotide (NADH). None of these methods are specific, but their selectivity can be improved considerably by separating the acetaldehyde from other aldehydes by distillation. The MBTH and 4-phenyl-phenol methods are the most sensitive. The wavelength maximum and the molar absorptivity or the fluorescence excitation and emission wavelengths, Beer's law range, analysis time, and the interferences are given for various precursors in Table 3.

The basic procedures for the analysis of a variety of mixtures for various precursors are given in Table 4.

Some representative procedures which can be used in the analysis of various acetaldehyde precursors are given in this section to facilitate assay for these and analogous compounds.

IV. ACETALS

In the absence of aliphatic aldehydes, acetals can be analysed directly by the following procedure.

A. Acetal assay

Heat 2 ml of aq test solution and 1 ml of 0·8% aq MBTH.HCl at 100° for 3 minutes. Cool to room temp and add 2 ml of 0·5% aq ferric chloride. After standing for 18 min read at 602 nm. With acetal a millimolar absorp-tivity of about 40·5 is obtained.

The method can be made more selective by distilling the volatile acet-aldehyde[26] or by washing a chloroform extract of the test substance with 2% aq sodium bisulphite to remove free acetaldehyde and related material.[161]

Using distillation and 4-phenylphenol as reagent, acetals and vinyl ethers have been assayed by the following procedure.[26]

Table 4. Analysis for acetaldehyde precursors in test mixtures

Mixture	Precursor	Procedure[a]	Ref.
Alcohol beverages	Acetal	$OH^- \rightarrow H^+ \rightarrow$ Distill $\rightarrow$ MBTH	154
Collagen	Aspartyl residues	$NH_2OH \rightarrow DNF \rightarrow OH^- \rightarrow H^+ \rightarrow$ MBTH	27
Blood	Ethanol	$Pp \rightarrow C \rightarrow NAD + ADH \rightarrow \lambda\ 340$ nm	50–53
Blood	Lactic acid	$Pp \rightarrow C^b \rightarrow H_2SO_4 + Cu^{2+} \rightarrow HQ \rightarrow \lambda\ 420$	104
Blood	Lactic acid	$Ce(SO_4)_2 \rightarrow$ Diff. $\rightarrow SC \rightarrow \lambda\ 223$ nm	90
Blood	Lactic acid	$Pp \rightarrow C^b \rightarrow H_2SO_4 + Cu^{2+} \rightarrow$ 4-PP	106
Body fluids	Ethanol	$Pp \rightarrow$ Chromate $\rightarrow$ Diff. $\rightarrow TSC \rightarrow \lambda\ 262$ nm	60
Brain (rat)	Lactic acid	$Pp \rightarrow C^b \rightarrow H_2SO_4 + Cu^{2+} \rightarrow$ 4-PP	96
Brain (animal)	Threonine	Extn $\rightarrow CC \rightarrow$ Sap $\rightarrow$ Extn $\rightarrow CC \rightarrow H_5IO_6 \rightarrow$ Diff. $\rightarrow H_2SO_4 + Cu^{2+} \rightarrow$ 4-PP	147
Poly(vinyl acetate) emulsions	Vinyl acetate	$OH^- \rightarrow Fe^{3+} +$ N-HBS	152
Protein hydrolysates	Threonine	$H_5IO_6 \rightarrow$ Diff. $\rightarrow H_2SO_4 + Cu^{2+} \rightarrow$ 4-PP	5
Serum and tissues	Lactic acid	$Pp \rightarrow H_2SO_4 \rightarrow$ 4-PP	100
Tissue	Lactic acid	$Pp \rightarrow H_2SO_4 \rightarrow$ 1-Naphthol	105
Urine	Lactic acid	$Ce^{4+} \rightarrow H_2SO_4 + Cu^{2+} \rightarrow$ 4-PP	94
Urine	21-Deoxycorticosteroids	$H_5IO_6 \rightarrow H_2SO_4 + Cu^{2+} \rightarrow$ 4-PP	118,138
Wine	Lactic acid	$CC \rightarrow Ce^{4+} \rightarrow Na_3Fe(CN)_5NO +$ Pip	91,97
Wine	Lactic acid	$Pb(OAc)_2 \rightarrow$ Filter $\rightarrow H_2SO_4 + Cu^{2+} \rightarrow$ 4-PP	98

[a] The first line translates as treatment with alkali followed by acidification, distillation and then determination of the acetaldehyde in the distillate in the 3-methyl-2-benzothiazolinone hydrazone procedure. ADH = alcohol dehydrogenase, C = centrifugation, CC = column chromatography, Diff. = diffusion, DNF = 2,4-dinitrofluorobenzene, Extn = extraction, N-HBS = N-hydroxybenzenesulfonamide, HQ = hydroquinone, NAD = nicotinamide adenine dinucleotide, Pip = piperidine, Pp = protein precipitation, 4-PP = 4-phenylphenol, Sap = saponification, SC = semicarbazide, and TSC = thiosemicarbazide.

[b] Protein-free centrifugate is treated with copper sulphate and calcium hydroxide to remove dextrose and other interfering substances.

B. Assay for acetals and vinyl ethers

Reflux 10 ml of cold 10% aq sulphuric acid (v/v), 1 or 2 ml of chloroform test solution and 1–2 mg of carborundum powder for 15 min in a 50 ml distilling flask. Then distil until about 3 ml of solution is left, collecting in 5 ml of 2% aq sodium bisulphite solution. Wash condensers, delivery tube, and chloroform with cold water. Combine aq extracts in 50 ml volumetric flask. Extract solution with 5 ml of redistilled hexane to remove chloroform.

Add 1 ml of aq aliquot with swirling to 8 ml of cold acid (mix 5 ml of 5% $CuSO_4.5H_2O$ with 500 ml conc sulphuric acid) followed by 0·2 ml of reagent (1 g 4-phenylphenol in 25 ml of hot 8% aq sodium hydroxide solution. Add 75 ml water before cooling). Allow tube to stand in dark at room temp for 1 hour. Heat at 100° for 90 s. Let stand in dark for 30 minutes. Read at 572 nm.

Acetal, acetaldehyde bound to bisulphite and free acetaldehyde have been determined in alcoholic beverages with the help of MBTH by appropriate changes in pH.[159]

V. 2-ALKENES

2-Alkenes can be ozonized at −70° after gas chromatographic separation, excess ozone removed by purging with nitrogen, and the ozonide thermally decomposed to the carbonyl compounds.[23] For example, 1-phenyl-2-butene forms phenylacetaldehyde and acetaldehyde while 2,4-hexadienal is converted in 83% yield to acetaldehyde and glyoxal. The detection limit is about 15 ng of the dienal.

Alternatively solutions of the 2-alkenes in carbon disulphide or ethyl acetate can be ozonized and cleaved reductively in the presence of triphenylphosphine to give acetaldehyde and other compounds.[24, 25]

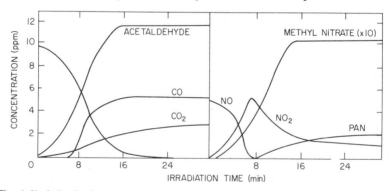

FIG. 1. Variation in the concentrations of reactants and products with time for the irradiation of a mixture of *trans*-but-2-ene, NO, NO_2 and air.[160]

An example of a 2-alkene which reacts readily with ozone but not with nitrogen dioxide or peroxyacetyl nitrate is *trans*-but-2-ene.[32, 33] In attempts to understand and alleviate adverse photochemical smog effects such as eye irritation, reduced visibility, plant damage and damage to property, many simplified atmospheric-simulated smog chamber studies have been performed. Thus, in the ultraviolet irradiation of *trans*-but-2-ene in the presence

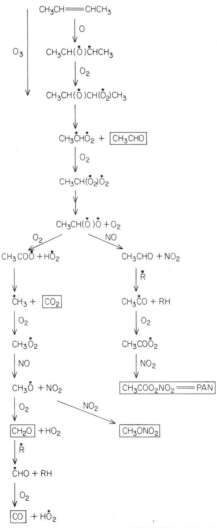

FIG. 2. Photo-oxidation of *trans*-but-2-ene in the presence of nitric oxide and nitrogen dioxide: skeleton reaction scheme initiated by oxygen atoms or ozone.[33]

of nitric oxide, nitrogen dioxide and air, the changes that take place as found by a long-path infrared spectrophotometer are depicted in Fig. 1. The postulated skeleton reaction scheme is given in Fig. 2. These types of reactions take place in the atmosphere but in some respects are much more complicated because of the widely varied brew of chemicals that are present.

VI. 2,3-BUTANEDIOL

The presence of 2,3-butanediol in wort and beer can be readily determined following the oxidation of this glycol to acetaldehyde as shown in the following procedure.

Owing to the colour of the alkaline nitroprusside solution, the calibration curve does not start at zero, but at an absorbance of 0·062. In constructing a calibration curve, dilutions of the purest 2,3-butanediol must be used. The range of dilutions should be chosen so that the 2,3-butanediol content of the beer samples can be read directly from the observed absorbance value.

A. The determination of 2,3-butanediol in beer[31]

Reagents. 0·05 M periodic acid (10·696 g $NaIO_4$ dissolved in water containing 50 ml N H_2SO_4, filtered, and diluted to 1 litre with water); 27% sodium acetate solution (270 g anhydrous sodium acetate, dissolved in water, filtered and made to 1 litre); 10% piperidine solution (10 ml piperidine diluted to 100 ml); 2% sodium nitroprusside solution (2 g sodium nitroprusside dissolved and made to 100 ml). The last reagent must be used within two days after preparation.

Procedure. Pipette 20 ml of decarbonated beer into a short-neck round-bottom flask. Connect the flask to a Widmer column with Liebig condenser. With careful heating distil 6 ml of liquid. Cool the round-bottom flask briefly, *e.g.* by replacing the heating mantle by a beaker of cold water. Disconnect the flask containing the residual 14 ml sample and connect to a steam distillation apparatus. Force the superheated steam through the sample flask (which should be heated to prevent premature condensation of steam) so as to transfer all 2,3-butanediol present in 60 min to the 200 ml receiver flask. Dilute the distillate to 200 ml and shake thoroughly.

Colorimetry. Into a 25 ml graduated cylinder with glass stopper add the 5 ml aliquot containing 2,3-butanediol, 5 ml of the sodium acetate solution, and 5 ml of the periodic acid solution, with shaking after each addition. Allow the mixture to react for exactly two minutes. Then, in quick succession, add 2·5 ml of sodium nitroprusside and 2·5 ml of piperidine solution. Shake the mixture and fill the 1 cm cuvette. Colour development reaches its maximum after only 45 s. Read the absorbance at 560 nm.

VII. 6-DEOXYHEXOSES

6-Deoxyhexoses, e.g. fucose, can be determined by an oxidative MBTH procedure, Fig. 3.[162] Other sugars and glycolic derivatives can be determined by this procedure.

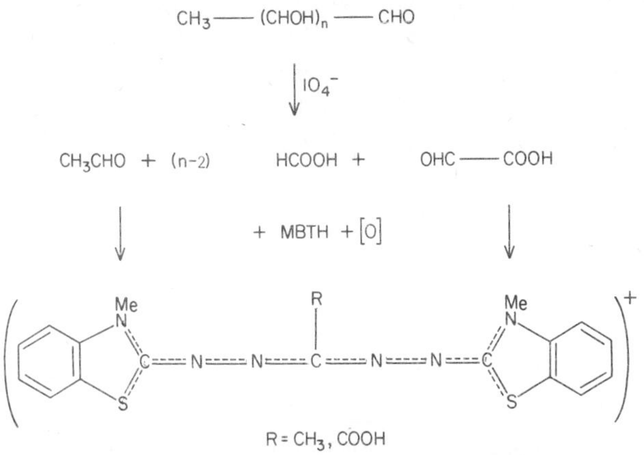

$$CH_3 \longrightarrow (CHOH)_n \longrightarrow CHO$$

$$\downarrow IO_4^-$$

$$CH_3CHO + (n-2) \quad HCOOH + \quad OHC \longrightarrow COOH$$

$$+ \text{ MBTH } + [O]$$

$$R = CH_3, COOH$$

FIG. 3. Postulated equation for the MBTH assay for 6-deoxyhexoses.

A. Assay for 6-deoxyhexoses

Add 0·2 ml of 0·5% periodic acid (H_5IO_6) in water–sulphuric acid (280:1) to 1 ml of an aq test solution. After 15 min add 0·4 ml of 2% sodium arsenite in water–conc hydrochloric acid (20:1) and then after 2 min add 1 ml of 0·8% aq MBTH.HCl. Heat in a boiling water bath for 3 min and then cool to room temp under tap water. Add 2 ml of 0·5% aq ferric chloride. Read absorbance at 15–25 min at 619 nm. Rhamnose and fucose gave millimolar absorptivities of 67 and 44, respectively.

In an alternative procedure a Conway unit was used with semicarbazide as the reagent.[40] The yield of acetaldehyde obtained with this procedure for various 6-deoxyhexoses and analogous compounds was D-rhamnose 99%, DL-threonine 99%, D-fucosamine HCl 90%, L-fuculose-o-nitrophenylhydrazone 80%, colitose 81%, 3-O-methyl-L-fucose 62%, and diethyl dithioacetal 86%. The yield could be increased by a longer oxidation time. It was concluded that oxidation of a 6-deoxyhexose with periodate releases acetaldehyde only when the contiguous hydroxyl groups at C-4 and C-5 are free. With this procedure, free 6-deoxyhexoses can be determined in the presence of glycosidically-bound sugar.

B. Assay for free 6-deoxyhexoses

Fill the sealing compartment of a Conway unit (68 mm diam) with 0·1 ml of 0·025% NPX Tergitol and 2·8 ml of water. Place in the reaction chamber 0·5 ml aq test solution (containing 0·05–0·2 μmol of fucose, etc.) and 2 drops of the NPX solution. In the central compartment place 2·5 ml of semi-carbazide hydrochloride (0·0067 M in 0·06 M NaH_2PO_4 and 0·14 M Na_2HPO_4, pH 7), then add 2 ml periodate reagent (0·2 M periodic acid–0·2 M NaOH–0·2 M glycine (10:15:12), pH 7·4–7·5) to the reaction chamber and place the lid immediately in position. Agitate occasionally for the next two hours. Mix the semicarbazide solution thoroughly and measure absorbance at 224 nm against a reagent blank.

VIII. ETHYLENE OXIDE

Ethylene oxide has been reported to be a precursor of acetaldehyde.[66] A tertiary amine has been found to be a catalyst for this reaction. In the preparation of polyoxyethylene alkylamines by the reaction of an alkylamine with ethylene oxide it was found that the polymeric product acted as a catalyst in rearranging ethylene oxide to acetaldehyde.

IX. ETHYLIDENECYCLOHEXANE

Ethylidene cyclohexane has also been postulated to form a malozonide with ozone; in the presence of *tert*-butyl methyl ketone this decomposes to a dioxethane which, on rapid heating at 170°, emits bluish-white light and erupts violently to discharge acetaldehyde to the atmosphere.[67] The postulated mechanism is shown in Fig. 4.

X. LACTIC ACID

Lactic acid in blood and urine has been determined with 4-phenylphenol reagent.[101, 106] Acetaldehyde and pyruvaldehyde are the most serious interferences; acrolein and propylene glycol are somewhat less serious.

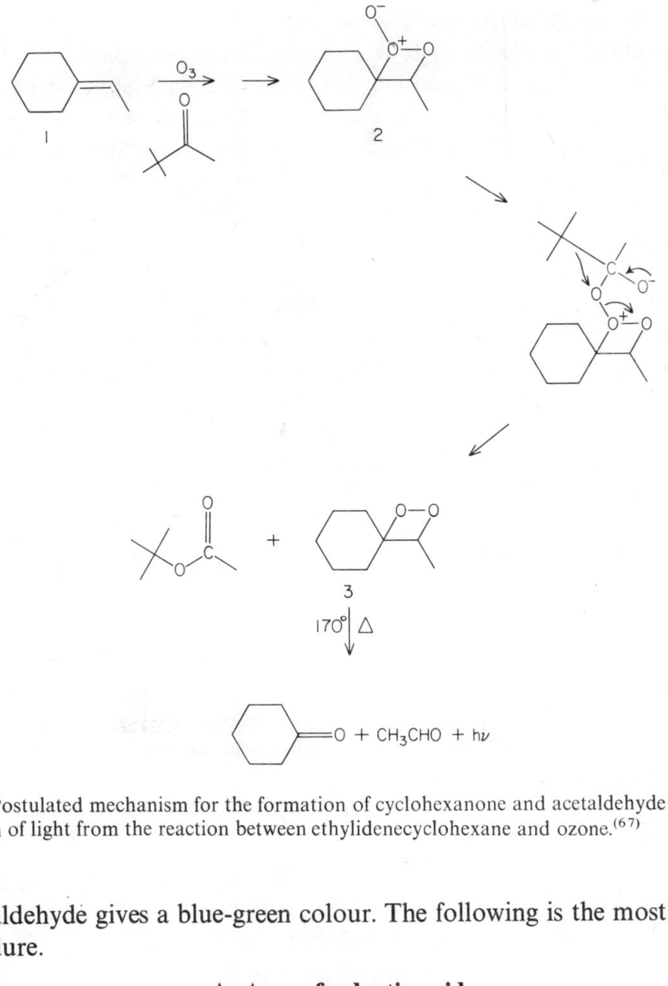

FIG. 4. Postulated mechanism for the formation of cyclohexanone and acetaldehyde and the emission of light from the reaction between ethylidenecyclohexane and ozone.[67]

Formaldehyde gives a blue-green colour. The following is the most popular procedure.

A. Assay for lactic acid

To a mixture of 1 part blood or urine, 7 parts water and 1 part 10% zinc sulphate $(ZnSO_4.7H_2O)$ add 1 part of 0·5 N NaOH and mix again. Centrifuge. To 1 ml aliquot add 0·5 ml of 20% copper sulphate and 3·5 ml water. Mix. Add 0·5 g $Ca(OH)_2$ powder. Shake tubes vigorously. Let stand for 15 min, shake, then let stand for 15 min again. Centrifuge. To 1 ml of aliquot add 1 drop of 4% copper sulphate. Freeze. Layer 6·0 ml of cold conc sulphuric acid under the aq solution. Mix very gradually so that the temperature of the mixture remains below 10°. Heat for 5 min in a boiling water bath without agitation. Cool to room temperature under the tap. Add 0·1 ml reagent (dissolve 1·5 g pure 4-phenylphenol in 10 ml 5% NaOH by warming and

B

stirring and dilute to 100 ml with water) directly on to the surface of the mixture. Disperse precipitated reagent by lateral shaking. Let stand for 1 h at room temp with occasional shaking. Heat in boiling water for 90 s to sulphonate the excess of reagent and stabilize the colour. Cool under tap. Read absorbance at 570 nm. A standard and a blank are run at the same time.

A more recent modification of the 4-phenylphenol procedure for lactic acid is applicable to blood plasma, cerebrospinal fluid or urine after precipitation of proteins.[107] Lactic acid is converted into acetaldehyde by heating with sulphuric acid, the acetaldehyde then reacts with 4-phenylphenol to yield the chromogen. Cupric copper is used to catalyse the conversion of lactic acid into acetaldehyde. The reaction obeys Beer's law up to values of about 80 mg per 100 ml of test solution. The colour is stable for at least one hour. Blank values give an absorbance of 0·05 and the 40 mg standard about 0·45; 100 mg of glucose gives a colour equivalent to 1 mg of lactic acid.

B. p-Phenylphenol determination of body fluid lactic acid[107]

Reagents. Precipitating reagent: Dissolve 10 g of sodium tungstate in 800 ml of water, add 22 ml of 90% orthophosphoric acid, followed by 5 g of copper sulphate; make up to 1 litre with water. Standard solution: Add 213 mg of lithium lactate to a little water, followed by 0·5 ml of conc sulphuric acid, and dilute the solution to 500 ml with distilled water. The final concentration is 40 mg of lactic acid per 100 ml. All reagents are stable for several years at room temperature.

Procedure. Collect blood and preserve in fluoride bottles. Freeze plasma, cerebrospinal fluid or urine until analysed. Introduce 3·95 ml of precipitating reagent into each of 3 centrifuge tubes, and then add 0·05 ml of plasma or cerebrospinal fluid; for urine use 3·8 ml of precipitating reagent and 0·2 ml of sample. Mix and centrifuge for 5 min at 2000 rev min^{-1}. Transfer 1 ml of supernatant liquid to $6 \times \frac{3}{4}$-inch Pyrex tubes. Add rapidly 6 ml of conc H_2SO_4. Let stand for 1–2 min and then mix. Place tubes in tap water to cool for 2–3 min. Introduce 0·1 ml of 1·5% 4-phenylphenol in dimethylformamide to each tube. Mix well and let stand for 10 min. Heat at 100° for 90 s. Cool in tap water. Read the absorbance at 565 nm.

If milk at any stage during production or manufacture is subjected to bacterial action, there will almost invariably be an increase in the lactic acid content. Normal milk has on a dry weight basis 0·9 mg/100 g. For this reason the following method has been developed. The colour is very stable and Beer's law is obeyed.

C. Estimation of lactic acid in skim milk powder [108]

Reagents. Reconstituted skim milk: weigh 1·00 g of skim milk powder into a 6 in. × 1 in. test tube. By pipette add 10·0 ml of water, stopper the tube, and shake for a few min to reconstitute the powder to liquid skim milk (final volume 10·6 ml). Copper sulphate solution: 25% solution of the penta-hydrate. Calcium hydroxide suspension: 30·0 g of calcium hydroxide slaked with 140 ml of water; shake before use. Conc sulphuric acid: 98% H_2SO_4. *p*-Hydroxydiphenyl reagent: dissolve 1·00 g in 100 ml of 0·08 N caustic soda solution. Standard solution: Dissolve 106·5 mg of lithium lactate in a little water, add 0·25 ml of sulphuric acid and make to 1 litre with distilled water. The final concentration is 10 mg of lactic acid per 100 ml.

Procedure. Pipette 1·00 ml of the reconstituted liquid skim milk into a 15 ml centrifuge tube. Add 7·00 ml of water and mix. Add 1·00 ml of the copper sulphate solution, mix and stand for 10 minutes. Add 1·00 ml of the shaken lime suspension, stopper the tube, mix by inversion, and then allow to stand for 10 min at room temp. Centrifuge for 10 min at 2000 rev min^{-1} to obtain a clear supernatant.

To a 1·00 ml aliquot of the supernatant in a test tube add 6·0 ml of conc sulphuric acid from a burette, shake for 1 min and place the tube in a boiling water bath for five minutes. Cool the tube with running water, add 0·05 ml of *p*-hydroxydiphenyl reagent, shake for 1 min, stand for 1 h and read the absorbance in a 1 cm cell in a spectrophotometer set at 570 nm. By replac-ing the 1·00 ml aliquot of the liquid skim milk with dilutions of the standard lactate solution (10 mg/100 ml) a calibration curve relating absorbance at 570 nm to lactate content can be established.

It has been reported that replacement of the conc H_2SO_4 with conc H_2SO_4–25% $CuSO_4.5H_2O$ (300:0·5, v/v) results in a 100% increase in absorbance. [109]

1-Naphthol can also be used to determine lactic acid. [79] The method is based on the oxidation of lactic acid to acetaldehyde and reaction of the latter with 1-naphthol to form the chromogen. The colour is stable for 3–4 h and the method is sensitive to 5 µg of lactic acid. Amino acids, alde-hydes other than acetaldehyde, organic acids and inorganic ions do not interfere.

D. Determination of lactic acid in natural water with 1-naphthol [79]

Evaporate 100–500 ml of test solution at pH 8–9 to 10–15 ml, adjust the pH to 2–3 with HCl (1:1), and extract with butanol (3 × 15 ml). Extract the lactic acid from the butanol layer into 1–3 ml of 0·1 N NaOH, and dilute the aq extract to 5 ml. Cool 1 ml of this solution in ice, add 2 ml of conc H_2SO_4

over 10–15 min, set aside for 30 min, and then heat for 10 min at 130°–150°. To the hot solution quickly add 0·2 ml of fresh 0·5% ethanolic 1-naphthol, cool, and measure the absorbance at 430 nm.

Samples of beet process juice or molasses solution can be analysed by the following procedure. Recoveries range from 97–103%, with no interference from other acids present in beet.[93] Results of duplicate determinations differ by <2·5 μg of lactic acid per ml of eluate.

E. Measurement of lactic acid in beet-sugar processing[93]

Pass 100 ml of the test solution containing up to 20 mg of lactic acid through columns containing (i) 10 ml of Zeo-Karb 225 resin (H^+ form) and (ii) 10 ml of De-Acidite FF resin (CO_3^{2-} form). Remove sugars with about 1·5 litres of water and then elute lactic acid from the anion exchange resin with 100 ml of 0·1 M NaCl. Incubate aliquots of eluate containing up to 200 μg of lactic acid for 2 h with saturated ceric sulphate solution in 6 N H_2SO_4 at 37° ± 3° in a Conway unit. Absorb the acetaldehyde liberated in buffered 6·7 mM semicarbazide (pH 7) and determine the absorbance at 224 nm.

XI. PARALDEHYDE

Paraldehyde, another precursor of acetaldehyde, can be determined enzymatically[114] or colorimetrically with 4-phenylphenol.[115]

In the former procedure the decrease in absorbance at 360 nm is proportional to the acetaldehyde content.

A. Enzymatic determination of paraldehyde [114]

Add 0·4 ml of 0·1 N HCl to 0·1 ml of serum or standard solution (0·2 mg of paraldehyde per ml) in a 3 ml glass tube. Heat-seal the tube, heat in a boiling water bath for 10–15 min to depolymerize the paraldehyde and chill in ice. Determine acetaldehyde by reduction to ethanol with NADH catalyzed by alcohol dehydrogenase.

When the usual 1:10 tungstic acid filtrate is further diluted 10 times or more, the colour can be developed directly with a 1 ml aliquot for blood levels of from 2–25 mg per cent paraldehyde.[115] For these and smaller amounts distillation[163] is necessary. Urinary paraldehyde can also be determined by the distillation method; a preliminary precipitation of an aliquot with phosphotungstic acid (25 ml of 25% phosphotungstic acid per 100 ml of urine) and removal of the precipitate to avoid excessive foaming during the distillation. Acetaldehyde would interfere but normally there is *ca.* 0·02–0·05 mg per cent in blood and this would not increase above 2–3 mg per cent even in acute alcoholism.

B. Determination of paraldehyde with 4-phenylphenol[115]

To 1 ml of the test solution (containing 0·2–2·5 μg of paraldehyde) add 0·05 ml of 5% copper sulphate. Cool in an ice bath and add slowly 8 ml of conc H_2SO_4 with agitation. Deliver 0·2 ml of 1% p-phenylphenol in 0·5 N NaOH directly into the solution. Let stand for 1 h at room temp with occasional shaking. Heat at 100° for 1·5 minutes. Cool, and read the absorbance at the long wavelength maximum.

XII. PHENOTHIAZINES

Persulphate oxidation of phenothiazine compound, **II**, gives formaldehyde and acetaldehyde.[126] These aldehydes can be determined by procedures described in the appropriate section.

II

XIII. 1,2-PROPANEDIOL AND OTHER GLYCOLS

The oxidation of ethyleneglycol and 1,2-propanediol to acetaldehyde and propionaldehyde, respectively, has been found useful in the direct recording of dioldehydratase (propanediol hydro-lyase, EC 4.2.1.28) activity.[124] Essentially dioldehydratase-catalysed dehydration of diols to aldehydes has been coupled to the NADH and alcohol dehydrogenase systems. The enzyme activity is measured through the rate of disappearance of NADH at 366 or 340 nm. Negative results are given with glycerol, ribitol, 1,2,4-butanetriol, 2,3-butanediol, 1,2-dihydroxy-2-methylpropane, 1,2-butyleneglycol, cyclohexanediol, mercaptoethanol, isopropanolamine, ethanolamine, chloroethanol, fluoroethanol, lactaldehyde and 1,2-dithiopropane.[164]

XIV. PYRUVIC ACID

Pyruvic acid can also be determined through acetaldehyde by a micro and an ultramicro method.[129] The chromogen is extracted into methylene chloride before measurement.

A. MBTH ultramicro determination of pyruvic acid[129]

Dilute 0·03–0·15 ml of test solution (containing 0·26–1·3 µg of pyruvic acid) to 0·2 ml with water. Add 0·04 ml of 2·76% MBTH in 0·1 N HCl followed by 0·04 ml of 5% aq ferric chloride. After 10 min, dilute to 5 ml with water. Read the absorbance after an additional period of 30 minutes.

XV. STEROIDS

Acetaldehydogenic steroids can also be determined with either the oxidative MBTH or oxidative 4-phenylphenol procedures. The following procedure can be used for pregnanetriol and other analogous compounds.[138]

A. Assay for urinary 21-deoxy-17,20-dihydroxycorticosteroids

Adjust 5 ml urine to pH 4–5 with 1 N NaOH and then to pH 4·5 with 0·5 ml buffer (13·6 g sodium acetate and 8·9 ml glacial acetic acid diluted to 100 ml with water). Add 0·5 ml Ketodase (Warner–Chilcott). After 17–20 h, cool, shake vigorously with 6·5 ml methylene chloride for at least 1 min, let stand for 5 min, and discard the upper layers. Wash the lower layers with 2 ml 1 N NaOH, Shake for 1 min, centrifuge, and discard the aqueous phase. Dry a 5 ml aliquot. Dissolve residue in 0·1 ml warm acetic acid and then cool to about 3°. Add 1 ml of ice-cold oxidation reagent (0·12 M periodic acid–1% glycine (both in 0·4 N sulphuric acid) (1:1, v/v), made just before use) to the dissolved extract. Transfer an aliquot (0·95 ml) of the mixture promptly to the outer compartment of a Conway unit (with the lid damped with 0·4 N H_2SO_4, almost covering the unit) whose inner compartment has already been filled with 0·53 ml of fresh aq 1% sodium bisulphite. Close the unit and let stand for 2·5 hours. Transfer 0·5 ml of the central trap solution to a tube and add 3·5 ml of the acid reagent. Cool to 12° and add 0·8 ml of reagent (0·45 g 4-phenylphenol dissolved in 10 ml 0·5 N NaOH at 60° with shaking. Dilute to 30 ml). After 20 min, heat at 100° for 90 s. Read the absorbance at 565 nm against the blank. Run a standard at the same time.

Alternatively, a more complicated but more selective procedure can be used involving paper chromatography, oxidation, aeration and colour formation with 4-phenylphenol, in that order.[103]

XVI. THREONINE

The assay for threonine has usually been made more selective through the use of an aeration[146] or a Conway diffusion[5] apparatus to separate the volatile acetaldehyde from interferences. Oxidation followed by the 4-phenylphenol[5, 146] or MBTH[45, 145] procedures can then be used for threonine or other acetaldehyde precursors, e.g. ephedrine and analogous compounds. Where these interferences are absent the procedure can be used directly as shown with the MBTH procedure.[145]

A. Assay for threonine

Add 1 ml of 0·02 M aq sodium metaperiodate to 0·5 ml of aq test solution. Mix and let stand for 10 min. Add 1 ml of 1·5 M aq sodium meta-arsenite followed by 1 ml of 1 M aq H_2SO_4 and 1 ml 0·8% aq MBTH.HCl. Heat for 3 min on a boiling water bath and then cool under the tap. Add 2 ml of 0·5% aq ferric chloride and let stand for 15 minutes. Read the absorbance at 629 nm. Threonine gives $m\varepsilon = 64$.

XVII. VINYL ACYLATES

Vinyl acylates can also be hydrolysed to acetaldehyde. Use has been made of this property to assay lipase.[153] Essentially lipase (glycerol-ester hydrolase, EC 3.1.1.3) hydrolyses vinyl oleate to vinyl alcohol which tautomerizes to acetaldehyde, the latter then being determined with MBTH.

REFERENCES

1. P. W. Clutterbuck and F. Reuter. *J. Chem. Soc.* **1935**, 1467.
2. E. J. Baum, L. D. Hess, J. R. Wyatt and J. N. Pitts, Jr. *J. Am. Chem. Soc.* **91**, 2461 (1969).
3. J. R. Cooper. *Biochem. Pharmacol.* **13**, 795 (1964).
4. O. Wiss. *Helv. Chim. Acta.* **31**, 22 (1948).
5. B. F. Folkes. *Analyst* **78**, 496 (1953).
6. B. Alexander and A. M. Seligman. *J. Biol. Chem.* **159**, 9 (1945).
7. S. L. Tompsett. *Anal. Chim. Acta* **19**, 360 (1958).
8. P. Roine and N. Rautanen. *Acta Chem. Scand.* **1**, 854 (1947).
9. A. I. Virtanen and N. Rautanen. *Biochem. J.* **41**, 101 (1947).
10. C. Fromageot and P. Heitz. *Mikrochim. Acta* **3**, 52 (1938).
11. A. S. M. Selim, M. E. A. Ramadam and M. M. El-Sadr. *J. Biol. Chem.* **227**, 871 (1957).
12. A. I. Kendall and T. E. Friedemann. *J. Infectious Diseases* **47**, 171 (1930).

13. T. E. Friedemann and A. I. Kendall. *J. Biol. Chem.* **82**, 23, (1929).
14. O. Furth, R. Scholl and H. Herrmann. *Biochem. Z.* **251**, 404 (1932).
15. E. W. McChesney. *Proc. Soc. Exptl. Biol. Med.* **32**, 94 (1934).
16. R. J. Block, D. Bolling and M. Webb. *J. Biol. Chem.* **133**, XIV (1940).
17. J. J. Gordon and J. H. Quastel. *Biochem. J.* **33**, 1332 (1939).
18. B. F. Miller and J. A. Muntz. *J. Biol. Chem.* **126**, 413 (1938).
19. S. E. G. Aqvist. *Acta Physiol. Scand.* **13**, 297 (1947).
20. E. Aubel and J. Asselineau. *Biochem. Biophys. Acta.* **2**, 198 (1948).
21. A. E. Braunshtein and S. M. Bychkov. *Biokhimiya,* **8**, 234 (1943); through *Chem. Abstr.,* **39**, 254 (1945).
22. J. D. Coyle. *J. Chem. Soc.* 2254 (1971).
23. D. A. Cronin and J. Gilbert. *J. Chromatog.* **87**, 387 (1973).
24. M. Beroza and B. A. Bierl. *Anal. Chem.* **39**, 1131 (1967).
25. B. P. Moore and W. V. Brown. *J. Chromatog.* **60**, 157 (1971).
26. M. C. Bowman, M. Beroza and F. Acree, Jr. *Anal. Chem.* **33**, 1053 (1961).
27. O. O. Blumenfeld and P. M. Gallop. *Biochemistry* **1**, 947 (1962).
28. R. Preussmann, H. Hengy, D. Lubbe and A. Von Hodenberg. *Anal. Chim. Acta* **41**, 497 (1968).
29. B. L. Van Duuren, C. Katz, B. M. Goldschmidt, K. Frenkel and A. Sivak. *J. Nat. Cancer Inst.* **48**, 1431 (1972).
30. H. Winterscheidt. *Seifen-Oele-Fette-Wachse* **81**, 16 (1955).
31. A. Scherrer. *Wallerstein Lab. Comm.* **35**, 5 (1972).
32. J. J. Bufalini. *Env. Sci. Technol.* **2**, 703 (1968).
33. J. A. Kerr, J. G. Calvert and K. L. Demerjian. *Chemistry in Britain* **8**, 254 (1972).
34. F. Feigl and V. Anger. "Spot Tests in Organic Analysis," 7th Ed., Elsevier, Amsterdam. 1966, p. 440.
35. N. Kobayasi and M. Fugimaki, *Agric. Biol. Chem.* **29**, 698 (1965).
36. B. H. Nicolet and L. A. Shinn. *J. Am. Chem. Soc.* **63**, 1456 (1941).
37. M. C. Cameron, A. G. Ross and E. G. V. Percival. *J. Soc. Chem. Ind.* **67**, 161 (1948).
38. J. R. Helbert and K. D. Brown. *Anal. Chem.* **33**, 1610 (1961).
39. S. B. Zimmerman and G. Sandeen. *Anal. Biochem.* **14**, 269 (1966).
40. A. K. Bhattacharya and D. Aminoff. *Anal. Biochem.* **14**, 278 (1966).
41. P. Hoffee, O. M. Rosen and B. L. Horecker. *Methods in Enzymology* **9**, 545 (1966).
42. D. P. Groth. *Methods in Enzymology* **9**, 549 (1966).
43. S. Ohkua. *J. Pharm. Soc. Japan* **75**, 232 (1955); through *Chem. Abstr.,* **49**, 8046 (1955).
44. R. Preussmann, H. Hengy and A. Von Hodenberg. *Anal. Chim. Acta* **42**, 95 (1968).
45. M. Pays and O. Danlos. *Ann. Pharm. Franc.* **25**, 533 (1967).
46. A. Wickstrom. *Ann. Pharm. Franc.* **8**, 86 (1950).
47. A. Wickstrom and B. Salvesen. *Medd. Norsk. Farm. Selskap* **14**, 97 (1952).
48. L. Chafez. *J. Pharm. Sci.* **52**, 1193 (1963).
49. L. Chafetz, M. Elefant and P. R. Amin. *J. Pharm. Sci.* **56**, 1528 (1967).
50. R. K. Bonnichsen and H. Theorell. *Scand. J. Clin. Lab. Invest.* **3**, 58 (1951).
51. R. K. Bonnichsen in H. U. Bergmeyer, Ed. "Methods of Enzymatic Analysis," Academic Press, New York, 1963, p. 285.
52. R. K. Bonnichsen and G. Lundgren. *Acta Pharmacol. Toxicol.* **13**, 256 (1957).
53. H. V. Malmstadt and T. P. Hadjiioannou. *Anal. Chem.* **34**, 455 (1962).

54. F. W. Ellis and J. B. Hill. *Clin. Chem.* **15**, 91 (1969).
55. R. A. Syed. *Clin. Biochem.* **2**, 135 (1968).
56. R. K. Bonnichsen and N. G. Brink in S. P. Colowick and N. O. Kaplan, Eds "Methods in Enzymology," Vol. 1, Academic Press, New York, 1955, p. 495.
57. E. A. Carter and K. J. Isselbacher. *Anal. Biochem.* **45**, 337 (1972).
58. N. O. Kaplan and M. M. Ciotti, in S. P. Colowick and N. O. Kaplan, Eds, "Methods in Enzymology," Vol. III, Academic Press, New York, 1957, p. 254.
59. I. M. Kolthoff and A. I. Medalia. *J. Am. Chem. Soc.* **71**, 3777 (1949).
60. O. Schmidt and R. Manz. *Klin. Wochschr.* **33**, 82 (1955).
61. A. Dirscherl. *Mikrochim. Acta* **1962**, 155.
62. F. Feigl and C. Stark. *Chemist Analyst* **45**, 39 (1956).
63. M. Pesez and J. Bartos. *Ann. Pharm. Franc.* **22**, 609 (1964).
64. F. Feigl and E. Silva. *Analyst* **82**, 582 (1957).
65. Ref. 25, p. 166.
66. I. Katsura, H. Kawaguchi and T. Yamamoto. *Nippon Kagaku Kaishi,* 1733 (1973).
67. P. R. Story, E. A. Whited and J. A. Alford, *J. Am. Chem. Soc.* **94**, 2143 (1972).
68. J. A. Sibley and A. L. Lehninger. *J. Biol. Chem.* **177**, 859 (1949).
69. D. Aminoff and W. T. J. Morgan. *Biochem. J.* **48**, 74 (1951).
70. E. F. Annison and W. T. J. Morgan. *Biochem. J.* **50**, 460 (1952).
71. A. H. Wardi and Z. P. Stary. *Anal. Chem.* 1093 (1962).
72. B. Smith, R. Ohlson and A. Olson. *Acta Chem. Scand.* **16**, 1463 (1962).
73. M. J. Rosen. *Anal. Chem.* **27**, 114 (1955).
74. See ref. 25, p. 365.
75. R. Milton. *Analyst* **61**, 91 (1936).
76. G. A. Horrop, Jr. *Proc. Soc. Exptl. Biol. Med.* **17**, 162 (1919–1920).
77. A. Hansen, O. Riesser and T. Nagaya. *Biochem. Z.* **196**, 301 (1928).
78. Z. Dische and D. Laszlo. *Biochem. Z.* **187**, 344 (1927).
79. A. G. Stradomskaya and I. A. Goncharova. *Gidrokhim. Mater.* **48**, 72 (1968).
80. B. F. Avery and A. B. Hastings. *J. Biol. Chem.* **94**, 273 (1931).
81. S. W. Clausen. *J. Biol. Chem.* **52**, 263 (1922).
82. H. T. Edwards. *J. Biol. Chem.* **125**, 571 (1938).
83. T. E. Friedemann, M. Cotonio and P. A. Shaffer. *J. Biol. Chem.* **73**, 335 (1927).
84. O. von Furth and D. Charnass. *Biochem. Z.* **26**, 199 (1910).
85. E. Ronzini and Z. Wallen-Lawrence. *J. Biol. Chem.* **74**, 363 (1927).
86. W. B. Wendel. *J. Biol. Chem.* **102**, 47 (1933).
87. S. R. Elsden and Q. H. Gibson. *Biochem. J.* **58**, 154 (1954).
88. H. Ryan. *Analyst* **83**, 528 (1958).
89. H. J. Starck. *Klin. Wochschr.* **34**, 153 (1956).
90. P. F. Scholander and E. Bradstreet. *J. Lab. Clin. Med.* **60**, 164 (1962).
91. H. Rebelein. *Deutsch Untersuchungsanst.* **64**, 9 (1968).
92. J. Savory and A. Kaplan. *Clin. Chem.* **12**, 559 (1966).
93. J. F. T. Oldfield and M. Shore. *Int. Sug. J.* **72**, 3 (1970).
94. M. V. Tsao, M. L. Baumann and S. Wark. *Anal. Chem.* **24**, 722 (1952).
95. J. Jeandet and H. Lestradet. *Rev. Franc. Etudes Clin. Biol.* **6**, 953 (1961); through *Chem. Abstr.,* **56**, 9039 (1962).
96. J. Krivanek. *Physiol. Bohemoslov.* **12**, 586 (1963).
97. H. Rebelein. *Deutsch. Lebensmitt-Rdsch.* **59**, 129 (1963).
98. D. Schaelderle and M. Hasselmann. *Ann. Falsif.* **54**, 421 (1961).
99. S. L. Bonting. *Arch. Biochem. Biophys.* **56**, 307 (1955).

100. N. J. Hochella and S. Weinhouse. *Anal. Biochem.* **10**, 304 (1965).
101. W. E. Huckabee. *J. Appl. Physiol.* **9**, 163 (1956).
102. R. P. Hullin and R. L. Noble. *Biochem. J.* **55**, 289 (1953).
103. J. A. Russell. *J. Biol. Chem.* **156**, 463 (1944).
104. W. S. Hoffman. "Photelometric Clinical Chemistry," Wm. Morrow and Co., New York, 1941, p. 195.
105. J. Wohnlich. *Bull. Soc. Chim. Biol.* **47**, 2166 (1965).
106. S. B. Barker and W. H. Summerson. *J. Biol. Chem.* **138**, 535 (1941).
107. J. D. Pryce. *Analyst* **94**, 1151 (1969).
108. A. J. Lawrence. *Aust. J. Dairy Technol.* **25**, 198 (1970).
109. S. B. Barker in "Methods in Enzymology" Vol. III, 241 (1957).
110. H. Irving and V. S. Mahnot. *Talanta* **15**, 811 (1968).
111. R. E. Strange and L. H. Kent. *Biochem. J.* **71**, 333 (1959).
112. F. Feigl and D. Goldstein. *Anal. Chem.* **29**, 1521 (1957).
113. L. R. Jones and J. A. Riddick. *Anal. Chem.* **28**, 254 (1956).
114. J. H. Thurston, H. S. Liang, J. S. Smith and E. J. Valentini. *J. Lab. Clin. Med.* **72**, 699 (1968).
115. W. W. Westerfeld. *J. Lab. Clin. Med.* **30**, 1076 (1945).
116. R. Preussmann, A. Von Hodenberg and H. Hengy. *Biochem. Pharmacol.* **18**, 1 (1969).
117. J. L. Williams and H. D. Graham. *Anal. Chem.* **36**, 1345 (1964).
118. R. I. Cox. *Biochem. J.* **52**, 339 (1952).
119. S. Dal Nosgare, T. O. Norris and J. Mitchell, Jr. *Anal. Chem.* **23**, 1473 (1951).
120. I. M. Baumel. *Anal. Chem.* **26**, 930 (1954).
121. L. Maros and E. Schulek. *Acta Chim. Acad. Sci. Hung.* **21**, 91 (1959).
122. L. Maros, I. Perl and E. Schulek. *Magyar Kém. Folyoirat* **67**, 203 (1961).
123. L. Maros, I. P. Molnár and E. Schulek. *Magyar Kém. Foyoirat* **66**, 321 (1960).
124. G. L. Sottocasa, N. Stagni and B. de Bernard. *Experientia* **27**, 1247 (1971).
125. See ref. 25, p. 167.
126. V. T. Beyrich. *Pharmaz. Zhalle* **108**, 837 (1969).
127. W. B. Wendel. *J. Biol. Chem.* **94**, 717 (1932).
128. A. Schellenberger, G. Hubner and H. Lehmann. *Angew. Chem.* **80**, 907 (1968).
129. M. Pays, P. Malangeau and R. Bourdon. *Ann. Pharm. Franc.* **24**, 763 (1966).
130. M. A. Paz, O. O. Blumenfeld, M. Rojkind, E. Henson, C. Furfine and P. M. Gallop. *Arch. Biochem.* **109**, 548 (1965).
131. G. C. Butler and G. F. Marrian. *J. Biol. Chem.* **119**, 565 (1937); **124**, 237 (1938).
132. R. I. Cox. *J. Biol. Chem.* **234**, 1693 (1959).
133. S. C. Pan. *J. Chromatog.* **9**, 81 (1962).
134. M. Finkelstein. Pregnanetriolone, an Abnormal Urinary Steroid, in R. I. Dorfman, Ed., "Methods in Hormone Research," Academic Press, New York and London, 1962, pp. 169–197.
135. P. Cristol and M. F. Jayle. *Bull. Soc. Chim. Biol.* **42**, 655 (1960).
136. D. Exley and J. K. Norymberski. *J. Endocrin.* **29**, 303 (1964).
137. R. I. Cox and G. F. Marrian. *Biochem. J.* **54**, 45 (1953).
138. M. G. Metcalf. *Anal. Biochem.* **13**, 483 (1965).
139. R. Gomer and W. A. Noyes, Jr. *J. Am. Chem. Soc.* **72**, 101 (1950).
140. R. J. Block and D. Bolling. *Proc. Soc. Exptl. Biol. Med.* **40**, 710 (1939); *J. Biol. Chem.*, **130**, 365 (1939).
141. R. H. Dainty. *Biochem. J.* **104**, 46P (1967).
142. D. M. Greenberg. *Methods in Enzymology* **5**, 931 (1962).

143. M. Flavin and C. Slaughter. *Anal. Chem.* **31**, 1983 (1959).
144. B. H. Nicolet and L. A. Shinn. *J. Am. Chem. Soc.* **61**, 1615 (1939).
145. E. Sawicki and C. R. Engel. *Chemist-Analyst* **56**, 7 (1967).
146. B. A. Neidig and W. C. Hess. *Anal. Chem.* **24**, 1627 (1952).
147. M. Hayashi, Y. Nakajima, K. Inoue and K. Miyaki. *Chem. Pharm. Bull., Japan* **11**, 1200 (1963).
148. L. A. Shinn and B. H. Nicolet. *J. Biol. Chem.* **138**, 91 (1941).
149. A. J. P. Martin and R. L. M. Synge. *Biochem. J.* **35**, 294 (1941).
150. T. Winnick. *J. Biol. Chem.* **142**, 461 (1942).
151. A. L. Dounce and G. B. Thannhauser. *J. Biol. Chem.* **173**, 159 (1948).
152. S. Hayashi and T. Motoyama. *Chem. High Polymers, Japan* **18**, 95 (1961).
153. H. Brockerhoff, R. J. Hoyle and P. C. Hwang. *Anal. Biochem.* **37**, 26 (1970).
154. V. E. Davis in M. K. Roach, W. M. McIsaac and P. J. Creaven, Eds., "Biological Aspects of Alcohol," Univ. of Texas Press, Austin, 1971, pp. 293–312.
155. G. Cohen, in M. K. Roach, W. M. McIsaac and P. J. Creaven, Eds., "Biological Aspects of Alcohol," Univ. of Texas Press, Austin, 1971, pp. 267–284.
156. M. J. Walsh in M. K. Roach, W. M. McIsaac and P. J. Creaven, Eds. "Biological Aspects of Alcohol," Univ. of Texas Press, Austin, 1971, pp. 233–259.
157. E. B. Truitt, Jr., in M. K. Roach, W. M. McIsaac and P. J. Creaven, Eds., "Biological Aspects of Alcohol," Univ. of Texas Press, Austin, 1971, pp. 212–232.
158. Worthington Enzyme Manual, Worthington Biochem. Corp. Freehold, N.J., 1972, p. 192.
159. J. L. Owades and J. M. Dono. *J. Assoc. Offic. Anal. Chemists* **51**, 148 (1968).
160. C. S. Tuesday in R. D. Cadle, Ed., "Chemical Reactions in the Lower and Upper Atmospheres," New York City, Interscience, 1961.
161. P. A. Giang and F. F. Smith. *J. Agric. Food Chem.* **4**, 623 (1956).
162. E. Sawicki, R. Schumacher and C. R. Engel. *Microchem. J.* **12**, 377 (1967).
163. E. Stotz. *J. Biol. Chem.* **148**, 585 (1943).
164. H. A. Lee, Jr. and R. H. Abeles. *J. Biol. Chem.* **238**, 2367 (1963).

2. β-ACETYLACROLEIN, PRECURSORS

I. DIPHENYLAMINE REACTION MECHANISM

It has been postulated that β-acetylacrolein[1,2] and precursors of widely varying structures such as 2-hydroxylevulinaldehyde, furfuryl alcohol, and DNA react with diphenylamine in acid solution to give a diarylmethane cationic resonance structure, **I**. The various precursors are given in Table 5.

I

It has also been postulated that **I** reacts further with acetylacrolein: the aldehyde group of acetylacrolein condenses with the methyl group of **I**, losing water, and the ketonic carbon of the acetylacrolein attaches itself ortho to the imino group of the nearest benzene ring.[53] No conclusive evidence has been presented for these structures. Attempts to isolate the chromogen have resulted in the isolation of seven fractions, two of which give bands near 600 nm in acidic solution. One would expect a cation such as **I** to absorb at wavelenths longer than 600 nm.

These precursors could not be expected to be analysed through the ultraviolet absorption spectrum of β-acetylacrolein, since the isospectral compound β-propionylacrolein absorbs at 215 nm, mε 7·4 in methanol,[54] wavelengths too short to be of use. Its vinylogue, 2,4-heptadiene-6-onal, absorbs at 273 nm, mε 50,[55] so its possible precursors, such as 2-deoxyheptose, could be analysed through the ultraviolet absorption spectrum of this aldehyde.

The formation of β-acetylacrolein, **II**, from furfuryl alcohol, **III**, and

Table 5. Precursors of β-acetylacrolein[a]

Compound[b]	Ref.
Arabinal	3–6
3-Deoxyhexoses[c]	7
2-Deoxyribose	2, 8–11
2-Deoxyribose anilide	3
β-2-Deoxy-D-ribose pentaacetate	3
2-Deoxyxylose	8
DNA	2–6, 8, 9, 12–49
3,6-Dideoxyhexoses[d]	30
2,5-Dideoxyxylose	30
Digitoxose[e]	30
4,5-Dihydroxy-2-methyl-4,5-dihydrofuran	39
2,5-Dimethoxy-2-methyl-2,5-dihydrofuran	39
Dimethyl derivative of β-methyl-2-deoxy-L-ribopyranoside	30
Furfuryl alcohol	1–6, 8, 9, 37, 38
Hexoses[f]	50, 51
2-Hydroxylevulinaldehyde	2, 8, 52
5-Hydroxymethylfurfural[f]	50, 51
2-Methoxylevulinaldehyde dimethylacetal	35
α-Methyl-2-deoxy-L-ribopyranoside	3
β-Methyl-2-deoxy-L-ribopyranoside	3
α-Methyl-α,α'-dimethoxyfuran	2
Mycarose[g]	30
Sodium thymonucleate	3
Xylal	8

[a] Both *cis-* and *trans-* forms react with diphenylamine to give a chromogen absorbing near 595 nm.
[b] For each compound, reaction with diphenylamine solution gives a chromogen absorbing near 595 nm.
[c] Negative results are obtained with this compound; preliminary oxidation with periodate forms a 2-deoxypentose which gives a positive result in the test.
[d] Negative results are obtained with this compound; preliminary oxidation with periodate forms a 2,5-dideoxypentose which reacts positively.
[e] Forms β-propionylacrolein.
[f] See discussion.
[g] Forms β-propionylcrotonaldehyde.

2-deoxy-D-ribose, **IV**, is postulated as taking place in the following manner, Fig. 5.[2]

II. PARAMETERS OF THE DIPHENYLAMINE METHOD

The determination of β-acetylacrolein and its precursors with diphenylamine in aq sulphuric acid has its interferences, Table 6. The importance of

Table 6. Interferences in the determination of DNA with diphenylamine

Interferences	Type	Removal	Ref.
Albumin	Interfering band at shorter λ	Albumin added to blank or extn with water	35
Aldehydes, aromatic	Weak band near 660 nm	Usually not present	3
Aldehydes, heteroaromatic	Weak band near 660 nm[a]		3
Chloride ion	Decreases intensity[b]		13
2-Deoxyribose	Same precursor, so large interference	Extn with CCl_3COOH	27
2-Deoxyribosides	Same precursor, so large interference	Extn with CCl_3COOH	27
2-Deoxyribotides	Same precursor, so large interference	Extn with CCl_3COOH	27
Excess reagent	Decreases colour stability	Reaction with 2,4-pentanedione	48
Ketohexoses	Weak band near 660 nm	Correction through heating time study	3, 12
Galacturonic acid	Bands at 500 and 650 nm		15
Lipids	Formation of emulsion	Extn with acetone, then ether	35
Mercapto compounds	Decreases absorbance		33
Miscellaneous interferences	Decreased reliability of results	Pptn of cadmium salt of DNA	32
Miscellaneous interferences	Decreased reliability	Extn of chromogen into n-butanol	46
Reduced lipoic acid	Inhibited production of colour	Alkylation of interferant with chloracetamide	36
Salts	Decreased colour	Dialysis against water	41
Sialic acid	Bands in same region of spectrum	Procedure modified	17
Skimmed milk constituents	Decreased reliability of results	Separation of leucocytes	34
H_2SO_4 in reagent	Improper concn decreased intensity	Concn of acid adjusted	18, 21

[a] $m\varepsilon = \sim 0.1$ for 5-hydroxymethylfurfural and 2·6 for 2-deoxy-D-ribose.
[b] Wavelength maximum shifts from 600 to 515 nm.

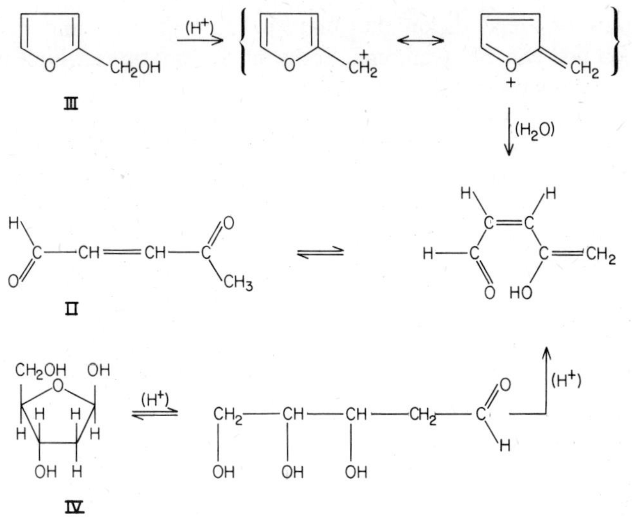

FIG. 5. Formation of β-acetylacrolein from furfuryl alcohol or 2-deoxyribose.[2]

Table 7. Mixtures analysed for DNA

Mixture	Ref.
Adipocytes	35
Animal tissues	28, 29, 48
Bacteria, *Escherichia coli*	40[a]
Bacteria, *Proteus vulgaris*	40[a]
Bovine spermatozoa	49[a]
Brains and brain sections	47
Drosophila larva	19
Human gastric washings	17, 22
Hypocotyls of *Lupinus albus*	56
Leucocyte concentration in milk[b]	34
Pea internodes	21
Plant extracts	15, 21, 46[a], 57, 58
Pollen	21
Protomyces inundatus	21
Rat mammary glands	26
Sea urchin eggs	59
Tissues grown *in vitro*	27
X-irradiated tissue	45[a]

[a] Analysis with *p*-nitrophenylhydrazine procedure. Remainder assayed with diphenylamine.
[b] Indole method preferred because of much lower blank readings.

any interference depends on the mixture being assayed and how readily the interference can be overcome. Some of the mixtures which have been assayed are shown in Table 7.

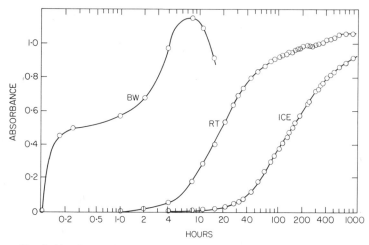

FIG. 6. Absorbance of the colour produced by deoxyribose and diphenylamine. Temperature (boiling water, room temperature and ice) and heating time varied.[10]

Aliphatic aldehydes give a weak blue colour which disappears when the mixture is heated. Bis-(2-furfurylmethyl)ether and 5-hydroxymethyl-furfural give bands near 660 nm with $m\varepsilon$ values of about 0·5 and 0·1, respectively.[3] Of course, with changes in the procedure and for the reagent composition, these intensities can be considerably increased, if so desired.

Negative results were obtained with ω-hydroxylevulinaldehyde, RNA, ribose, fructose, mannose, cinnamaldehyde, malonaldehyde, 2,4-pentane-dione, 2,5-hexanedione, furan (precursor of succinaldehyde), and 2-ethoxy-2,3-dihydropyran (precursor of glutaraldehyde) in the diphenylamine-sulphuric acid test.[2] Weak positive results were given by β-acetylpropion-aldehyde and its precursors α-methylfuran and 2,3-dideoxyribose.

Time and temperature parameters were studied in the Dische[14] and Burton[25] diphenylamine procedures for 2-deoxyribose. In the former procedure, the colour is developed by heating for 10 min in a boiling water bath followed by colorimetry at 595 nm, while in the latter method colour development is specified at 30° for 17 h followed by colorimetry at 600 nm. Considering the curves in Fig. 6, where room temperature is 17°, colour development at 10 min in the boiling water bath is far from an optimal condition, while Burton's specification of colour development for 17 h

Table 8. Intensity (mε) values at 580 nm in the diphenylamine determination of some β-acetylacrolein precursors[3]

2-Methoxylevulinaldehyde[a]	4·2
Furfuryl alcohol	3·1
D-Arabinol	3·1
2-Deoxy-D-ribose	2·6
Sodium thymonucleate	2·2
β-Methyl-2-deoxy-L-ribopyranoside	2·1
Dimethyl derivative of above	0·6

[a] For structure see discussion in (8).

at 30° may be optimal. At ice water temperature the reaction is much too slow.

Using Dische's diphenylamine procedure[14] the mε values of some β-acetylacrolein precursors have been reported at the wavelength maximum of 580 nm, Table 8. The Burton modification is reported to have greater selectivity and sensitivity,[25] but the procedure has been modified with reported increases in sensitivity of 25%[17] and 70%.[21] The Burton modification has been applied on a micro scale so that the DNA content of a single *Drosophila* larva was measured with a range in measurement of 0·3–1·8 μg of DNA.[19] The minimum detectable concentrations have been compared for various methods of determining DNA (Table 9).

In this section we will discuss procedures for the determination of DNA involving hydrolysis of DNA to 2-deoxy-D-ribose and dehydration of the latter to β-acetylacrolein. Hydrolysis and measurement of DNA and RNA has been thoroughly discussed.[65, 66]

III. ADIPOCYTES

Adipocytes were analysed by the following method.[35] Adipose cells isolated from 5–30 mg sample of subcutaneous fat tissues were digested and

Table 9. Minimum detectable concentrations of DNA

Method	Determination limit μg	Ref.
Indole	2·5	60
Diphenylamine	5	25
p-Nitrophenylhydrazine	10	40
Carbazole	25	61
Cysteine	50	62
Tryptophan	100	63
Schiff's reagent	500	64

gently washed with a modified Krebs–Ringer phosphate buffer which contained half of the recommended calcium concentration and 4% albumin adjusted to pH 7·4 with 0·154 N NaOH. For the digestion stage the buffer also contained 0·04% collagenase and 0·1% glucose. After estimation of oxygen consumption the lipids were removed from the cell suspension by repeated extractions with acetone followed by a single extraction with ether. A white water-soluble powder was obtained which contained "fat-free adipocytes," albumin, and salts from the buffer.

A. Determination of DNA in washed adipocytes[35]

Dissolve the powder in 0·3 ml water. Add 0·5 ml of reagent (1 g of diphenylamine in 2 ml conc H_2SO_4 and 98 ml glacial acetic acid, stable for one week in refrigerator) and 0·05 ml of 70·7% perchloric acid. Shake until precipitate dissolves. Heat at 100° for 5 min, then cool under tap water. Read the difference in absorbance at 610 and 660 nm against a blank prepared from 0·5 ml of the Krebs–Ringer phosphate buffer with 4% albumin.

IV. SIALIC ACID INTERFERENCE

Sialic acids interfere with the estimation of DNA by most procedures[12, 17] because of the purple colour which sialic acids form when heated with the diphenylamine reagent at 100°.[23] Human gastric washings were treated with acid, the DNA precipitated, extracted and hydrolysed and then assayed by the following procedure wherein the interference of sialic acid has been decreased considerably.

A. Estimation of DNA in the presence of sialic acid[17]

Diphenylamine reagent. Dissolve 1 g of diphenylamine in about 40 ml of acetic acid in a 50 ml volumetric flask. Add 1 ml conc H_2SO_4 and dilute to volume with acetic acid. Add 0·25 ml of 2% aq acetaldehyde (kept at 4°). Use on day of preparation.

DNA solution. Dissolve 40 mg of highly polymerized calf thymus DNA in 100 ml of 5 mN NaOH and store at 4°. The solution used contained 0·836 μg atom of P/ml.

DNA hydrolysates—working standards. Dilute 0·25, 0·5 and 1 ml samples of the DNA solution in glass-stoppered test tubes to 6·8 ml with water and add 0·2 ml of 50% (w/v) trichloroacetic acid solution to each tube. Heat the tubes at $90 \pm 1°$ for exactly 15 min, cool in running water and store at 4°. Hydrolysates are stable for at least 6 months.

Procedure. Add 2 ml of hydrolysate to 0·2 ml of 60% (w/v) perchloric acid (sp. gr. 1·54) in a glass-stoppered test tube. Dilute specimens containing more than 0·15 μg atom of DNA P/ml with 5% trichloroacetic acid so as to bring them into the range of 0·01–0·15 μg atom of DNA P/ml. The blank consists of 2 ml of 5% trichloroacetic acid. Set up a 2 ml sample of each of the three working standards with each series of estimations. To each mixture add 2 ml of 2% diphenylamine reagent, and leave the mixtures for 48–54 h in a refrigerator kept between 6 and 13°. After removal from the refrigerator keep the coloured solutions in ice-water until they are transferred to cuvettes. Read the absorbances at 550 and 600 nm. Calculate the concentration of DNA from the absorbance at 600 nm. The absorbance at 550 nm indicates whether significant interference by sialic acid has occurred. The absorbance produced by sialic acid increases preceptibly at 550 nm on standing at room temperature. The absorbance produced by DNA at 600 nm shows little change with time at room temp over 115 hours.

V. PLANT TISSUE

Plant tissues and some of the mixtures described in Table 7 have been assayed with a modification of the Burton method[25] which is 70% more sensitive.[21] The blank is considerably reduced in this procedure. Calf thymus DNA in 10% perchloric acid is used as the standard. Turbidity arising from precipitation of impurities in the DNA extracts of plant tissues is a source of error which is cancelled by measuring the 595–700 absorbance difference in the following method.

A. Estimation of DNA in plant tissues[21]

To 2 ml of the test solution containing DNA in 10% perchloric acid add 2 ml of 4% diphenylamine in glacial acetic acid followed by 0·1 ml of aq 1·6 mg/ml acetaldehyde. After incubation at 30° overnight, read the absorbance difference at 595–700 nm.

This procedure has been useful for the estimation of DNA in plant tissues, where low levels of DNA are usually encountered and interference from cell-wall breakdown products is high.[58] These problems are particularly severe in fibrous plant tissues such as sugarcane leaf.[57] A modification of the procedure [21] has been described as having 30% higher sensitivity, a lower reagent blank, and greater convenience in use.[57] Acetaldehyde in the procedure is replaced by paraldehyde which is easier to store and handle and which can be added to the diphenylamine reagent with no adverse effects. This reagent mixture is stable for up to one month. Because of the increased sensitivity and convenience, the modified procedure is recommended for general use with non-plant as well as plant materials. The sensitivity of the method can be increased by extracting the chromogen into a volume of amyl acetate smaller than the reaction volume.[44] A three-fold gain in sensitivity can thus be obtained.

B. Diphenylamine determination of DNA[57]

Calf thymus DNA, 0·0413 mg hydrolysed DNA/ml 0·02 N $HClO_4$. Prepare by dissolving 10·33 mg of DNA in 8·33 ml of water in a 250 ml flask. Immerse flask in a bath at 70° and add slowly with swirling 1·67 ml of 3 N $HClO_4$. Continue heating for about 20 min (or until DNA has dissolved), cool, and then dilute to volume with water. Store solution at 4°.

Reagent. 0·01% paraldehyde and 4% diphenylamine in glacial acetic acid (add paraldehyde first). Store in the dark at room temperature.

Procedure. Mix 2·5 ml of test solution containing about 20 μg of DNA/ml of 1·5 N $HClO_4$ with 1·5 ml of reagent. Let stand for 18–24 h and read absorbance at 600 nm. If desirable for increased sensitivity, extract the chromogen with 1 ml of amyl acetate. Centrifuge the upper layer and read the absorbance at 600 nm. About 96% of the chromogen is extracted into amyl acetate.

VI. PYRIMIDINE DEOXYRIBONUCLEOTIDES

The diphenylamine reagent, as with many other reagents used for the analysis of DNA, does not react with pyrimidine deoxyribonucleotides because the pyrimidine–deoxyribose bond is stable to acid. However, the pyrimidine sugar bond can be broken by acid hydrolysis if the 5,6-double bond of the pyrimidine is first saturated and then the reduced ring is cleaved by mild alkaline hydrolysis.[67] Saturation of the 5,6-double bond of the pyrimidine has been accomplished through catalytic reduction[68] or through reaction with bromine water to produce a 5-bromo-6-hydroxy-5,6-dihydropyrimidine deoxyribonucleotide.[36] The dihydropyrimidine ring is then cleaved by mild alkaline hydrolysis to yield an acid–labile phosphodeoxyribosyl derivative. The reaction with bromine water appears to be complete within one minute.

VII. RIBONUCLEOTIDE REDUCTASE

The ribonucleotide reductase present in crude extracts of *Lactobacillus leichmannii* reduces ribonucleotides to deoxyribonucleotides in amounts which can be estimated by a suitable colorimetric method.[36, 69] However, lipoic acid present in the enzymic assay seriously inhibits colour formation. In the estimation of the acid–labile purine deoxyribonucleotides the dihydrolipoate is deactivated by alkylation with chloroacetamide, while in the estimation of the acid-stable pyrimidine deoxyribonucleotides, lipoic acid is extracted at acid pH with petroleum ether. The following procedures based on these principles have been reported.

A. Assay for ribonucleotide reductase by estimation of purine deoxyribonucleotides[36]

Mix 0·5 ml of the enzymic reaction mixture containing up to 0·35 μmol of purine deoxyribonucleotide with 0·4 ml of 0·5 M chloroacetamide in 0·25 M potassium phosphate buffer, pH 7·3, and heat for 10 min on a steam bath. Cool to room temp and add 2 ml of reagent (dissolve 2 g of diphenylamine in 100 ml of acetic acid and add 2·75 ml of conc H_2SO_4). Incubate at 38° for 4 h and then read the absorbance at 595 nm.

Beer's law was obeyed up to 0·35 μmol of *d*-AMP or *d*-GMP. At this higher concentration both compounds gave an absorbance of about 1·25 at 595 nm.

The presence of small amounts of reduced lipoic acid or dithiothreitol completely eliminates colour production. Although the Blakely alkylation step[36] is effective in cancelling the interference of dithiols up to 20 μmol/ml, colour development is seriously inhibited at higher concentrations while the presence of the B_{12} coenzyme results in a positive interference.[70] The addition of various amounts of mercuric chloride to constant amounts of dithiol eliminated the colour interference when the $HgCl_2$/dithiol molar ratio reached 1·5:1. Concentrations of the B_{12} coenzyme up to 50 nmole ml^{-1} were completely co-precipitated with the Hg-dithiol complex. An added advantage of $HgCl_2$ treatment is that it removes 80–93% of the protein, thus reducing the chance of turbidity during incubation with the diphenylamine reagent. The following procedure was recommended.[70]

Routine incubation mixtures for the measurement of ribonucleotide reductase activity contained the following (per ml): fungal protein (treated with DNAse and dialysed), 1·0–2·2 mg; adenosine triphosphate, 3 μmol; reduced lipoic acid or dithiothreitol, 10–50 μmol, B_{12} co-enzyme, 10–100 nmoles, magnesium acetate, 5 μmol, and phosphate buffer (pH 6), 50 μmol. In tests during the development of the assay method for the production of *d*-ATP in this system, amounts of *d*-AMP or *d*-ATP were added in the range of 10–100 nmol per ml of sample. Control samples contained all components except deoxynucleotide. One millilitre of incubation mixture was added to an equal volume of DPA reagent (4% DPA in glacial acetic acid with 10% H_2SO_4) containing 25 µl of an aq solution of 8% acetaldehyde per 10 ml of reagent. After 2 h at 26° or 5 h at 18°, read the absorbance at 595 nm.

B. Assay for ribonucleotide reductase by estimation of pyrimidine deoxy-ribonucleotides[36]

Add 0·2 ml of 1 N HCl to 0·5 ml of the enzymic reaction mixture containing up to 0·35 µmol of pyrimidine deoxyribonucleotide. Extract twice with 2 ml portions of petroleum ether (b.p. 60–80°). Agitate the mixture on a Vortex stirrer when less than 0·1 mg of protein is present and centrifuge for 1 min at 300 *g*. When larger amounts of protein are present, gently agitate the mixture for a longer period so as not to form a troublesome emulsion. After centrifugation, remove the petroleum ether with a pipette and perform a second extraction in exactly the same manner. Remove traces of petroleum ether by aerating the surface of the liquid for a few minutes. Mix the solution with 0·2 ml of saturated bromine water and let the mixture stand at room temp for 1–10 minutes. After the addition of 0·5 ml of 5 N NaOH, let the mixture stand at room temp for 10 min for estimation of *d*-CMP, or 40 min for estimation of *d*-UMP. Add 2 ml of the diphenylamine reagent and incubate for 4 h at either 50° in the case of *d*-CMP or 38° for *d*-UMP. Read the absorbance at 595 nm.

Beer's law was obeyed up to 0·35 µmol of *d*-CMP or *d*-UMP. For the upper limit of concentration, absorbances of 0·9 and 1·15 were obtained for *d*-UMP and *d*-CMP, respectively.

VIII. BRAIN DNA

The diphenylamine procedure can also be used for the quantitative determination of DNA in preserved brains and brain sections.[47] Neonatal and mature chicken, rat and bullfrog (*Rana catesbiana*) tadpole brains were used in the study. It was found that one hemisphere could be used as a control for the other, and that tissue preserved in 75% (v/v) ethanol is equivalent to fresh tissue, as far as DNA is concerned. On the basis of published data[71] for the DNA content of one diploid frog cell ($1·5 \times 10^{-5}$ µg) the total number of cells in the cerebral hemispheres of a bullfrog tadpole close to metamorphosis is estimated to be $1·2 \times 10^6$ and of a frog immediately after metamorphosis $1·9 \times 10^6$.[47] Thus, colorimetric determination of DNA and derivation of cell number in such small brains appears feasible.

A. Diphenylamine determination of DNA in brain samples[47]

Weigh the sample, freeze and treat as follows.[72, 73] Homogenize the frozen brain tissue with 4 ml of cold 6% (w/w) trichloracetic acid in a Ten–Broeck homogenizer. Rinse the homogenizer with an additional 3–4 ml of cold 6% trichloracetic acid and combine the homogenate and rinse in a polyethylene centrifuge tube. After centrifugation at 18 000 g for 40 min, discard the supernatant fluid and resuspend the pellet in 2 ml of 1 M perchloric acid (for brains weighing 100–500 mg) or in 4 ml of 1 M perchloric acid (for brains weighing 500–1500 mg) and warm at 70° for 15 minutes. Recentrifuge, resuspend pellet in 2 ml of 1 M perchloric acid, and repeat hot extraction step. Combine the two supernatant fractions. In the case of larger brains a third extraction step was necessary with the first supernatant fluid kept separate from the combined second and third. Adjust concentration of perchloric acid to 0·5 M and assay for DNA content at 30° by reading the difference in absorbance values at 610 and 650 nm for both the tissue extracts and the standard (calf thymus DNA, after treatment with hot perchloric acid).[25] A micromethod was used for small brains by scaling down to one-tenth the volumes in all the foregoing extraction and colorimetric procedures.

IX. CHROMOGEN EXTRACTION

A fourfold increase in sensitivity of the diphenylamine reaction has been obtained by the addition of a simple single-step organic extraction procedure utilizing amyl acetate.[44] Reliable and accurate determinations become possible for DNA concentrations as low as 1·5 μg/ml solution. Turbidity is not a problem. Extraction appears to be quantitative except when the DNA concentration is greater than 50 μg/ml solution. The use of this extraction procedure is probably necessary only when concentrations of DNA are in the range of 1·5–12·5 μg/ml or for turbid solutions. The procedure has been adapted for use with human serum with similar results by utilizing the modification of the Giles and Myers reaction[21] described by Tan et al.,[74] plus the amyl acetate extraction step.

A. Diphenylamine extraction procedure for DNA[44]

Add 1 ml portions of calf thymus DNA at concentrations of 50, 25, 12·5, 6·25, 3·13, and 1·55 μg ml^{-1} in a solution of 0·145 M NaCl to 1 ml of 20% perchloric acid. Add 2 ml of 4% diphenylamine in glacial acetic acid followed by 0·1 ml of 0·16% (w/v) aq acetaldehyde and vortex. Incubate for 1 h at 56°. Read absorbance at 595 nm and then add 1 ml amyl acetate. Vortex the mixtures, centrifuge at 1600 rev min^{-1} for 1 min at room temp, remove the clear blue layer, and read the absorbance at 595 nm.

X. DNA IN SEA URCHIN EGGS

The determination of DNA in sea urchin eggs and its subcellular distribution are possible even in the presence of a great deal of other chromogenic materials.[59] Most of the cytoplasmic DNA was found to be associated with the mitochondria ($>90\%$) and only a small portion was detected in the yolk granule fraction. Through a combination of milder extraction and colorimetric procedures and appropriate blank correction a more accurate assay of the DNA content in sea urchin eggs became possible. In the colorimetric method reported here[17] the absorbancy at 600 nm which is specific to DNA is proportional to the contents of DNA in spite of the presence of N-acetylneuraminic acid. In the other methods[25, 75] sialic acid is a serious interference. The blank correction is necessary since it corresponds to 20–40% of the apparent estimate of DNA in the whole egg homogenate. This correction is found to be predominantly ascribable to the yolk fraction.

Before development of the method four conventional extraction procedures were tried.[76–79] The latter procedure was found to be most suitable with slight modification. Three colorimetric procedures were investigated.[17, 25, 75] The Croft–Lubran method[17] was found to most suitable with a blank correction. The complete procedure is as follows.

A. Determination of DNA in sea urchin eggs[59]

Preparation of eggs and sperm. Sea urchins under study were *Pseudocentrotus depressus*, *Hemicentrotus pulcherrimus*, and *Anthocidaris crassispina*. Eggs and sperm were spawned by the conventional KCl method. Treatment of the eggs in slightly acidified sea water, pH 5·0, removed their jelly coat. Extraction of DNA.[79] Homogenize the eggs (about 5–10 ml packed cell volume or several $\times$ 10^7 cells) with water and add 3 vol of ethanol or homogenize directly with ethanol. Store the ethanolic homogenates at 0° for 2 h and centrifuge at 3000 rev min for 10 min. Wash the pellet four–six times with ethanol, and three times with ethanol–ether (3:1 v/v) mixture. Wash the residue again with ethanol and then with cold 10% NaCl acidified with perchloric acid (PCA) (pH 2·0). Suspend the washed pellet in 3 vol of 10% NaCl, adjusted to pH 9–10 by adding Na_2CO_3, heat in a boiling water bath for 60 min, and then centrifuge. Repeat this hot extraction procedure once more for 30 minutes. Combine the first and the second extracts (supernatants), mix with 3 vol of cold ethanol, and allow the mixture to stand at 0° overnight.

Spin the precipitates down by centrifugation, re-suspend in 1 N KOH, and incubate the alkaline suspension at 37° for 20 hours. Add ice-cold 20% PCA up to 5% concentration. Collect the precipitates containing DNA by centrifugation, wash twice with cold 5% PCA and suspend in 5% PCA. Heat the suspension at 90° for 15 min and then centrifuge. Use the supernatant thus obtained for DNA colorimetry.

Colorimetry. Mix an equal volume of DNA extract with the reagent (1 g diphenylamine, 49 ml glacial acetic acid, 1 ml conc H_2SO_4, and 0·25 ml of 2% acetaldehyde in water). Keep the mixture at 10° for 72 hours. For samples other than egg materials DNA can be measured at 600 nm using calf thymus DNA as standard. For egg materials, the following procedure is used. Divide DNA extract into two equal parts. To one part add an equal volume of reagent and to another part add an equal volume of reagent minus diphenylamine. After 72 h at 10° measure the difference in absorbance at 600 nm to get the DNA content.

XI. *p*-NITROPHENYLHYDRAZINE—MECHANISM OF REACTION

Another reagent that has been used for the determination of DNA, 2-deoxyribose, etc. through the derived β-acetylacrolein is *p*-nitrophenylhydrazine.

The chemistry of the reaction between various β-acetylacrolein precursors and *p*-nitrophenylhydrazine has been investigated.[7, 39, 40] The sequence shown in Fig. 7 has been proposed. A pyridazinium cation is formed from

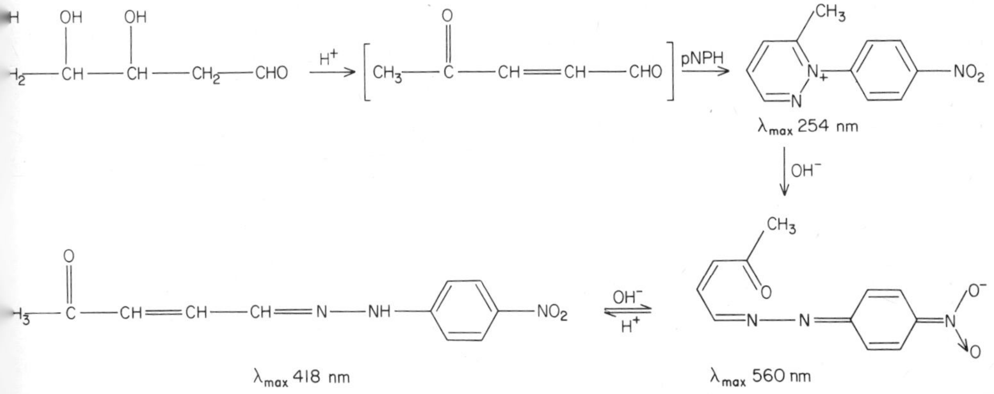

FIG. 7. Mechanism of the Webb–Levy reaction[40] as proposed by Himmelspach and Westphal.[7]

which is derived the purple anionic resonance structure, which is subsequently measured spectrally. The evidence indicates that the same chromogen is obtained from 2-deoxyribose, 2,5-dimethoxy-2-methyl-2,5-dihydrofuran, furfuryl alcohol or DNA. The pure pyridazinium perchlorate is prepared from either furfuryl alcohol or DNA. This material can be used as the chromogen standard since alkali readily cleaves the ring to the final chromogen, β-acetylacrolein p-nitrophenylhydrazone anion.[39]

XII. DNA IN TISSUES AND MICROORGANISMS

In the original method[40] for the determination of DNA in tissues and microorganisms, biological material was prepared for analysis by the method of Schneider[76] followed by dehydration with ether and drying *in vacuo* to give a dry powder from which convenient samples could be taken for analysis. In the first 5 min after the addition of alkali, the colour faded by 2% per min and then the rate of fading decreased. Beer's law is obeyed from about 30 ($A = 0.1$) to 300 μg of DNA. It was also claimed that the intensity obtained in this procedure was five times as great as obtained with the diphenylamine procedure.[14] Recovery of DNA added to liver powder ranged from 93–101%. Little or no colour developed under the conditions of the test with ribose, hydrolysed RNA, hydrolysed ribosides, maltose, fructose, glucose, saccharose, methyl glucoside, hydrolysed glycogen, xylose, arabinose, casein, zein, hydrolysed inulin when their final volumes, made alkaline after the butyl acetate extraction, contained the equivalent of 1 mg of ribose, glucose, etc. A satisfactory degree of precision was obtained over the range of 20–300 μg of DNA.

A. p-Nitrophenylhydrazine determination of DNA[40]

Hydrolysis. Suspend material in 3 ml of 5% trichloroacetic acid and heat for 30 min at 100°. Use 3–60 mg of dried powder containing 15–450 μg of DNA which is equivalent to 18–360 mg of fresh tissue. Carry out hydrolysis in a 15 ml conical centrifuge tube, in the mouth of which place an inverted sealed ampoule tube. Cool in cold water. Add 3 ml of 5% trichloroacetic acid. Mix and centrifuge. Prepare a stock solution of standard hydrolysed DNA as follows: place 25 mg of DNA and 20 ml of 5% trichloroacetic acid in a 25 ml volumetric flask, cover with a sealed ampoule tube and heat for 30 min at 100°. Cool and dilute to 25 ml with 5% trichloroacetic acid.

Colorimetry. To duplicate 2 ml aliquots of hydrolysed material containing 10–300 μg of DNA and 2 ml of a standard solution containing 100 μg of hydrolysed DNA add 2 ml of 5% trichloroacetic acid followed by 0·2 ml of 0·5% *p*-nitrophenylhydrazine in ethanol (prepare fresh daily). Heat for 20 min at 100° with a sealed ampoule tube for a condenser. Cool in cold water, add 10 ml *n*-butyl acetate to each tube. Stopper and shake for 5 minutes. Centrifuge and discard most of organic layer. To 3 ml of the aq layer add 1 ml of 2 N NaOH and dilute to 5 ml with water. Read absorbance immediately at 560 nm.

In a modified procedure DNA contents of tissues were measured after whole-body X-irradiation.[45]

Ten per cent homogenates in 8·5% sucrose were prepared from each tissue. Five ml aliquots (0·5 g tissue) were pipetted to 10 ml centrifuge tubes and extracted twice with 5% trichloroacetic acid (TCA). The mixtures were treated at 4° for 10 min in an International PR-2 centrifuge at 2600 g. The supernatants were decanted and the pellets frozen until analysed.

DNA analyses were performed using a modified Webb and Levy technique.[3] Changes involved the use of 3 ml of hydrolysed extract, 3 ml of TCA, and 0·3 ml of reagent.

Herring sperm DNA (Calbiochem grade C) was used for standard preparations. Standards and samples were hydrolysed for 30 min in boiling water using 5% TCA. A 0·5% solution of *p*-nitrophenylhydrazine in ethanol was the reagent. The aq phase was read at 560 nm after extraction with *n*-butyl acetate and addition of NaOH. The method is reproducible, reads 10% lower than the diphenylamine method, but agrees more closely with the *P* determinations. Advantages of the method are that tissues do not require fat extraction before analysis, proteins or their degradation products do not interfere to the extent they do when using diphenylamine, and ribose at a concentration of 1 mg/ml^{-1} does not interfere.

XIII. DNA IN PLANT TISSUE

Another modification has been applied to the extraction and identification of DNA in plant leaf tissue.[46] The main improvements have been the removal of interfering substances and a reduction of the rate of fading to essentially 1% per hour. The range of recovery of DNA added to *Prunus* leaf extracts was 98–109%. Similar results were obtained when known amounts of DNA were added to yeast RNA and to mixtures containing known amounts of the three commonly occurring pentoses (arabinose, ribose and xylose). Anywhere from 2–8 μg DNA/ml of salmon sperm DNA could be assayed.

A. *p*-Nitrophenylhydrazine determination of DNA in plant tissue[46]

Preparation of leaf tissue. Use either fresh leaf tissue or lyophilized material.

Grind fresh material (10–15 g) in a blender with 100 ml cold ethanol. Pour the suspension on to Whatman No. 3f paper in a Buchner funnel, wash with 100 ml portions of acetone under suction and finally dry in a vacuum desiccator. Prepare the more convenient lyophilized material according to Levitt[80] for potato tuber slices (frozen with liquid air or dry ice, dried over alumina, and ground in a Wiley Mill using 50-mesh screen). To remove interfering substances, treat weighed sample (2–300 mg) on a suction filter with organic solvents in the following sequences (25 ml aliquots of each) acetone–water–methanol (80:16:4); 0·05 ml formic acid in methanol, 5% perchloric acid in 80% ethanol; ethanol–ethyl ether (1:1); and ethyl ether. Air-dry before use. Hydrolysis. Weigh 200–300 mg tissue into a 50 ml centrifuge tube and wet with a small amount of ethanol. Add 10 ml 0·5 N NaOH and heat the suspension at 100° for 15–20 minutes. Cool the tube in ice, and add 20 ml ethanol and 1 ml glacial acetic acid to precipitate the DNA. After 30 min in the ice bath, centrifuge the material, discard the supernatant, and heat the precipitate with 30 ml 5% TCA for 30 min at 100°. Centrifuge the cooled solution and wash the precipitate with 10 ml 5% TCA and recentrifuge. Combine the supernatants and make up to 30 ml volume, 15 ml of this being used for each determination of DNA. During heating, cover the tubes loosely with a glass ampoule to retard evaporation.

Prepare a stock solution of DNA from highly polymerized material at a concentration of 100 μg ml^{-1} in 0·05 N NaOH. Make dilutions of twice the required strength with distilled water, and hydrolyse with an equal volume of 10% TCA to give the desired final concentration in 5% TCA.

Colorimetry. Add 0·5 ml of 0·5% PNPH in ethanol to each of the 50 ml tubes containing the DNA solution (15 ml in 5% TCA). Loosely cover to retard evaporation and place in a boiling water bath for 20 minutes.

If a reddish colour develops at the end of the heating period, rather than the purple one specific for the PNPH–deoxyribose reaction, too much TCA has been destroyed during the process and all the excess PNPH will not be extracted by the iso-amyl acetate. Remedy this by adding 1 ml 30% TCA at this point. (It cannot be added earlier since a high concentration of TCA will destroy some of the deoxyribose during the heating at 100°.) Cool the tubes and saturate with NaCl by adding a slight excess. Add 10 ml iso-amyl acetate, stopper and mix on a mechanical shaker for 5 minutes. Allow the layers to separate and discard the top one. Repeat the procedure with a further 10 ml iso-amyl acetate and finally with 10 ml ethyl ether, the organic layer being discarded in each case. Evaporate any remaining ether. Add 5 ml n-butanol, cool. Add 5 ml 50% NaOH, shake on a shaker for 5 min, centrifuge, and read the absorbance of the n-butanol phase at 580 nm in 1 cm cells.

XIV. DNA IN SPERMATOZOA

The previous modification[46] has been applied to animal tissue so as to take advantage of the increased colour stability. In the following procedure nucleoprotein is extracted according to Borenfreund et al.[81]

A. p-Nitrophenylhydrazine determination of DNA in bovine spermatozoa[49]

To a suspension of 100 mg of bovine spermatozoa in a beaker containing 20 ml of 0·5 M sodium chloride–0·005 M sodium citrate add 2-mercaptoethanol to a final concentration of 2%. Incubate the mixture at 4° for 2 h with gentle stirring. Add 10 mg trypsin and continue incubation for 1 h at room temperature.[46] Centrifuge and save the supernatant. Repeat incubation with trypsin twice, combine supernatants, and precipitate the nucleoprotein by the addition of two volumes of ethanol. Collect the precipitate with a glass rod and dry over calcium chloride. Hydrolyse DNA with 5% trichloroacetic acid and bring to volume with this acid solution. Develop colour by the method previously described[46] and read the absorbance at 580 nm to determine the DNA. The colour is stable for at least 1 hour.

XV. IMPROVED NPH METHOD FOR DNA

In a more recent method the following improvements over the original method[40] are claimed.[48]

(a) Combination of the extraction of DNA with hot acid with the reaction with p-nitrophenylhydrazine to obviate destruction of deoxyribose.

(b) Use of pure acetylated reagent and inclusion of metabisulphite in the reaction mixture to improve reproducibility.

(c) More effective removal of excess p-nitrophenylhydrazine by reaction with 2,4-pentanedione, instead of the multiple extractions with butyl acetate, to improve the stability of the final chromogen.

(d) Extraction of the final chromogen with butanol, which purifies and concentrates the chromogen, thus stabilizing it.

Study of the reaction with deoxyribonucleosides and deoxyribonucleotides revealed that the reaction of the purine derivatives was complete after 120 min at 90° in 0·86 M perchloric acid, but that appreciable reaction of the corresponding pyrimidine derivatives also occurred under these conditions. Attempts to have both derivatives or only the purine derivatives react completely were unsuccessful. A linear standard curve was obtained for salmon sperm DNA. The parameters for the line of "best fit" were 0·02 absorbance unit for the intercept and $6·72 \times 10^{-3}$ absorbance unit/µg

DNA for the gradient. The 95% confidence limits for these parameters were 0·003 and 0·04, and $6·61 \times 10^{-3}$ and $6·82 \times 10^{-3}$, respectively. Tissue samples and the DNA standard gave comparable reproducibilities. Nine replicates of a homogenate of a rat lung gave a mean absorbance value of 0·444 with a standard deviation of 0·013. The limit of sensitivity is approx 15 μg DNA in 4 ml 1 M perchloric acid.

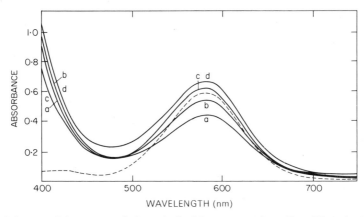

FIG. 8. Spectra of chromogen solutions obtained from preparations of small intestine (a), heart (b), kidney (c), and brain (d) by application of standard procedure for the NPH reaction after treatment with cold perchloric acid. For comparison, the broken line represents the spectrum of the butanolic solution obtained by application of the standard chromophore development procedure to an acidic aqueous solution of chromogen perchlorate.[48]

The specificity of the method was also studied in terms of the possible interferences and the spectra obtained with various tissues as compared to the spectrum of the pure chromogen, Fig. 8.[48] Preparations from liver, submaxillary gland, spleen, bone marrow, sperm and lung gave similar spectra in the 580 nm region. Ribose (and its derivatives such as adenosine monophosphate and adenosine triphosphate) and fructose (and its derivatives such as sucrose) gave chromogens which had significant absorption at 580 nm, e.g. 0·02 μmol deoxyribose gave the same absorbance as 2 μmol ribose and 0·2 μmol fructose. The corresponding figures for glucose, sialic acid, and N-acetylgalactosamine were 20, 5 and 15 μmol, respectively. Samples from this p-nitrophenylhydrazine procedure can be used for RNA estimation by orcinol.[82]

A TLC study[83] showed that 89–98% of the final chromogen material obtained from a wide range of rat tissue preparations (bone marrow, brain, heart, kidney, liver, lung, small intestine, sperm, spleen, and submaxillary gland) had the same spectral and chromatographic characteristics as the pure chromogen and the chromogen from DNA, thus confirming a relative absence of interfering materials. The spectrum of the material eluted from the major interfering component of the RNA and ribose chromatograms showed equal absorbance at 580 and 680 nm so that routine correction for the interference by RNA in the estimation of DNA may be made by subtraction of the absorbance at 680 nm from that at 580 nm. The use of this correction was applicable to ribose–deoxyribose and RNA–DNA mixtures in ratios up to 20:1 and 10:1, respectively.

There was no evidence of any fructose chromogen in the chromatograms from tissue samples. Thus, the interference by fructose is probably inconsequential.

The stoichiometric yield of chromogen from deoxyribose is about 50%.[48] For purine deoxyribonucleoside monophosphates the yield was greater than 0·9 mol deoxyribose/g-atom of phosphorus, whereas for the pyrimidine derivatives it was less than 0·3. The results for deoxyribose 5-phosphate, deoxythymidine 3′,5′-diphosphate, and DNA were 0·85, 0·09 and 0·44 mole deoxyribose/g-atom phosphorus, respectively.

This method[48] was evaluated by comparison with a modification[28, 84] of the diphenylamine method.[25] Agreement between the p-nitrophenylhydrazine method and the "kinetic" diphenylamine procedure was evaluated statistically. The results show that the destruction of deoxyribose during extraction with acid impairs the precision of the diphenylamine method even when the conditions of extraction are identical for both the test sample and the DNA standard. Both the "kinetic" diphenylamine method and the p-nitrophenylhydrazine procedure overcome this problem but the former is too laborious for routine use.

A. Selective estimation of DNA with p-nitrophenylhydrazine[48]

Reagents. Acetylated reagent: Dissolve 2·5 g of p-nitrophenylhydrazine in 40 ml glacial acetic acid by heating at 100° for 60 minutes. Cool, collect the precipitate by filtration, and wash with about 15 ml cold ethanol. Yield of orange–yellow needles was 2·2 g. Recrystallization from boiling ethanol (30 ml/g), using hot filtration and a little charcoal, gave very pale yellow needles in 70–80% yield (m.pt. 211·5–212·5°). Reagent solution contains 1% of crystals in methanol. Store aq solutions of deoxyribose and DNA at 5°; 5% aq 2,4-pentanedione at room temperature. These three solutions keep for at least several weeks. Prepare 0·05 M potassium metabisulphite and methanolic NaOH daily, the latter by diluting 10 M aq NaOH tenfold with methanol.

Procedure. Centrifuge a sample of tissue homogenate containing 10 µg–4 mg

DNA and an equal volume of cold 0·4 M perchloric acid in a 16 × 100 mm screw-cap culture tube at about 1500 rev min^{-1} for a few min in a refrigerated centrifuge. Wash residue 3 times with cold 0·2 M perchloric acid. Discard the supernatants and suspend final residue in 2 ml water. Treat 2 ml samples of this solution, water (blank) and DNA standards successively with 0·2 ml of 0·05 M potassium metabisulphite, 0·15 ml of acetylated *p*-nitrophenyl-hydrazine reagent, and finally 2 ml of 2 M perchloric acid. Cap tubes, shake, and heat at 90° for two hours. Chill in an ice bath, remove caps and add 0·2 ml of 5% aq 2,4-pentanedione to each tube. Heat recapped tubes at 90° for 30–60 min, chill, centrifuge, and transfer supernatants to stoppered graduated 25 ml test tubes. After washing precipitates twice with 1 M perchloric acid, dilute combined washings and supernatants to 10 ml with 1 M perchloric acid. Treat each solution with 5 ml water-saturated butanol followed by 2 ml 10 M NaOH. Stopper the tubes, and shake immediately. Transfer 3 ml aliquot of upper organic phase to another tube and to clarify treat with 0·5 ml of 1 M NaOH in 90% methanol. Between 5 and 30 min after addition of the alkali, measure the absorbance of the blue solution at both 580 nm and 680 nm. After correcting for blank readings, the difference in absorbance at the two wavelengths is taken as the measure of DNA in the sample.

XVI. ANTHRONE DETERMINATION OF HEXOSES

In the determination of hexoses with anthrone a blue-green colour is obtained.[85-87] The reactions involved in this procedure are complex as shown by the variety of final chromogens obtained in the determination of glucose.[87] These reactions will be discussed mainly in the 2,5-dioxo-3-hexenal precursors section.

However, one of the chromogens isolated from the reaction is reported to contain a β-acetylacrolein moiety, e.g. chromogen **II**.[50]

II

The neutral chromogen absorbs at 473 nm in benzene and at 635 nm and 655 nm in 70% and 82% H_2SO_4, respectively. In comparison to this methyl-substituted tetramethine derivative the simple dimethine derivative absorbs at 444 nm in benzene and 620 nm in 70% H_2SO_4. The neutral chromogen was isolated in pure crystals following column chromatographic separation of the products obtained by heating glucose with anthrone in H_2SO_4.

XVII. DIPHENYLAMINE DETERMINATION OF FRUCTOSE

In the same way in the determination of fructose in sperm[51] with diphenyl-amine or anthrone at 620 nm, one wonders if β-acetylacrolein and/or 2,5-dioxo-4-hexenal are incorporated in one of the structures of the final blue chromogens.

Regression and variance analyses showed that the diphenylamine method was suitable while the anthrone method was not suitable for the determination of fructose in sperm.

A. Diphenylamine determination of fructose in sperm[51]

Mix 0·1 ml of test solution with 8 ml of cadmium sulphate reagent (13 g $CdSO_4$ and 63·5 ml of 0·5 M H_2SO_4 diluted to 1 l) and 1 ml 1 M NaOH. Mix, centrifuge for 10 min and filter. To 4 ml of filtrate add 2 ml conc HCl and 0·4 ml of 10% diphenylamine in abs ethanol. Stopper and heat for 15 min at 100°, cool for 3 min in cold water, add 4 ml of n-propanol, let stand for 20 min at room temp and read the absorbance at 620 nm.

REFERENCES

1. L. Birkofer and R. Dutz. *Ann.* **608**, 7 (1957).
2. C. Izard-Verchere, P. Rumpf and C. Viel. *Bull. Soc. Chim. France* 2134 (1971).
3. R. E. Deriaz, M. Stacey, E. G. Teece and L. F. Wiggins, *J. Chem. Soc.* 1222 (1949).
4. W. G. Overend, F. Shafizadeh and M. Stacey. *J. Chem. Soc.* 1027 (1950).
5. W. G. Overend. *J. Chem. Soc.* 1484 (1951).
6. R. Allerton, W. G. Overend and M. Stacey. *J. Chem. Soc.* 255 (1952).
7. K. Himmelspach and O. Westphal. *Ann.* **668**, 165 (1963).
8. C. Izard-Verchere, P. Rumpf and C. Viel. *Bull. Soc. Chim. France,* 2118 (1971).
9. C. Izard-Verchere and C. Viel. *Bull. Soc. Chim. France* 2122 (1971).
10. D. F. Clausen. *Tech. Bull. Regist. Med. Techn.* **39**, 186 (1969).
11. L. Birkofer and R. Dutz, *Ann. Chem.* **657**, 94 (1962).
12. J. B. Lee. *Nature* **200**, 264 (1963).
13. W. W. Ackermann, F. Sokol and A. J. Brandau, Jr. *Anal. Biochem.* **12**, 332 (1965).
14. Z. Dische. *Microchem.* **8**, 4 (1930); in E. Chargoff and J. N. Davidson, Eds. "The Nucleic Acids", Academic Press, New York, 1955, p. 285.
15. M. Holden. *Analyst* **78**, 542 (1953).
16. G. Toennies, F. Feng, J. J. Kolb and P. M. Luttner, *Anal. Biochem.* **11**, 473 (1965).
17. D. N. Croft and M. Lubran. *Biochem. J.* **95**, 612 (1965).

C

18. K. Konopka and B. Skoczylas. *Chem. Anal., Warsaw* **8**, 807 (1963).
19. V. Nigon and J. Daillie. *Biochim. Biophys. Acta* **29**, 246 (1958).
20. P. Defrane and J. B. LePecz. *Pathol. Biol. Semaine Hop.* **9**, 2341 (1961); through *Chem. Abstr.* **56**, 14566 (1962).
21. K. W. Giles and A. Myers. *Nature* **206**, 93 (1965).
22. D. N. Croft. *Brit. Med. J.* **ii**, 897 (1963).
23. T. F. Slater and D. Lovell. *Experentia* **17**, 272 (1961).
24. R. Steele, T. Sfortunato and L. Ottolenghi. *J. Biol. Chem.* **177**, 231 (1949).
25. K. Burton. *Biochem. J.* **62**, 315 (1956).
26. T. Slater. *Biochim. Biophys. Acta* **51**, 193 (1961).
27. S. L. Bonting and M. Jones. *Arch. Biochem. Biophys.* **66**, 340 (1957).
28. S. Lovtrup and L. Roos. *Biochim. Biophys. Acta* **33**, 1 (1961).
29. A. S. Orlov and E. I. Orlova. *Biokhimiya* **26**, 834 (1961).
30. R. F. Martin, J. M. Radley and G. S. Hodgson. *Proc. Aust. Biochem. Soc.* **4**, 108 (1971).
31. G. Delmon, R. Babin and P. Blanquet. *Bull. Soc. Pharm. Bordeaux* **91**, 211 (1953).
32. D. W. Hatcher and G. Goldstein. *Anal. Biochem.* **31**, 42 (1969).
33. E. C. Short, Jr., H. R. Warner and J. F. Koerner. *Anal. Biochem.* **26**, 251 (1968).
34. A. de Langen. *Australian J. Dairy Technol.* 36 (1967).
35. M. Novak. *Anal. Biochem.* **36**, 454 (1970).
36. R. L. Blakely. *J. Biol. Chem.* **241**, 176 (1966).
37. R. Pummerer, O. Guyot and L. Birkofer. *Ber.* **68**, 480 (1935).
38. N. Clauson-Kaas and J. T. Nielsen. *Acta Chem. Scand.* **9**, 475 (1955).
39. R. F. Martin. *Aust. J. Chem.* **25**, 401 (1972).
40. J. M. Webb and H. B. Levy, *J. Biol. Chem.* **213**, 107 (1955).
41. P. K. Ganguli. *Rev. Can. Biol.* **29**, 261 (1970).
42. E. Tan, P. H. Schur, R. I. Carr and H. G. Kunkel, *J. Clin. Invest.* **45**, 1732 (1966).
43. R. M. Kothari. *J. Chromatog.* **64**, 85 (1972).
44. G. N. Abraham, C. Scaletta and J. H. Vaughan. *Anal. Biochem.* **49**, 547 (1972).
45. C. L. Burger. *Anal. Biochem.* **20**, 373 (1967).
46. R. E. Brown, B. Zawadzka and D. F. Millikan. *Phytochemistry* **2**, 221 (1963).
47. S. Zamenhof, L. Grauel, E. V. Marthens and R. A. Stillinger. *J. Neurochem.* **19**, 61 (1972).
48. R. F. Martin, D. C. Donohue and L. R. Finch. *Anal. Biochem.* **47**, 562 (1972).
49. D. E. Grogan and D. F. Millikan. *Nature* **206**, 1156 (1965).
50. H. Hörmann and T. L. Nagabhushan. *Z. Physiol. Chem.* **335**, 280 (1964).
51. G. Peter and V. Hauenstein. *Z. Klin. Chem. Klin. Biochem.* **10**, 569 (1972).
52. K. G. Lewis. *J. Chem. Soc.* 531 (1957).
53. C. Izard-Verchere, P. Rumpf and C. Viel. *Compt. Rend.* **271**, 1326 (1970).
54. A. R. Pinder and B. W. Staddon. *J. Chem. Soc.* 2955 (1965).
55. J. Novak and F. Sorm. *Coll. Czech. Chem. Comm.* **23**, 1126 (1958).
56. K. W. Giles and A. Myers. *Biochim. Biophys. Acta* **87**, 460 (1964).
57. G. M. Richards. *Anal. Biochem.* **57**, 369 (1974).
58. H. N. Munro and A. Fleck. *Methods of Biochemical Analysis* **14**, 129, 163, 164 (1966).
59. T. Kaneko and H. Terayama. *Anal. Biochem.* **58**, 439 (1974).
60. G. Ceriotti. *J. Biol. Chem.* **198**, 297 (1952).
61. S. Gurin and D. B. Hood. *J. Biol. Chem.* **139**, 775 (1941).
62. P. K. Stumpf. *J. Biol. Chem.* **169**, 367 (1947).

63. S. S. Cohen. *J. Biol. Chem.* **156**, 691 (1944).
64. G. Widstrom. *Biochem. Z.* **199**, 298 (1928).
65. W. C. Hutchinson and H. N. Munro. *Analyst* **86**, 768 (1961); **87**, 303 (1962).
66. H. N. Munro and A. Fleck. *Analyst* **91**, 78 (1966).
67. W. E. Cohen and D. G. Doherty. *J. Am. Chem. Soc.* **78**, 2863 (1956).
68. L. Grossman and G. R. Hawkins. *Biochim. Biophys. Acta* **26**, 657 (1957).
69. R. L. Blakley. *J. Biol. Chem.* **240**, 2173 (1965).
70. F. Stutzenberger. *Anal. Biochem.* **56**, 294 (1973).
71. A. E. Mirsky and H. Ris. *J. Gen. Physiol.* **34**, 451 (1950–51).
72. F. C. Margolis. *J. Neurochem.* **16**, 447 (1969).
73. S. Zamenhof, H. Bursztyn, K. Rich and P. J. Zamenhof. *J. Neurochem.* **11**, 505 (1964).
74. E. Tan, P. H. Schur, R. I. Carr and H. G. Kunkel. *J. Clin. Invest.* **45**, 1732 (1966).
75. G. Cerioitti. *J. Biol. Chem.* **214**, 59 (1955).
76. W. C. Schneider. *J. Biol. Chem.* **161**, 293 (1945).
77. W. C. Schneider. *J. Biol. Chem.* **164**, 747 (1946).
78. M. Ogur and G. Rosen, *Arch. Biochem.* **25**, 262 (1950).
79. E. P. Tyner, C. Heidelberger and G. A. LePage. *Cancer Res.* **13**, 186 (1953).
80. J. Levitt. *Physiol. Plantarum* **5**, 470 (1952).
81. R. Borenfreund, R. F. H. Fitt and A. Bendich. *Nature* **191**, 1375 (1961).
82. R. F. Martin and G. S. Hodgson. *Anal. Biochem.* **52**, 462 (1973).
83. R. F. Martin. Ph.D. Thesis, University of Melbourne, 1970.
84. S. Lovtrup. *Acta Biochim. Pol.* **9**, 411 (1962).
85. R. Dreywood. *Ind. Eng. Chem., Anal. Ed.* **18**, 499 (1946).
86. E. W. Yemm and A. J. Willis. *Biochem. J.* **57**, 508 (1954).
87. T. Momose, Y. Ueda, K. Sawada and A. Sugi. *Pharm. Bull. (Tokyo)* **5**, 31 (1957); *Chem. Abstr.* **51**, 17864 (1957).

3. ACROLEIN, PRECURSORS

I. FORMATION REAGENTS

Some examples of compounds from which acrolein can be derived through dehydration, hydrolysis or oxidation are shown in Table 10. Some of the basic precursor structures are listed in Table 11.

Examples of dehydration are (a) the conversion of β-hydroxypropionaldehyde to acrolein by heating with 2N HCl, the acrolein being characterized as the 2,4-dinitrophenylhydrazone[19] and (b) the conversion of glycerol to acrolein in hot sulphuric acid,[12–18] e.g.

$$CH_2OH-CHOH-CH_2OH \xrightarrow[\Delta]{H_2SO_4} CH_2{=}CH-CHO + 2H_2O \tag{1}$$

Several types of oxidation reactions have been shown to form acrolein. Photo-oxidation of simple artificial atmospheres containing nitrogen oxides, ozone or oxygen and 1,3-alkadienes and sometimes other chemicals has shown that acrolein and formaldehyde can be formed from the diene.[4–8] Acrolein accounts for approx 3–10% (on a molar basis) of the total aldehydes in automobile exhaust.[28, 29] Of the aldehydes present in the atmosphere 50% is present as formaldehyde and 5% as acrolein.[30–32] The average range of acrolein in the urban atmosphere is approx 0·1–2 $\mu g\,m^{-3}$.[33]

Acrolein can be formed by oxidation of propene with mercuric sulphate.[21] These two form a complex which, when heated for 1 h at 60°, gives a quantitative yield of acrolein, as determined by absorption at 322 nm. The postulated equation is:

$$CH_3-CH{=}CH_2 + H_2O + Hg^{+2} \rightarrow H^+ + CH_3CH(OH)-CH_2-Hg^+$$

$$CH_3CH(OH)-CH_2-Hg^+ + 3Hg^{+2} \rightarrow CH_2{=}CH-CHO + 4Hg^+ + 3H^+ \tag{2}$$

2,4-Dinitrophenylhydrazine can also act as an oxidizing agent.[20] 1,3-Propanediol in a saturated solution of this hydrazine in 10% hydrochloric acid forms a turbid mixture containing the precipitated hydrazone within 10 min.

Enzymatic methods of oxidation for molecules containing the 1,3-propanediamine or allylamine structures have been described.[1, 2, 26, 27] Thus,

Table 10. Formation of acrolein from precursors

Precursor	Reagent	Reaction[a]	Ref.
Allylamine	Spermine oxidase	(O)	1, 2
Allylidene diacetate	H_2SO_4	H	1, 3
1,3-Butadiene	Nitrogen oxides, ozone or oxygen	(O)[b]	4–8
Cyclophosphamides	$H_2O_2 \rightarrow$ pH 7·2 at 37°	(O) → H + D	9
3,3'-Diaminodipropylamine	Spermine oxidase	(O)	1, 2
3,3-Diethoxy-1-propene	Acid	H	1
3,3-Dimethoxy-1-propene	H_2SO_4	H	3
4-(2,4-Dinitrophenoxy)-1,2-butanediol	Periodate → alkali	(O) → H	10–11
Glycerol and triglycerides	H_2SO_4	D	12–18
4-Hydroxycyclophosphamides	pH 7·2 at 37°	H + D	9
β-Hydroxypropionaldehyde	2 N HCl	D	19
2-Methyl-1,3-pentadiene	Nitrogen oxides, hν	(O)	4–8
1,3-Pentadiene	Nitrogen oxides, hν	(O)	4–8
Propane-1,3-diol	2,4-Dinitrophenylhydrazine	(O)	20
Propene	Mercuric sulphate	(O)	21–25[c]
Spermidine	Spermine oxidase	(O)	1, 2, 26, 27
Spermine	Spermine oxidase	(O)	1, 2, 26, 27
1,3,3-Triethoxypropane	Acid	H	2
1,3,3-Trimethoxypropane	Acid	H	2

[a] D = dehydration; H = hydrolysis; (O) = oxidation.
[b] Photooxidation
[c] Catalytic oxidation with a copper catalyst.[23]

Table 11. Basic acrolein precursor structure

CH_2=CH—CH_2X,	X=H, OH, NH_2
CH_2=CH—CH$(OR)_2$,	R=H, alkyl, acyl
HO—CH_2—CH_2—CHO	
$CH_2(OR)$—CH(OR)—CH_2OR,	R=H, alkyl, acyl
CH_2=CH—CH=CR_2,	R=H, alkyl
X—CH_2—CH_2—CH_2—X,	X=OH, NH_2, NHR
ArO—CH_2CH_2—CHOH—CH_2OH	

spermine or spermidine incubated at 37° for 24 h with calf serum forms acrolein.[1]

Monooxidation at C-4 of cyclophosphamide appears to be responsible for the activation of this antitumor agent by the drug-metabolizing enzymes of the liver.[34-36] Studies of the activities of the various *in vitro* active metabolites of the cyclophosphamides should reveal more about the role that is played by their conversion to aldophosphamide and by their spontaneous breakdown, both intra- and extracellularly, to the two cytotoxic substances, acrolein and N,N-bis(2-chloroethyl)phosphorodiamidic acid.[37] The reactions are shown in Fig. 9. The occurrence of aldophosphamide after activa-

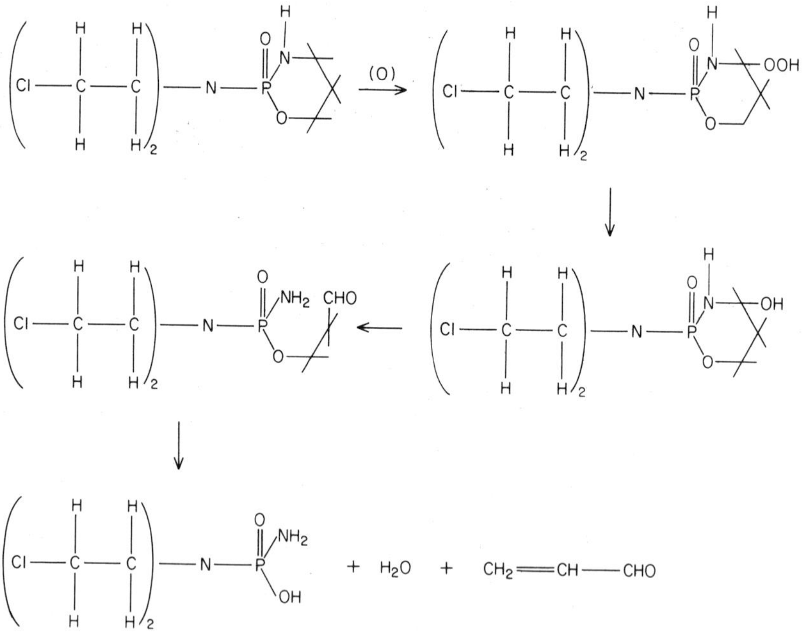

FIG. 9. Probable metabolism and *in vitro* Fenton oxidation of cyclophosphamide to acrolein and N,N-bis(2-chloroethyl)phosphorodiamidic acid.[9]

tion of cyclophosphamide by microsomal preparations[34, 35] and the production of acrolein under such conditions[38] are understandable on the basis of prior C-4 hydroxylation.[9]

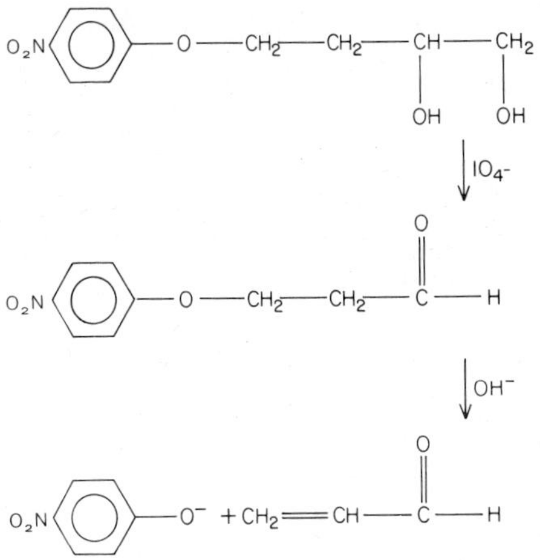

$$O_2N-C_6H_4-O-CH_2-CH_2-\underset{\underset{OH}{|}}{CH}-\underset{\underset{OH}{|}}{CH_2}$$

$$\downarrow IO_4^-$$

$$O_2N-C_6H_4-O-CH_2-CH_2-\overset{\overset{O}{\|}}{C}-H$$

$$\downarrow OH^-$$

$$O_2N-C_6H_4-O^- + CH_2\!\!=\!\!CH-\overset{\overset{O}{\|}}{C}-H$$

FIG. 10. Reactions involved in the formation of acrolein from 4-(p-nitrophenoxy)-1,2-butanediol.

An accurate and sensitive method for measuring periodate concentration quantitatively utilizes 4-(p-nitrophenoxy)1,2-butanediol or 4-(2,4-dinitrophenoxy)1,2-butanedione as reagents.[10] These substances are readily oxidized by periodate to β-(di)nitrophenoxy aldehydes which undergo a facile β-elimination in alkali to yield the coloured (di)nitrophenolate ion and acrolein, Fig. 10. Other 4-aryloxy-1,2-butanediols could be oxidized, hydrolysed and dehydrated to acrolein in a similar fashion. They could then be analysed through acrolein. Such a method could probably be used to measure alkaline phosphomonoesterase (orthophosphoric monoester phosphohydrolase, EC 3.1.3.2) and acid phosphomonoesterase (orthophosphoric monoester phosphohydrolase, EC 3.1.3.2).[11]

The reagents which have been used in the determination of the acrolein derived from precursor molecules are given in Table 12.

II. m- AND o-AMINOPHENOLS

The relative fluorescence intensities obtained with acrolein and some of its precursors in the reaction with m-aminophenol are given in Table 13.[2] As discussed in the acrolein section of the first volume 7-hydroxyquinoline is the fluorogen formed in the reaction. The following procedure has been used for the 1,3-diaminopropane type of precursors.

A. *m*-Aminophenol determination of spermine or spermidine[2]

To 2 ml of test solution, 0·05 M in tris(hydroxymethylamino)methane, add 0·5 ml of calf serum. Incubate at 50° for 3 h. Precipitate protein with 0·5 ml of aq trichloroacetic acid. Filter or centrifuge. To a 2 ml aliquot add 0·5 ml of reagent (250 mg of *m*-aminophenol plus 300 mg of hydroxylamine hydrochloride dissolved in 25 ml 1 N HCl) and 0·5 ml of 5 N HCl. Heat on a boiling water bath for 10 min. Cool in tap water. Read at $F400/510$. Fluorescence is stable for several hours.

A somewhat similar reagent which has been used in the analysis of the acrolein precursor, glycerol and its glycerides, is *o*-aminophenol.[13] With this reagent serum triglycerides were determined with the following steps: removal of interfering materials by silicic acid, alkaline hydrolysis of glycerides to glycerol which is heated with *o*-aminophenol in the presence of conc sulphuric acid and arsenic acid to form 8-hydroxyquinoline, followed by chelation with Mg^{2+} in an alkaline solution to form a fluorescent complex, Fig. 11. The fluorogen is pH-dependent.

The method is specific for triglycerides. Inositol, glucose, and other hexoses, serine, choline, and ethanolamine do not affect the results. Possible interfering substances, such as methanol, ethanol, fatty acids, sterols, glycero-

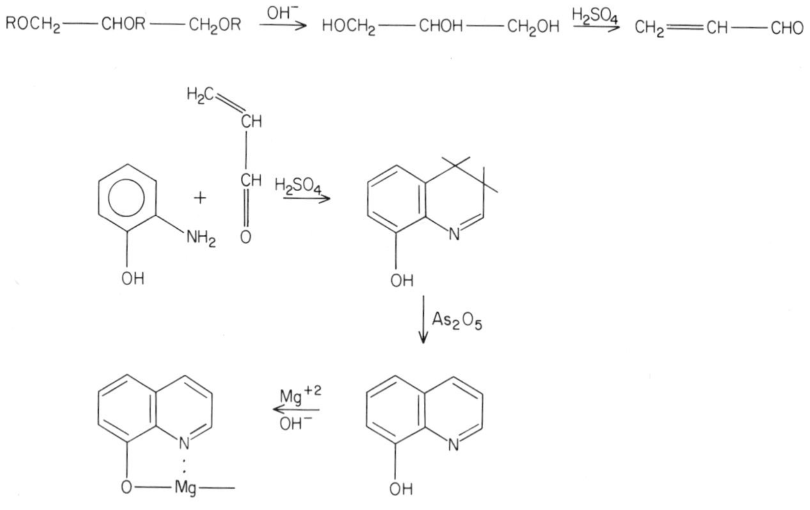

FIG. 11. Determination of glycerides with *o*-aminophenol.

phosphatides, sphingomyelin, and free serum glycerol are all removed by clean-up steps in the procedure. This fluorimetric procedure, given below, compares favourably with other methods.

B. o-Aminophenol determination of serum triglycerides[13]

Shake 0·3 ml serum with 1·2 g of activated silicic acid and 7·5 ml isopropyl ether. Treat a triolein standard similarly. Evaporate 5 ml aliquots of the supernatant liquids, dissolve residues in 3–4 drops of ether, 0·5 ml methanol and 3 drops of 2% methanolic KOH solution, and saponify at 60–70° for 30 minutes. Add 2 drops of 6% methanolic acetic acid, evaporate to dryness, dissolve the residue in 6 ml light petroleum and add 0·5 ml 10 N H_2SO_4. Shake the mixture, centrifuge, and discard the petroleum layer. Transfer duplicate 0·1 ml aliquots of the aq layers to tubes in which 0·1 ml of 1·6% o-aminophenol in acetone was evaporated. Add 0·4 ml of a 0·6% solution of arsenic acid in conc sulphuric acid and heat the mixture at 140° for 15 minutes. After cooling in ice water, add 1 ml of aq magnesium sulphate solution (120 μg of Mg per ml), followed by 5 ml of 28% aq ammonia solution. Shake the mixture and read in a filter fluorimeter. In this work a Farrand fluorimeter with aperture 6 and Corning 5874 (primary) and 2424 (secondary) filters were used. Recoveries of triolein added to serum ranged from 97–103%. The method can be used to determine glycerophosphatides.

III. ANTHRONE

Anthrone has been used to determine various types of acrolein precursors, Table 12. Benzanthrone cation is the fluorogen formed in the reaction. The intensity of fluorescence of this cation in sulphuric acid increases uniformly when the concentration of acid is between 85 and 98%; below 85% the fluorescence is erratic.[12] In the determination 85% sulphuric acid and reaction at 120° gave maximal production of benzanthrone and a minimal decomposition of the anthrone. In the presence of organic materials, such as sugars, the reaction mixture can become dark. To overcome this difficulty 6 ml of water can be added to the mixture followed by 2 extractions with 6-ml volumes of benzene. Following evaporation of the benzene and solution of the residue in sulphuric acid, readings can be made at $F350–500/575$.

The procedure to be described can be used to determine glycerol in the concentration range of 10–75 μg with an accuracy of ± 5 μg. A linear relation is found over this concentration. Unlike the sugars which interfere significantly only when present in greater than 100-fold amounts, tartaric acid, formaldehyde, ethylene glycol and acetone cause far more serious interference in 10-fold amounts. Thus, tartaric acid and formaldehyde quench

Table 12. Determination of acrolein precursors

Precursor	Reagent	$F_{exc/em}$ or $\lambda_{max/(me)}$	Other data	Ref.
Allylamine[a]	m-Aminophenol	400/510	Detn limit ~ 10 ng	2
Allylidene diacetate[b]	Anthrone	485/560	Detn limit −0·5 μg	3
1,3-Butadiene[c]	4-Hexylresorcinol	605 (20)[d]		8
Glycerol	Anthrone	~ 350–500/575	Detn limit − 10 μg	12
Glycerol	o-Aminophenol + Mg^{2+}		No interference from hexoses	13
Propane-1,3-diol	2,4-Dinitrophenylhydrazine		Carbonyl compounds interfere	20
Propene	—[e]	322	1-Alkenes and other UV absorbers	21

[a] Also allylidene diacetals, 3,3'-diaminodipropylamine, spermine (detm. limit 5 ng) and spermidine (detm. limit 10 ng).
[b] Also 3,3-dimethoxy-1-propene, detm. limit 0·4 μg.
[c] Also other 1,3-alkadienes.
[d] Obtained with pure acrolein.
[e] No reagent.

the fluorescence of benzanthrone to a large extent while ethylene glycol suppresses the fluorescence to a lesser but still significant extent. Acetone enhances the fluorescence.

Table 13. Determination of acrolein precursors with m-aminophenol[2]

Compound	Relative fluorescence intensity, $F352/495$
Acrolein	100
Allylidene diacetate	160
3,3-Diethoxy-l-propene	127
1,3,3-Triethoxypropane	90
1,3,3-Trimethoxypropane	87
Spermine	18
Allylamine	13
Spermidine	9

A. Anthrone determination of glycerol[12]

Add 1 ml of 0·1 % (w/v) solution of anthrone in 85 % sulphuric acid to 1 ml of an 85 % sulphuric acid test solution. Heat for exactly 15 min in an oil-bath at 120°. Allow to cool, dilute with 5 ml of 98 % sulphuric acid and thoroughly mix the two layers. Read at $F350-500/575$.

Easily-hydrolysable acrolein precursors can be determined with anthrone by another simple precedure.[3] Acrolein, malonaldehyde and its precursors give the same fluorogen, the benzanthrone cation, so these compounds could be considered interferences in the determination of acrolein. Pyruvaldehyde and its precursors give an entirely different fluorogen which emits at much shorter wavelengths. The procedure is as follows.

B. Anthrone determination of easily-hydrolysable acrolein precursors[3]

To 2 ml of aq test solution add 3 ml of 0·1 % anthrone in conc sulphuric acid. Allow the mixture to stand for 10 min and then add 3 ml of glacial acetic acid. Cool and read at $F485/560$. Allylidene diacylates, 3,3-dialkoxy-1-propenes and 1,3,3-trialkoxypropanes are determined in this fashion.

IV. HEXYLRESORCINOL AND SCHIFF'S REAGENT

4-Hexylresorcinol has not seen much use in the analysis of acrolein precursors, probably because it has never been investigated with this purpose in mind.

Since allyl alcohol can be oxidized readily to acrolein with the help of chloramine T,[39]

$$CH_2{=}CH{-}CH_2OH + CH_3.C_6H_4SO_2NClNa \rightarrow$$
$$CH_2{=}CH{-}CHO + CH_3.C_6H_4SO_2NH_2 + NaCl$$

allyl alcohol could be determined with 4-hexylresorcinol.

Unlike tissue-bound formaldehyde, acrolein bound to tissue gives a direct reaction with Schiff's reagent.[40]

REFERENCES

1. R. A. Alarcon. *Arch. Biochem. Biophys.* **113**, 281 (1966).
2. R. A. Alarcon. *Anal. Chem.* **40**, 1704 (1968).
3. E. Sawicki, R. A. Carnes and R. Schumacher, *Mikrochim. Acta* 929 (1967).
4. A. P. Altshuller and J. J. Bufalini. *Photochem. Photobiol.* **4**, 97 (1965).
5. E. A. Schuck and G. J. Doyle. Photooxidation of Hydrocarbons in Mixtures Containing Oxides of Nitrogen and Sulfur Dioxide, Report No. 29, Air Pollution Foundation, San Marino, Calif. (1959).
6. J. E. Sigsby, Jr., T. A. Bellar and L. J. Leng. *J. Air Pollution Control Assoc.* **12**, 522 (1962).
7. E. R. Stephens, *et al. Int. J. Air Water Pollution* **4**, 79 (1961).
8. I. R. Cohen and A. P. Altshuller. *Anal. Chem.* **33**, 726 (1961).
9. J. van der Steen, E. C. Timmer, J. G. Westra and C. Benckhuysen. *J. Am. Chem. Soc.* **95**, 7535 (1973).
10. D. H. Rammler, R. Bilton, R. Haugland and C. Parkinson. *Anal. Biochem.* **52**, 198 (1973).
11. D. H. Rammler and C. Parkinson. *Anal. Biochem.* **52**, 208 (1973).
12. F. A. Lyne, J. A. Radley and M. B. Taylor. *Analyst* **93**, 186 (1968).
13. D. Mendelsohn and A. Antonis. *J. Lipid Res.* **2**, 45 (1961).
14. F. Schutz. *Papierfabrikant* **36**, 55 (1938).
15. J. A. Radley. *J. Sci. Food Agric.* **1**, 222 (1950).
16. C. F. H. Allen and S. C. Overbaugh. *J. Am. Chem. Soc.* **57**, 1322 (1935).
17. F. Feigl and O. Frehden. *Mikrochim. Acta* **1**, 137 (1937).
18. C. A. Kohn. *cf.* W. Fresenius. *Z. Anal. Chem.* **30**, 619 (1891).
19. J. Pawelkiewicz and B. Zagalak. *Acta Biochim. Polon.* **12**, 207 (1965).
20. D. Welti and D. Whittaker. *Chem. Ind.* **1962**, 986.
21. B. C. Fielding and H. L. Roberts. *J. Chem. Soc.* **1966A**, 1627.
22. S. A. D. Macallum. U.S.P. 2, 197, 258 (1940).
23. K. Herstein. U.S.P. 2, 270, 705 (1942).
24. F. E. Mertz and O. C. Dermer. *Proc. Oklahoma Acad. Sci.* 134 (1949).
25. V. P. Latyshev and N. I. Popova. *Izvest. Sibir. Otdel., Akad. Nauk. S.S.S.R.* **1959**, 48; through *Chem. Abstr.* **54**, 6408d (1960).
26. R. A. Alarcon. *Arch. Biochem. Biophys.* **106**, 240 (1964).
27. T. Unemoto, I. Keiko, H. Makoto and M. Komei. *Chem. Pharm. Bull. Japan* **11**, 148 (1963).
28. A. P. Altshuller, I. R. Cohen, M. E. Meyer and A. F. Wartburg, Jr. *Anal. Chim. Acta* **25**, 101 (1961).

29. M. F. Fracchia, F. J. Schuette and P. K. Mueller. *Env. Sci. Technol.* **1**, 915 (1967).
30. A. P. Altshuller and S. P. McPherson. *J. Air Pollution Control Assoc.* **13**, 109 (1963).
31. P. W. Leach, *et al. J. Air Pollution Control Assoc.* **14**, 176 (1964).
32. N. A. Renzetti and R. J. Bryan. *J. Air Pollution Control Assoc.* **11**, 421 (1961).
33. Preliminary Air Pollution Survey of Aldehydes, A Literature Review, National Air Pollution Administration Publication No. APTD 69–24, Nat'l Bureau of Standards Clearinghouse for Federal Scientific and Technical Information, Springfield, Virginia, 1969.
34. D. L. Hill. *Proc. Am. Assoc. Cancer Res.* **12**, 67 (1971).
35. D. L. Hill, W. R. Laster, Jr. and R. F. Struck. *Cancer Res.* **32**, 658 (1972).
36. A. Takamizawa, S. Matsumoto, T. Iwata, K. Katagiri, Y. Tochino and K. Yamaguchi. *J. Am. Chem. Soc.* **95**, 985 (1973).
37. O. M. Friedman, E. Boger, V. Grubliauskas and H. Sommer. *J. Med. Chem.* **6**, 50 (1963).
38. R. A. Alarcon and J. Meienhofer. *Nature, New Biol.* **233**, 250 (1971).
39. D. S. Mahadevappa and H. M. K. Naidu. *Talanta* **20**, 349 (1973).
40. M. Elleder and Z. Lojda. *Histochemie* **30**, 325 (1972).

4. 2-ACROLEYL-3-AMINOFUMARATE, PRECURSORS

I. 3-HYDROXYANTHRANILATE

Some tryptophan metabolites are believed to be causative agents of human urinary bladder cancer. One of these, e.g. 3-hydroxyanthranilic acid, has shown carcinogenic activity in animals. The excretion of this substance is increased in patients with cancer of the urinary bladder.[1] A specific method for the quantitative estimation of this compound through the formation of an aldehyde-precursor is available. The principle of the method is as follows. 3-Hydroxyanthranilic acid is metabolized with 3-hydroxyanthranilic acid oxidase (3-hydroxyanthranilate; oxygen oxidoreductase, E.C. 1.13.1.6; 3-OH-AO) to 2-acroleyl-3-aminofumarate.

The configuration of the reaction product has been proposed by Bonner and Yanofsky[2] and proven by Kuss.[3] The derived aldehyde is measured by means of its absorption maximum at 360 nm. A somewhat similar method has been used for the estimation of 3-hydroxyanthranilic acid oxidase activity.[4] The method can also be applied to the determination of 3-hydroxy-kynurenine, also a carcinogen, through degradation by kynureninase to 3-hydroxyanthranilic acid which is then degraded to 2-acroleyl-3-amino-fumarate.[5]

In the procedure for 3-hydroxyanthranilic acid, Beer's law was obeyed from 1–10 μg ml^{-1}. The relative standard deviation was $\pm 5 \cdot 68 \%$. Recovery experiments with 3-hydroxyanthranilic acid added to urine were around $100 \pm 2 \cdot 6 \%$.

A. Procedure for determination of 2-acroleyl-3-aminofumarate[5]

Urine is adjusted to pH 7·4 with 2 N NaOH or 1 N HCl respectively and then filtered.

For estimation of total 3-OH-A the urine is hydrolysed as follows: 5 ml urine are mixed with 0·02 ml of the hydrolysing enzyme and incubated for 2 h at room temp.

Assay. The analyses are performed in the same way with hydrolysed and non-hydrolysed urine at room temp. Samples are prepared in 3 ml cuvettes with 1 cm optical path:

Table 14

	Analysis (A)	Standard (S + A)	Blank (B)
Tris buffer	0·90	0·90	0·9
Urine	1·00	1·00	1·0
Standard solution	—	0·05	—
0·1 N NaOH	—	0·05	—
Cysteine-Fe solution	0·02	0·02	—
Enzyme solution	0·20	0·20	—
H$_2$O	0·10	—	0·22

The amount of standard substance added should be in correlation with the concentration of the analysis sample, i.e., 2–3 µg standard at a concentration of about 1 µg 3-OH-A/ml urine (Table 14).

Immediately after addition of the enzyme solution the extinction is measured against the blank at 360 nm. The extinction is registered as long as it increases; generally, this lasts for 10–20 minutes. The extinction of the standard sample is read every minute, the extinction of the analysis sample every second minute. During the incubation period the samples have to be thoroughly mixed several times (Fig. 12).

Calculation.

$$C = \frac{D_A}{D_{S+A} - D_A} \times 5 = \text{µg/ml 3-OH-A}$$

With variation of the amount of standard substance added, the factor 5 in this formula will have to be changed accordingly. As 1 ml of urine is used for

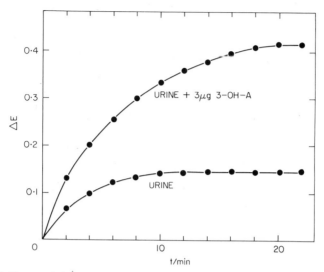

FIG. 12. Characteristic curve of absorption at 360 nm during enzymatic assay with normal human urine.[5]

analysis the result has to be multiplied with the 24 h amount (ml) of urine to calculate the 24 h excretion. If more than a few drops of NaOH or HCl have been used for adjustment of the pH, this dilution factor has to be considered.

REFERENCES

1. E. Boyland in D. M. Wallace, Ed. "Tumours of the Bladder," E. and S. Livingstone. Ltd., Edinburgh—London, 1959, p. 83.
2. D. M. Bonner and C. Yanofsky. *Proc. Natl. Acad. Sci. U.S.* **35**, 576 (1949).
3. E. Kuss. *Z. Physiol. Chem.* **345**, 195 (1966).
4. O. Wiss. *Z. Naturforsch.* **11b**, 54 (1956).
5. H. Schievelbein and E. Buchfink. *Clin. Chim. Acta* **18**, 291 (1967).

5. ADIPALDEHYDE, PRECURSOR

Ruthenium tetroxide is better than osmium tetroxide in rupturing the double bond of cyclohexene.[1] The following reaction takes place:

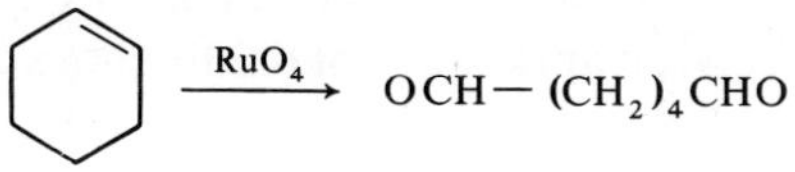

$$\text{[cyclohexene]} \xrightarrow{\text{RuO}_4} \text{OCH}-(\text{CH}_2)_4\text{CHO}$$

The adipaldehyde can then be determined by any one of the aldehyde reagents, e.g. MBTH, DNPH, NPH, etc.

REFERENCE

1. L. M. Berkowitz and P. N. Rylander. *J. Am. Chem. Soc.* **80**, 6682 (1958).

6. ALDEHYDE ACIDS (MISCELLANEOUS), PRECURSORS

Long-chain epoxy acids and esters can be oxidized readily by periodate to a mixture of two aldehydes.[1] Some of the precursors that undergo this type of reaction are shown in Table 15. The oxidations were usually performed in aq dioxane. Glycidyl stearate was not oxidized to an aldehyde under these conditions. However, when the stearate was treated with periodic acid dissolved in acetic acid and chloroform, formaldehyde and formylmethyl

Table 15. Internal cleavage of internal epoxides with periodic acid

Precursor	Aldehyde	Ref.
Methyl 9,10-epoxystearate	methyl azelaaldehydate pelargonic aldehyde	1
9,10-Dihydroxystearic acid	methyl azelaaldehydate pelargonic aldehyde	2
Glycidyl stearate	formylmethyl stearate[a]	3
Methyl 9,10:12,13-diepoxystearate	methyl azelaaldehydate	1
Methyl 12-hydroxy-9,10-epoxystearate	methyl azelaaldehydate	1
Methyl 12,13-epoxy-9-octadecanoate	methyl 11-formylundecanoate	1

[a] and CH_2O

Table 16. Solvent effect on periodate cleavage of methyl 9,10-epoxystearate

Solvent	Methyl azelaaldehydate yield, %
Nitromethane	89·9
1,4-Dioxane	89·1
Methyl acetate	77·6
Acetic acid	47·7

stearate were obtained in an almost quantitative yield. The importance of the solvent in the oxidation is shown in Table 16.

Use has not yet been made of determining these precursors through photometric analysis of the aldehydes.

REFERENCES

1. G. Maerker and E. T. Haeberer. *J. Am. Oil Chem. Soc.* **43**, 97 (1966).
2. G. King. *J. Chem. Soc.* 1826 (1938).
3. K. E. Bharucha and F. D. Gunstone. *J. Sci. Food Agric.* **6**, 378 (1955).

7. ALIPHATIC ALDEHYDES, PRECURSORS

I. INTRODUCTION

A fairly large number of organic molecules are available from which aliphatic aldehydes can be derived. As will be shown, use has been made of this property to characterize and analyse the precursor molecules present in the complex mixtures found in living tissue, in the material derived from the life forms inhabiting this planet and in the environment surrounding the human animal. Many examples of aldehyde formation cited in this section and in the volumes in Part II of this treatment have not yet been utilized in photometric analysis but are potentially of very considerable use. On the other hand, it must be emphasized that, under some conditions of analysis for aldehydes, there are precursors that react in terms of the derived aldehyde, so that an elevated value is obtained for the aldehyde. In a somewhat similar fashion analysis for an aldehyde precursor may give an elevated value through the presence of interfering aldehyde(s).

Of value in the separation and analysis of aldehydes and their precursors is a recent compilation concerned with the chromatographic properties of aliphatic aldehydes.[1] The industrial usage and the physiological properties of aliphatic aldehydes, such as acetaldehyde, acrolein, chloral, citronellal, and formaldehyde, have been reported.[2] This wide prevalence of the aldehydes in the human environment is important from several aspects. The aldehydes can be interferences in the determination of the precursors by methods of analysis for aldehydes. Also, since aldehydes are very reactive they can form precursors in the environment. Since many of the aldehydes are mutagenic,[2] some of their precursors could also be mutagenic and even carcinogenic under appropriate conditions. Some of the aliphatic aldehydes, e.g. acrolein, crotonaldehyde, and formaldehyde, have been shown to be highly cytotoxic to Ehrlich–Landschutz diploid ascites tumor cells *in vitro*.[3] It would appear that a thorough study is needed of those aldehyde precursors which can release the cytotoxic aldehyde *in vivo* in some appropriate human tissue.

Precursors, reagents and reactions useful in the derivation of aldehydes are listed in Table 17. To emphasize the large variety of these precursors

Table 17. Formation of aliphatic aldehydes from precursors

Precursors	Reagents	Reactions[a]	Ref.
Acids, fatty	H_2O_2 + fatty acid peroxidase	(O)	4
Acyl chlorides	$Na_2Fe(CO)_4$	(H)	5, 6
Alcohols[b]	$Pb(OAc)_4$	(O)	7
Alcohols, primary[c]	$Me_3N\text{-}C_6H_4N_2BF_4$ [d]	(O)	8, 9
Alcohols, primary	CrO_3 – graphite	(O)	10
Alcohols, primary[c]	$RuO_2 + IO_4^-$	(O)	11
Alcohols, primary	$NAD(P)^+$ + alcohol oxidoreductase	(O)	12–20
Aldehydes DNPHs[e]	MBTH	D	21
1,2-Alkanolamines	Ethanolamine ammonia-lyase	DP	22, 23
Alkenyl ethers	Alkenyl-glycerophosphinicocholine	H	24, 25
Alkenyl ethers (plasmalogens)	Mercuric chloride	H	26, 27
Alkenyl ethers (plasmalogens)	HCl or H_2SO_4	H	27–42
Alkylamines	Argentic picolonate	(OD)	43–45
Alkylamines	H_2O_2 + catalyst	(OD)	45–47
Alkylamines	O_2 + monoamine oxidase	(OD)	48–53
N-Alkylarylamines	Periodate	(O)	54
N-Alkylarylamines	Ce(IV) salts	(O)	55
N-Alkylarylamines	Dichromate	(O)	56
N-Alkylarylamines	$Pb(OAc)_4$	(O)	57
Alkyl halides	$Na_2Fe(CO)_4$	A	5, 6
Alkyl oxiranes	Periodate	(O)	58
Alkyl tosylates	$Na_2Fe(CO)_4$	A	5, 6
α-Amino acids	NaClO or NaBrO	(OD)	59, 60, 60a
α-Amino acids	Epicatechin + tea leaf extract	(OD)	61
α-Amino acids	Alloxan	(OD)	62
D-α-Amino acids	D-Amino acid oxidase → MBTH	(O)DC	63, 64
α-Amino acids	Perinaphthindantrione	(OD)	65, 66
α-Amino acids	Ninhydrin	(OD)	67–80

Table 17—continued

Precursors	Reagents	Reactions[a]	Ref.
α-Amino acid	$NH_2OH + DNF +$ alkali	LR	81
Amino alcohols + diamines	Periodate	(O)	82–88
Azoalkanes	Acid	Taut → H	89, 90
Benzylidenehexoses	Periodate	(O)	91
Collagen	Periodate	(O)[f]	92
vic-Cycloalkanediols	MnO_2	(O)	93
Cyclooctatetraene	$Pb(OAc)_4 + CH_3COOH + BF_3$	RC + (O)	94
2,2-Dialkyloxiranes	Acid + water	RO	95, 96
Enol ethers	$Pb(OAc)_4$	(O)	97
Epoxides	Periodate	H → (O)	98–105
Epoxides	BF_3	RO	106
Epoxides	Acid	RC + RO	107
Ethers	$Pb(OAc)_4$	(O)	108
Ethylene acetals	Periodate	(O)	109
Ethylene glycols	Permanganate	(O)	109a
Gangliosides	H_2SO_4	(O)	110
Glyceride oils	Air	(O)	111–116
α-Glycols	Periodate	(O)	117–135
α-Glycols	Air + Co(II)	(O)	136
α-Glycols	Ce(IV)	(O)	137
α-Glycols	$Pb(OAc)_4$	(O)	138
α-Glycols	$Pb(OAc)_4$, RuO_4, or Ag_2CO_3	(O)	139–143
α-Glycols	Dioldehydrase	DH	144
α-Glycols	Propanediol dehydratase	DH	145, 146
Hydrazines	$HgSO_4$ + acid	(O) → Taut → H	90, 147
Hydrocarbons (unsaturated)	$NO_x, O_x + h\nu$	(O)	148–158
Hydrocarbons	Air	(O)	159–163
Hydroperoxides[g]	Acid	H	112, 164–170

α-Hydroxy acids	Pb(OAc)$_4$	DC + (O)	171
α-Hydroxy acids	Periodate	DC + (O)	172
17-Hydroxysteroids	Pb(OAc)$_4$	RO + (O)	173
2-Ketocarboxylic acids	2-Ketodecarboxylase	DC	174
2-Ketocarboxylic acids	Pyruvate decarboxylase	DC	175
Lipids	DNPH	(O)	176
Methyl octadecenoate	Air	(O)	177
Methyl octadecenoate	O$_3$ → φ$_3$P	(O) → (H)	178
Nitroalkanes	Alkali → acid	H	179
1-Nitroalkanes	Permanganate	(O)	180
1-Nitroalkanes	Nitroethane oxidase	(O)	181
Nitrosamines	Acid + air	(O)	182
Nitrosamines	Enzymic (β + ω-hydroxylation)	(O)	183, 184
Olefins	Periodate	(O)	132, 185
Olefins	RuO$_4$	(O)	11
Olefins	Ozone → (CH$_3$)$_2$S	(O) → (H)	186, 187
Olefins	Ozone → (C$_6$H$_5$)$_3$P or Na$_3$AsO$_3$	(O) → (H)	187–189
Oximes	Tl(NO$_3$)$_3$	H	190
Ozonides	DNPH	H	191–195
Phenylhydrazones	Tl(NO$_3$)$_3$	H	190
2-Phosphonoacetaldehyde	Phosphonoacetaldehyde hydrolase	H	196
Pyruvic acids	Acid	DC	197
Semicarbazones	Tl(NO$_3$)$_3$	H	190
Styrenes, α-phenyl	Pb(OAc)$_4$	(O)	211, 212
Thiazoles, 2-methyl	RCl → Me$_3$OBF$_4$ → NaBH$_4$ → HgCl$_2$	A → A → (H) → H	199
Thiazolidine-4-carboxylic acids	Iodine	H	198, 200
Thiazolidines	HgCl$_2$	H	199
Thiazolines, 2-methyl	Me$_3$OBF$_4$ → NaBH$_4$ → HgCl$_2$	A → (H) → H	201
Unsaturated acids	Periodate	(O)	202–207
Unsaturated acids	Ozone	(O)	208
Unsaturated acids	Air	(O)	209
Unsaturated alcohols	Periodate	(O)	203

Table 17—*continued*

Precursors	Reagents	Reactions[a]	Ref.
Unsaturated aldehydes	Periodate	(O)	203
Unsaturated esters	Periodate	(O)	203
Vinyl ethers	Acid	H	210

[a] A = alkylation, DC = decarboxylation, DH = dehydration, D = displacement, DP = disproportionation, H = hydrolysis, (H) = reduction, LR = Loessen rearrangement, (O) = oxidation, OD = oxidative deamination, RC = ring contraction and RO = ring opening.
[b] where the quaternary C is next to the alcohol function.
[c] See Table 18.
[d] 2,6-Dichloro-4-trimethylammoniumbenzene diazonium fluoborate chloride.
[e] See Table 19.
[f] Derived aldehydes analysed with MBTH.
[g] In auto-oxidized oils and fats.

Table 18. Some oxygenated precursors of aliphatic aldehydes

Precursor	Aldehyde	Ref.
Acids, unsaturated		
Oleic	Nonanal	203
Petroselenic	Dodecanal	203
Alcohols, unsaturated		
Elaidyl	Nonanal	203
Oleyl	Nonanal	203
Selechyl	Nonanal	203
Vaccenyl	Heptanal	203
Aldehydes, unsaturated		
Crotonaldehyde		203
Aldehyde DNPHs, unsaturated		
2-Ethylhex-2-enal	Butanal	203
Hept-2-enal	Pentanal	203
cis-4-Heptenal	Propanal	203
cis-5-Heptenal	Acetaldehyde	203
Hexadec-2,4-dienal	Dodecanal	203
Hexadec-2-enal	Tetradecanal	203
trans-2-trans-6-Nonadienal	Propanal	203
Non-2-enal	Heptanal	203
trans-4-Nonenal	Pentanal	203
trans-5-Nonenal	Butanal	203
trans-6-Nonenal	Propanal	203
trans-7-Nonenal	Acetaldehyde	203
Epoxides or oxiranes		
1,2-Epoxybutane	Propanal	98
1,2-Epoxydecane	Nonanal	98
trans-2,3-Epoxydecane	Acetaldehyde + octanal	102
trans-4,5-Epoxydecane	Butyraldehyde + hexanal	102
trans-5,6-Epoxydecane	Valeraldehyde	102
cis-7,8-Epoxydecyl acetate	Propanal + 7-acetoxyheptanal	102
cis-7,8-Epoxyhexadecyl acetate	Nonanal + 7-acetoxyheptanal	102
2,3-Epoxy-2-methyloctadecane	Hexadecanal	102
7,8-Epoxy-7-methyloctadecane	Undecanal	102
7,8-Epoxy-8-methyloctadecane	Heptanal	102
7,8-Epoxy-9-methyloctadecane[a]	Heptanal + 2-methylundecanal	102
9,10-Epoxymethylstearate	Nonanal + methyl azelaaldehydate	98
9,10-Epoxyoctadecane	Nonanal	102
9,10-Epoxyoctadecanoic acid allyl ester[b]	Nonanal + ald. ester	102
cis-9,10-Epoxy-1-octadecanal	Nonanal	102
cis-9,10-Epoxytetradecyl acetate	9-Acetoxynonanal	102
Esters		
Methyl cis-5-eicosenoate	Pentadecanal	203
Methyl nervonate	Nonanal	203

Table 18—*continued*

Precursor	Aldehyde	Ref.
Methyl-*cis*-6-octadecenoate	Dodecanal	203
Methyl 12-octadecenoate	Hexanal	203
Methyl oleate	Nonanal	203
Methyl palmitoleate	Heptanal	203
Methyl petroselinate	Dodecanal	203
Methyl vaccenate[a]	Heptanal	203
Glycols		
Glyceryl-1-hexadecyl ether	Hexadecoxyacetaldehyde	98
Glyceryl-1-octadecyl ether	Octadecoxyacetaldehyde	98
1-Monopalmitin	Glycolaldehyde palmitate	98
1-Monostearin	Glycolaldehyde stearate	98
1,2-Propanediol	Acetaldehyde	98, 102
α-Hydroxy acids		
α-Hydroxymyristic acid	Tridecanal	98
DL-Lactic acid	Acetaldehyde	98, 102
Ketones		
Acetoin	Acetaldehyde	102
3-Pentanone	2-Ethylbutanal	210
Vinylidene (V) derivatives		
1-Bromo-2-ethoxy V	Bromoacetaldehyde	213
1-Bromo-2-ethylthio V	2-Ethylthioacetaldehyde	213
1-Ethoxy-2-ethylseleno V	2-Ethylselenoacetaldehyde	214
1-Ethoxy-2-ethylthio V	2-Ethylthioacetaldehyde	215
1-Ethylthio-2-ethylseleno V	2-Ethylselenoacetaldehyde	214

[a] *cis-* or *trans-*
[b] Methyl ester also.

present in the human environment some of the oxygenated precursors of aldehydes are listed in Tables 17 and 18.

II. ACIDS

Long chain aliphatic aldehydes can be derived from fatty acids such as lauric to stearic acids.[4] Fatty acid peroxidase (EC 1.11.1.3 Palmitate: hydrogen peroxide oxidoreductase) catalyses the following reaction, as shown for palmitate

$$Palmitate + 2H_2O_2 = Pentadecanal + CO_2 + 3H_2O$$

The reaction could be used to determine the fatty acids through the derived aldehydes.

III. ACYL HALIDES

Acyl halides can be reacted with disodium tetracarbonylferrate to form aldehydes,[5, 6] e.g.

$$RCOCl + Na_2Fe(CO)_4 \longrightarrow [RCOFe(CO)_4]^-$$

$$[RCOFe(CO)_4]^- \xrightarrow[25°]{H^+} RCHO$$

The dioxane complex of the tetracarbonylferrate is preferred as the reagent.

IV. PRIMARY ALCOHOLS

Primary alcohols have been determined through their derived aldehydes. Various oxidizing agents can be used in forming the aldehydes, such as ruthenium tetroxide and 2,6-dichloro-4-trimethylammoniumbenzenediazonium fluoborate chloride. The former reagent is obtained in the reaction

$$RuO_2 + 2IO_4^- \rightarrow RuO_4 + 2IO_3$$

The tetroxide then oxidizes the alcohol to an aldehyde, the latter being determined by any of the available methods. The equation for the oxidation with the diazonium salt is more complicated and shown in Fig. 13. The data obtained with these two oxidizing agents in the MBTH determination of primary alcohols are given in Table 19. The procedures used are as follows.

A. MBTH determinations of primary alcohols[9,11]

(a) To 3 ml of an acetic acid test solution add 0·1 ml of oxidant solution (agitate 10 mg of amorphous ruthenium dioxide suspended in 5 ml of carbon tetrachloride with 5 ml of 10% aq sodium metaperiodate and use the carbon tetrachloride layer). After 5 min add 0·5 ml of 0·5% aq MBTH·HCl. Then after 5 min add 0·2 ml of hydrogen peroxide, after 15 min add 5 ml of acetone, and after 5 min read at 660 nm.

(b) Add 0·5 ml of 0·5% aq 2,6-dichloro-4-trimethylammoniumbenzenediazonium fluoborate chloride to 0·5 ml of the aq test solution. After 10 min in bright light add 0·5 ml of aq MBTH.HCl, and then after 20 min 2·5 ml of 0·4% of aq ferric chloride. After a further 10 min dilute to 10 ml with water. Read between 610 and 650 nm.

With the help of enzymes primary alcohols can be converted to aldehydes.[12–20] Thus, with alcohol dehydrogenase (EC 1.1.1.1 Alcohol: NAD$^+$ oxidoreductase) primary or secondary alcohols or hemiacetals can react.[13–15] The animal, but not the yeast, enzyme oxidizes cyclic secondary

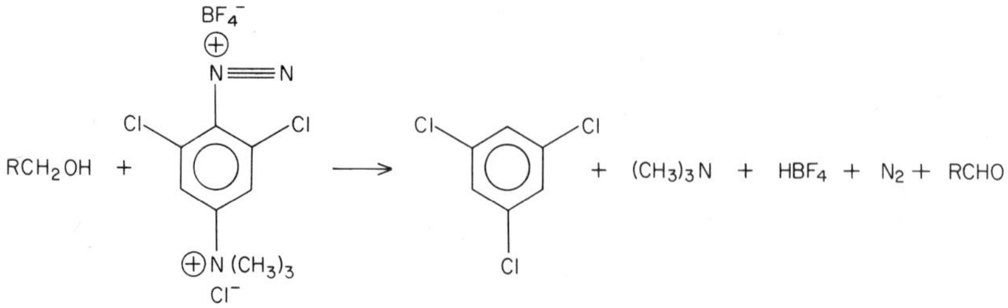

FIG. 13. Reaction of 2,6-dichloro-4-trimethylaminobenzenediazonium salts with primary alcohols.

alcohols to ketones. For a primary alcohol the reaction is

$$RCH_2OH + NAD^+ = RCHO + NADH + H^+.$$

With the enzyme alcohol: NADP$^+$ oxidoreductase, EC 1.1.1.2, the reaction is somewhat similar except that the receptor is NADP$^+$.[16–18] Some of the enzymes of this series oxidize only primary alcohols; others act more rapidly on secondary alcohols.

Another enzyme system has been shown to have greater selectivity for primary alcohols. Alcohol oxidase (EC 1.1.3.13 Alcohol:oxygen oxidoreductase) is a flavoprotein (FAD) which acts on lower primary alcohols and unsaturated alcohols, but does not affect branched-chain and secondary alcohols.[19] The reaction is essentially

$$RCH_2OH + O_2 = RCHO + H_2O_2$$

Methanol, ethanol, *n*-propanol, and allyl alcohol can be determined with alcohol oxidase.[12]

Saturated alcohols with a quaternary carbon next to the alcohol function lose, when treated with lead tetraacetate, either a proton or the tertiary

Table 19. MBTH determination of primary aliphatic alcohols

Alcohol	λ_{max}	mε^a	mε^b
Methanol	630	5·0	3·8
Ethanol	610	11·5	22·0
n-Propanol	610	8·6	16·1
n-Butanol	610	7·0	17·8
n-Pentanol	650	6·0	—

^{a} Oxidative procedure with 2,6-dichloro-4-trimethylammoniumbenzenediazonium fluoborate chloride.[9]

^{b} At λ_{max} 660 nm. Ruthenium tetroxide oxidation procedure.[11]

carbonium ion which then combines with the acetate ion,[7]

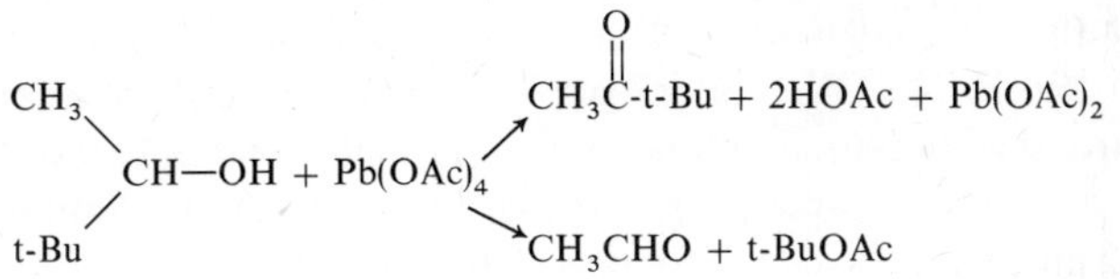

$$
\begin{array}{c}
CH_3 \\
\diagdown \\
CH-OH + Pb(OAc)_4 \\
\diagup \\
t\text{-}Bu
\end{array}
\quad
\begin{array}{c}
\nearrow \quad CH_3\overset{\displaystyle O}{\overset{\|}{C}}\text{-}t\text{-}Bu + 2HOAc + Pb(OAc)_2 \\
\\
\searrow \quad CH_3CHO + t\text{-}BuOAc
\end{array}
$$

Pinacolyl acetate and isobutene are also formed, the latter by loss of a proton from the tertiary carbonium ion. Since the yields depend on the solvent and the temperature, an analytical procedure could be developed for this type of alcohol by optimizing the various factors.

V. ALDEHYDE HYDRAZONES

Aldehyde hydrazones can also be determined with MBTH as shown in a figure (of the formaldehyde precursor section, Volume 4,) for the determination of 2,4-dinitrophenylhydrazones.[21] The spectrum obtained with the formaldehyde derivative is shown in another figure in that section. Alcohols can be used as the test solvent, but they have to be purified because they contain

Table 20. Spectral determination of aldehyde 2,4-dinitrophenylhydrazones[21]

Aldehyde	Melting point (°C)	mε at λ_{max} 667 nm
Formaldehyde	166	57
Acetaldehyde	168	77
Propanal	154	68
Butanal	122	64
2-Methylpropanal	187	36
Pentanal	98	60
2-Methylbutanal	125	44
Hexanal	104	59
Heptanal	107	58
Octanal	106	54
Nonanal	96	49
Decanal	104	30
Undecanal	104	24
Dodecanal	106	10
Acrolein	165	24
Crotonaldehyde	195	11

aldehydes; even after purification, aldehydes form fairly rapidly. The chromogen obtained in the procedure to be described is stable for 30 minutes. Beer's law is obeyed from 4–85 μg per 10 ml of final solution. The data is given in Table 20. Other aldehyde derivatives can be determined by the procedure, e.g. heptanal oxime and heptanal thiosemicarbazone give mε of 52·0 and 35·0, respectively, at the wavelength maximum of 667 nm. Aldehyde derivatives can be easily differentiated from ketone derivatives with this procedure.

A. Determination of aldehyde derivatives with MBTH[21]

Mix 2 ml of the 2-ethoxyethanol test solution with 2 ml of aq 0·3% MBTH. HCl. After standing for 1 h add 2 ml of aq 1% ferric chloride solution. Then let stand for 3 min and dilute to 10 ml with methanol. Read at wavelength 667 nm.

VI. *VIC*-ALKANOLAMINES

Various *vic*-alkanolamines could be oxidized with periodate to a variety of aliphatic aldehydes dependent on the structure of the alkanolamine. Enzymatic methods could also be used, e.g.

$$HOCH_2CH_2NH_2 = CH_3CHO + NH_3$$

The enzyme for this reaction is ethanolamine ammonia-lyase (EC 4.3.1.7).[22, 23] The usage of this reaction in the analysis for *vic*-alkanolamines has not been attempted as yet.

VII. ALKENYL ETHERS

1-(1′-Alk-1′-enyl)glycerophosphinicocholine could be determined through the aldehyde by the following reaction with the help of the enzyme alkenylglycerophosphinicocholine hydrolase (EC 3.3.2.2 1-(1′-Alk-1′-enyl)glycero-3-phosphinicocholine aldehydohydrolase)[24, 25]: 1-(1′-Alk-1′-enyl)glycero-3-phosphinicocholine + H_2O = an aldehyde + glycero-3-phosphinicocholine.

Plasmalogens or alkenyl glycerols or O-α-alk-1-enyl glycerols or aldehydogenic triglycerides have the following structure

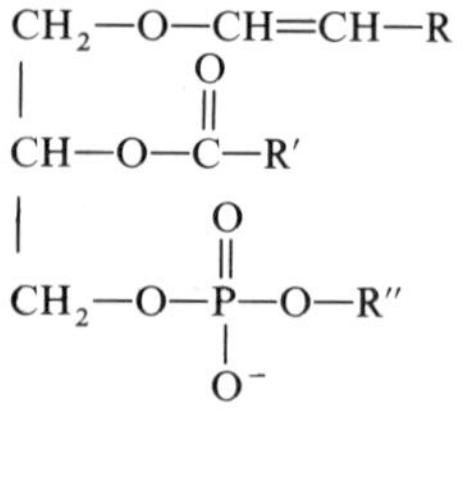

$$
\begin{array}{l}
CH_2-O-CH{=}CH-R \\
\qquad\quad\; O \\
\qquad\quad\; \| \\
CH-O-C-R' \\
\qquad\quad\quad O \\
\qquad\quad\quad \| \\
CH_2-O-P-O-R'' \\
\qquad\qquad\; | \\
\qquad\qquad\; O^-
\end{array}
$$

where HO—CH=CH—R represents the enolic forms of long chain aliphatic aldehydes containing saturated (mostly) chains of approximately 14 to 19 carbons,[26, 34, 35] HOOC—R′ long chain saturated and partially unsaturated fatty acids, and HR″ represents choline, ethanolamine or serine. The ethanolamine derivatives are the most widely distributed in nature; they are present in most animal tissues. The brain contains the highest concentration of plasmalogens, the liver the lowest.

Plasmalogens were discovered in 1924 by Feulgen. He found that cellular cytoplasm was stained purple with fuchsin—sulphurous acid after pretreatment with an acid fixative such as mercuric chloride. Since the enol ether structure is usually not found in other natural products, plasmalogens are responsible for the histochemical aldehyde reaction of cytoplasm. This is called the plasmal reaction. The following aldehyde-forming reactions of plasmalogen have been described, Fig. 14.

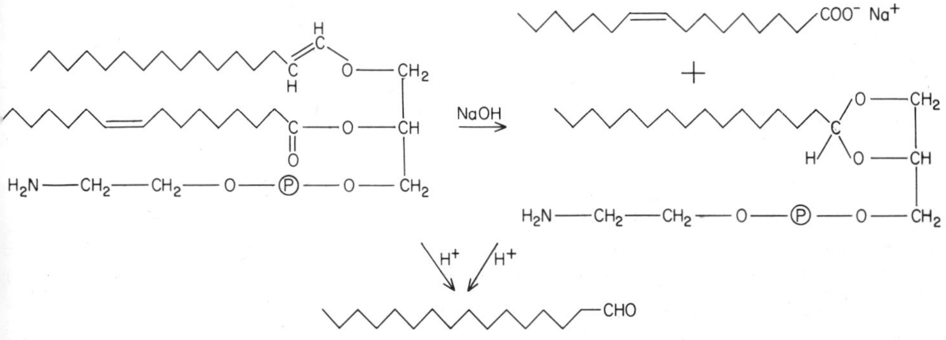

FIG. 14. Hydrolysis of a plasmalogen to an aldehyde.

A study of the plasmalogens in rat kidney showed that their hydrolysis was as rapid in 6 N HCl as in 1% HgCl$_2$. In 2 N HCl 5 min was necessary for maximum hydrolysis; in 1 N HCl, 15 min was required.[27] Ninety-eight percent hydrolysis of the alkenyl ether in a pig heart lecithin fraction to the aldehyde was obtained by treating the fraction with 90% acetic acid for 24 h at 37°.[26] Another method of hydrolysis involves vigorous shaking of an ether extract of the plasmalogen with an equal volume of conc hydrochloric acid for 1–2 min followed by another extraction of the aqueous layer with ether.[34] The combined ether extracts are washed twice with distilled water, evaporated to dryness under a stream of nitrogen and then dissolved in the appropriate solvent for the desired analysis. A phospholipid fraction can also be hydrolysed by coating a flask with a thin film of the material, allowing the film to be in contact with HCl gas for 20 min, dissolving the hydrolysed material in chloroform, then eluting the aldehydes through a silicic acid column with chloroform.[35]

Hydrolysis can also be accomplished on a thin-layer plate by treating the lipid sample in a band on a silica gel G plate with fumes from warm (50–60°) conc hydrochloric acid for 5 minutes.[29, 30] The plate is developed twice with hexane–diethyl ether (99:5). After spraying with 0·2% alcoholic 2′,7′-dichlorofluorescein and treatment with warm air or water, the aldehyde bands near the solvent front can be eluted with ether. In some separations p-nitrophenylhydrazine or DNPH[30] can be used in the location and analysis of these aldehydes.

A. Location of plasmalogens on a thin-layer plate[31]

Spray the plate with 0·4% DNPH in 2 N HCl. Compounds containing free carbonyl groups can be seen at this stage as brown to red spots. Plasmalogens are detected after heating the plate at 105° for 10 minutes. Brown, red or orange-red spots can be seen against a yellow background.

Plasmalogens stored in methanolic solutions lose their ether linkage because of addition to the double bond of the methanol and formation of an acetal[32] which readily reacts with p-nitrophenylhydrazine.[33] Another artifact may be the presence of free aldehydes in fresh tissue due to the presence of easily hydrolysable plasmalogens. This controversy[37] is still under investigation. But in some investigations care is taken to destroy free aldehydes (with alkaline hydrogen peroxide as in the following procedure) before assaying for the plasmalogens.

B. Pararosaniline determination of plasmalogens in the presence of free aldehydes[26]

Add 0·1 ml of test sample to 0·5 ml of 1 N KOH. Then add 0·5 ml of 1 M hydrogen peroxide. Mix gently and heat for 10 min at 70°. Cool and add 0·5 ml of a hydrolysing solution (consisting of 1 g of mercuric chloride dissolved in 5 ml of warm deionized water followed by 95 ml of glacial acetic acid). Mix, and immediately add 4 ml of fuchsin reagent (0·1 g of basic fuchsin dissolved in 100 ml of deionized water, filtered and added to 100 ml of deionized water saturated with sulphur dioxide). Mix well, and after 20 min extract the chromogen with 4 ml of isoamyl alcohol, separating the two layers by centrifugation. Read at 550 nm.

If only a measure of total aldehydes is desired, add the mercuric chloride solution directly to the dried lipid sample, then after 15 min add the fuchsin reagent and proceed as above.

Fatty aldehydes liberated from the neutral plasmalogen fraction of milk fat can be analysed by a two-phase bisulphite–DNPH column procedure.[216, 217] However, these columns (30 g) were difficult to use with microgram amounts of aldehydes. The procedure was miniaturized for use with melting point capillary columns containing 200 mg of impregnated Celite.[218] Since the method was tried with aliphatic, aromatic and heterocyclic aldehydes, it will be discussed more fully in the total aldehydes precursors section.

VIII. ALKYL AMINES

Argentic picolinate can be used to oxidize primary amines to the corresponding aldehydes in 30–71% yields.[44] Aldehyde oximes can be obtained in up to 85% yields by the treatment of primary amines with hydrogen peroxide and appropriate catalysts.[46, 47]

Enzymatic methods utilizing amine oxidase [EC 1.4.3.4 Amine:oxygen oxidoreductase (deaminating) (flavin containing)] could also be used to determine primary amines. This enzyme acts on primary, secondary and tertiary amines.[49–53] The reaction has been utilized to determine amine oxidase fluorimetrically.[49]

A somewhat different amine oxidase is EC 1.4.3.6, Amine:oxygen oxidoreductase (deaminating) (pyridoxal-containing). It is a pyridoxal–phosphate protein containing copper and consists of a group of enzymes which can oxidize primary amines and diamines, including histamine. Substrates can be primary alkyl amines, cadaverine, putrescine, hexamethylenediamine and benzylamine.[48] The method has been used to determine amine oxidase activity.

With either of these enzyme systems the following reaction takes place

$$RCH_2NH_2 + H_2O + O_2 = RCHO + NH_3 + H_2O_2$$

and thus primary amines could be determined through the aldehyde, as for example by reaction with DNPH, extraction of the chromogen into toluene and then into 1 N NaOH, followed by reading the absorbance at 450 nm.[50]

Various oxidative deamination methods are available for the obtainment of aldehydes from alkylamines. For example, with a primary or secondary amine the following reaction can take place, where R and R' are H or alkyl groups:

$$RCH_2NHR' \xrightarrow[\text{picolinate}]{\text{argentic}} RCH{=}NHR' \xrightarrow{H_2O} RCHO$$

D

Oximes of aldehydes can be obtained in up to 85% yield by the following reaction.[46, 47]

$$RCH_2NH_2 + H_2O_2 \xrightarrow{Na_2WO_4} RCH=NOH$$

Dialkyl and trialkylamines and trialkylamine oxides can be treated with nitrite to form nitrosamines which can then be decomposed in the test tube or in tissue to various aliphatic aldehydes (see the nitrosamine portion of this section and also the chapter on Nitrosamine Aldehyde Precursors. Thus, these types of amines could be analysed through their derived aldehydes.

IX. N-ALKYLARYLAMINES

In the formaldehyde precursor section it was shown that p-substituted N,N-dimethylanilines react with MBTH in the presence of a ferric salt to give the blue formazan cation.[219, 220] Many tertiary aromatic and hetero-cyclic amines containing N-methyl groups appear to form formaldehyde readily in this fashion and can be determined with this reaction with high sensitivity. Somewhat similar to this is the reaction of N,N,N',N'-tetraethyl-4, 4'-diaminoazobenzene with ceric ion.[55] A two-electron oxidation takes place to give the free radical,

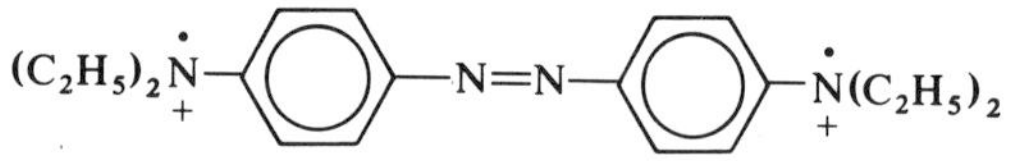

$$(C_2H_5)_2 \overset{\cdot}{\underset{+}{N}} \!\!-\!\!\bigcirc\!\!-\!\!N{=}N\!\!-\!\!\bigcirc\!\!-\!\!\overset{\cdot}{\underset{+}{N}}(C_2H_5)_2$$

which at room temperature slowly yields acetaldehyde.

Another somewhat similar reaction involves the oxidation of tertiary N-alkylarylamines with lead tetraacetate.[57] One alkyl group is oxidized to an aliphatic aldehyde and the acetyl derivative of the secondary amine is formed. The yield of aldehyde is between 50% and 90%.

$$ArNR(CH_2R') + Pb(OAc)_4 \xrightarrow[Ac_2O/20°]{CHCl_3} ArNR(Ac) + R'CHO$$

Periodate oxidation of N-alkylanilines has also been shown to give aliphatic aldehydes.[54]

Thus, it can be seen that many types of N-alkylarylamines can be analysed through their derived aliphatic aldehydes.

X. ALKYL HALIDES

Alkyl halides and tosylates can also be converted to aldehydes by a reaction somewhat similar to that reported for acyl halides[5, 6]

$$Na_2Fe(CO)_4 + RX \xrightarrow[\text{or } \phi_3P]{CO} [RCOFe(CO)_3 \cdot L]^- \text{ where } L = CO \text{ or } \phi_3P$$

$$\text{then } [RCOFe(CO)_3L]^- \xrightarrow[25°]{H^+} RCHO$$

Since the formation of the alkyl iron intermediate can be viewed as an S_N2 displacement of carbon, substrate reactivities follow the expected order ROTos $\sim$ RI > RBr > RCl and primary > secondary $\gg$ tertiary.

These reactions are of potential value for the analysis of acylating and alkylating agents many of which play a role in the carcinogenic process.

XI. α-AMINO ACIDS

Aliphatic aldehydes can also be obtained from α-amino acids. One method is through oxidation by hypochlorite,[59, 60] hypobromite, chloramine T, or N-bromosuccinimide,[60a] e.g.

$$RCH(NH_2)COOH + NaClO \rightarrow RCHO + NH_3 + CO_2 + NaCl$$

Another method of producing aliphatic aldehydes from α-amino acids is through reaction of the amino acid with epicatechin and tea leaf extract.[61] The aldehyde is believed to be derived from the reaction of the amino acid with o-quinone derived from the oxidation of epicatechin catalysed by polyphenol oxidase or peroxidase. The aldehydes were characterized through thin layer chromatography of the DNPH derivatives.

Other types of o-dicarbonyl type molecules have been shown to form aldehydes from amino acids. For example, alloxan derivatives are postulated as reacting in the following fashion, Fig. 15.[62] Another molecule which has been used in this fashion is perinaphthindantrione or its hydrate.[65, 66] The reaction is shown in Fig. 16.

Ninhydrin has been the most popular reagent for the conversion of amino acids to aldehydes containing one carbon atom less.[67-80] The equation is shown in a figure of the formaldehyde precursors section. The volatile aldehydes can be collected in an acid solution of DNPH and then the dinitrophenylhydrazones can be separated on magnesium sulphate and estimated colorimetrically.

Amino acids and peptides can be converted to hydroxamic acid derivatives which form aldehydes by Lossen rearrangement followed by MBTH determination of the aldehydes.[81]

D-Amino acids can be determined through their oxidation by D-amino acid oxidase (D-amino-acid:oxygen oxidoreductase, deaminating

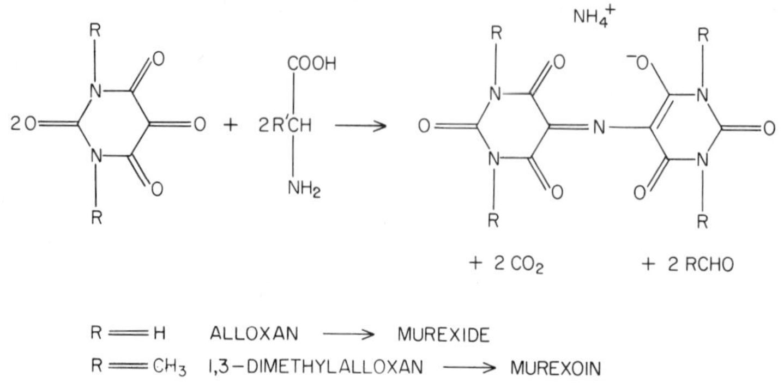

FIG. 15. Reaction of alloxans with amino acids.

EC 1.4.3.3)[63] to the 2-oxo acid which is determined subsequently with MBTH as the decarboxylated aldehyde,[64] e.g.

$$CH_3CH(NH_2)COOH + H_2O + O_2 = CH_3COCOOH + NH_3 + H_2O_2$$

$$CH_3COCOOH + MBTH \rightarrow Azine$$

$$Azine + MBTH \xrightarrow[-CO_2]{FeCl_3} Acetaldehyde \; formazan$$

XII. *VIC*-AMINOALCOHOLS AND DIAMINES

Aminoalcohols and β-hydroxy-α-amino acids containing the functional group —CH(OH)—CH(NRR′)— can be oxidized to aldehydes.[82–84]

$$\begin{matrix} R—CHOH \\ | \\ R′—CHNR″R‴ \end{matrix} \xrightarrow{IO_4^-} \begin{matrix} RCHO \\ R′CHO \end{matrix} + R″R‴NH + IO_3^-$$

1,2-Diamines react similarly. Primary and secondary amines are oxidized rapidly while tertiary amines are oxidized very slowly.[85] Acylation of the

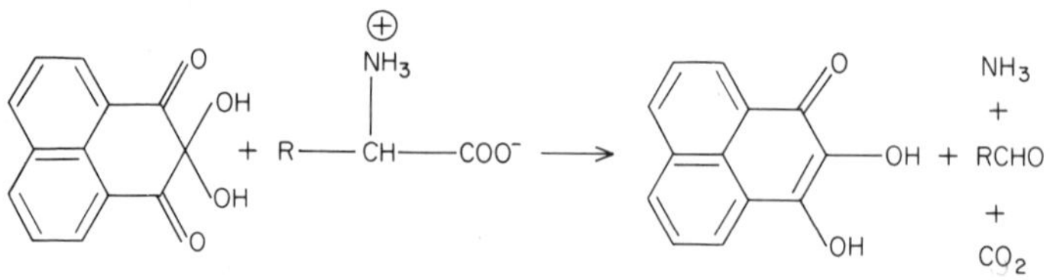

FIG. 16. Reaction of perinaphthindantrione hydrate with amino acids.

amino group of the amino alcohols interferes with the oxidation. The mechanism of oxidation of these and many other compounds with periodate has been discussed at length by Dryhurst.[86] The aminoalcohols and the diamines have been determined by the oxidative MBTH[87] and oxidative ethyl acetoacetate[88] procedures which have been described in the formaldehyde precursor section. In the MBTH procedure millimolar absorptivities of 50–125 can be obtained. The ethyl acetoacetate procedure depends on the formation of dihydropyridine fluorogen.

XIII. AZOALKANES

Azoalkanes have alkylating properties[89] and thus can have adverse physiological effects. Through tautomerism and hydrolysis aliphatic aldehydes can be formed (as shown in a figure in the aliphatic aldehydes section). The analytical procedure has been given in the formaldehyde section.[90]

XIV. BENZYLIDENEHEXOSES

Oxidation of these and analogous molecules can give m-dioxane aldehydes. An example of this oxidation is given in the reaction of 4,6-O-benzylidene-2-D-glucose with sodium periodate in aq methanol, Fig. 17.[91]

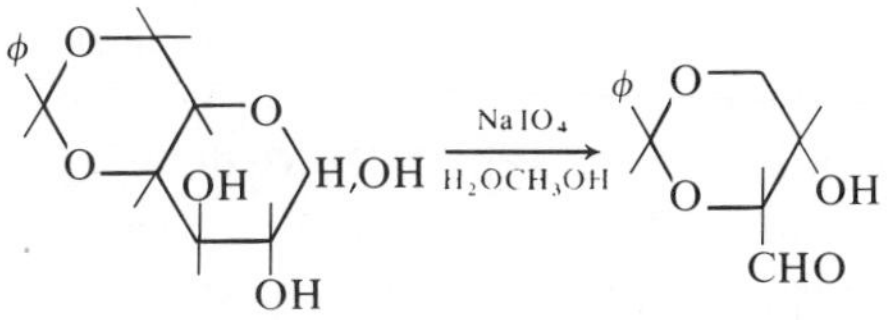

FIG. 17. Periodate oxidation of 4,6-O-benzylidene-α-D-glucose.

XV. CIGARETTE TOBACCO

The smoking of cigarette tobacco results in the formation of a variety of gas phase aldehydes which can be trapped separately or together. A small activated charcoal[221] or silica gel[222] trap will efficiently collect aldehydes from the gas phase of at least five cigarettes. The aldehydes can be recovered from silica gel by simple aqueous extraction with intermittent shaking for one hour. The aldehydes are then treated with DNPH, then with alkali, and measured at 480 nm, all operations being performed by an Auto Analyser, Fig. 18.[222]

XVI. COLLAGEN

Collagen after periodate treatment forms aliphatic aldehydes which can be determined with MBTH.[92]

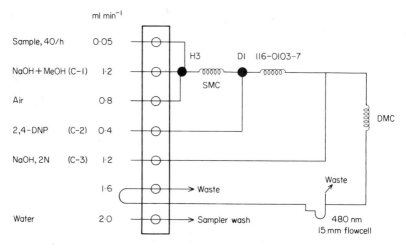

Fig. 18. Auto-analyser manifold for aldehydes in the gas phase.[222]

XVII. 1,2-DIOLS

Treatment of 1,2-diols of varying degrees of substitution with an excess of activated manganese dioxide and methylene chloride affords dicarbonyl fragments at room temperature.[93] For example, 1,2-cycloalkanediols would tend to form α,ω-alkanedials. Where the hydroxyl groups are secondary, dehydrogenation is also observed in addition to ring cleavage, e.g. oxidation of 1,2-*cis*-cyclododecanediol with manganese dioxide for 4 h gives 85% α,ω-dodecanedial, 14% 1,2-cyclododecanedione and traces of 2-hydroxy-cyclododecanone. Linear 1,2-diols will be discussed in the α-glycol part of this section.

XVIII. ENOL ETHERS

Enol ethers react under mild conditions with lead tetraacetate to give 2-acyloxyacylals,[97, 223–226] e.g.

$$CH_2{=}CHOR + Pb(OAc)_4 \rightarrow AcO{-}CH_2{-}CH(OR)OAc$$

The reactions are carried out at room temp in acetic acid or in benzene. Yields range from 50–90%. When methanol is used as the solvent, acetals are produced instead of acylals.[97]

$$CH_3CO{-}CH{=}CH{-}OCH_3 \xrightarrow[CH_3OH,\,20°]{Pb(OAc)_4} CH_3COCH{-}CH(OCH_3)_2$$
$$\underset{OAc}{|}$$

The acylals and acetals can be readily hydrolysed to aldehydes and then assayed by any of the reagents described in the aliphatic aldehyde and other sections.

XIX. EPOXIDES

Epoxide groups are found in many natural products, e.g. fatty acids, insect juvenile hormone, and sex attractants. They are used as reagents in the manufacture of dyes and surfactants and as intermediates in biological systems. Many of them are mutagenic and some are carcinogenic to animals.

Epoxides can be oxidized by periodiate to aldehydes.[98-103] Some examples are given in Table 18. For example, 2,3-epoxyoctane gives n-hexanal, 3,4-epoxyheptane gives n-propanal and n-butanal, 1,2-epoxydodecane gives undecanal, and methyl 9,10-epoxystearate gives n-nonanal and methyl azela-aldehydate.[100] On the other hand oxidation can take place on a column.[98] The epoxide in benzene or dichloromethane is oxidized by passage through a column containing periodic acid on calcium sulphate. The percolate is passed through a second column containing Celite impregnated with a solution of DNPH in phosphoric acid. The dinitrophenylhydrazones are eluted with hexane, and the eluate is passed through a third column containing alumina for isolation of individual derivatives. Analysis is by spectro-photometry.

The formation of the aldehyde consisted of the following reactions

$$R-\underset{\underset{\displaystyle O}{\diagdown\diagup}}{\overset{\displaystyle H}{\underset{|}{C}}-\overset{\displaystyle R'}{\underset{|}{C}}-R'' \xrightarrow[\text{H}_2\text{SO}_4\,\text{H}_2\text{O}]{\text{45 min. 45°}} R-\overset{\displaystyle H}{\underset{\underset{\displaystyle HO}{|}}{\overset{|}{C}}}-\overset{\displaystyle R'}{\underset{\underset{\displaystyle OH}{|}}{\overset{|}{C}}}-R'' \xrightarrow{\text{H}_5\text{IO}_6} R-\overset{\displaystyle H}{\underset{\underset{\displaystyle O}{\|}}{C}} + \overset{\displaystyle R'}{\underset{\underset{\displaystyle O}{\|}}{C}}-R'' + \text{HIO}_3$$

When phosphoric acid was used in the ring-opening, *cis* epoxides, 1,2-epoxides and trisubstituted epoxides were completely or almost completely hydrolysed within 5 min, while *trans* epoxides or hindered epoxides (alkyl substituted alpha to epoxide) were hydrolysed partially or in trace amounts.[103] The hydrolysis was essentially complete within 1 hr for all epoxides.

Periodic acid in ether or tetrahydrofuran can be used to effect hydrolytic cleavage of a monoalkyloxirane to give an aldehyde.[58] The method can be used for water-insoluble compounds, or where a cleavage product is sensitive to aqueous acid. For example, an 80% yield of the extremely water-sensitive 4-bromobutyraldehyde is obtained from the epoxide:

$$\text{BrCH}_2\text{CH}_2\text{CH}_2\underset{\underset{\displaystyle O}{\diagdown\diagup}}{\triangle} \xrightarrow[\text{ether}]{\text{H}_5\text{IO}_6^-} \text{BrCH}_2\text{CH}_2\text{CH}_2\text{CHO}$$

Reaction of methyl esters of epoxidized fatty acids with periodic acid leads to direct cleavage of the epoxide ring and the production of two aldehydes.[101, 105] Thus, the addition of aq periodic acid to a stirred solution of methyl 12-hydroxy-9,10-epoxystearate followed by stirring for 15 min at room temp gave an 83% yield of methyl azelaaldehyde hydrate and pelargonaldehyde.

Some epoxides can rearrange in acidic solution to form aldehydes as shown in Fig. 19.[106, 107]

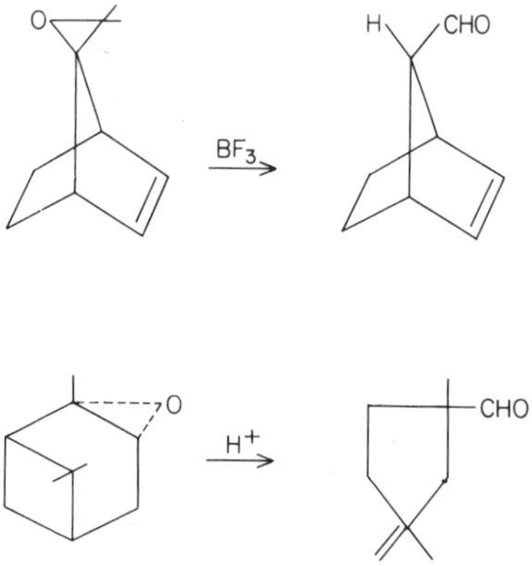

(106)

(107)

FIG. 19. Rearrangement of epoxides to form aldehydes.

Simple epoxides, such as the 1,1-dialkylethylene oxides, undergo ring cleavage in aq acidic solutions,[95] e.g.

$$R_2C\overset{O}{\frown}CH_2 \xrightarrow[H_2O]{H^+} R_2CHCHO$$

An example of this reaction is the formation of camphenilanaldehyde from camphene oxide,[96] e.g.

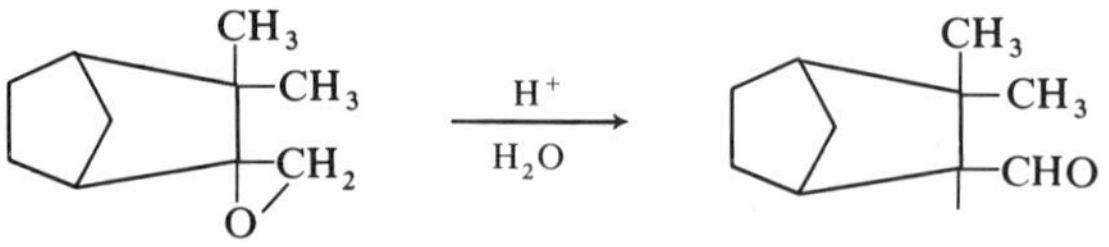

XX. ETHYLENE ACETALS OR 1,3-DIOXOLANES

Ethylene acetals in aq *p*-dioxane solution are oxidized by an equivalent amount of periodic acid. Thus, the ethylene acetal of octadec-9,12-diynal in *p*-dioxane is mixed with aq periodic acid, heated to boiling, cooled, and made neutral with aq sodium bicarbonate. Extraction with petroleum ether gave the aldehyde in quantitative yield,[109] e.g.

$$n\text{-}C_5H_{11}-C\equiv C-CH_2-C\equiv C-(CH_2)_7-C\overset{O}{\underset{O}{\diagdown}}$$

$$\Big\downarrow \overset{H_5IO_6}{\underset{H_2O\ -\ p\text{-dioxane}}{}} \overset{H}{}$$

$$n\text{-}C_5H_{11}-C\equiv C-CH_2-C\equiv C-(CH_2)_7-CHO + 2H_2CO$$

XXI. ETHYLENE GLYCOLS

Mono-, di- and triethylene glycols, frequently mixed with volatile aliphatic alcohols, have been used as de-icing agents for aircraft and airfield runways. Airfield drainage may subsequently contaminate surface waters with low levels of these glycols. The presence of these glycols in surface waters can be determined. They can be oxidized to aldehydes which can then be determined with MBTH. If CA were used as the reagent only ethylene glycol would be determined.[109a, 227, 228] With an MBTH method the three glycols can be monitored in surface waters at concentrations of upwards of 0.5 mg 1^{-1}.[109a] The oxidant chosen for the conversion of the glycols to aldehydes was acidic permanganate at $100°$.

Normal oxidation of the glycols would be expected to yield dialdehydes, e.g. glyoxal from ethylene glycol, $(OHC-CH_2)_2O$ from diethylene glycol, and $OHCCH_2-O-CH_2-CH_2-OCH_2CHO$ from triethylene glycol. Other possible products could be glyoxylic acid, glycolaldehyde, glycolic acid and oxalic acid. The millimolar absorptivities obtained for the mono-, di- and triethylene glycols in the procedure described below were 8.06, 5.6 and 8.9. Since one could expect $m\varepsilon$ values of about 100 for the postulated dialdehydes formed from the di- and triethylene glycols, optimization was far from reached and/or other types of oxidation products were formed. Typical surface water sample blanks indicated the general absence of a natural level of aldehydes which would be further oxidized by the permanganate and of a natural level of compounds containing primary alcohol groups. Domestic effluents showed exceptions to this. Volatile alcohols associated with de-icing glycols are seldom encountered in airfield run-offs at water temperatures greater than $0°$ because of their escape into the air. Because of aerial oxidation of organic constituents to aldehydes during evaporation, recovery experiments involving the concentration of surface-water samples on a water bath cannot be used. High blanks are thus obtained. A MBTH method for ethylene glycol contamination of surface waters is described in the formaldehyde precursors section.

The following method has been used successfully to monitor the biodegradation of low levels of glycols in river water. The final colour formed reaches a maximum response after 15 min and remains stable for a further 15 min.

A. Spectral determination of low levels of mono-, di- and triethylene glycols in surface waters[109a]

Reagents. $KMnO_4$: 0·012M (0·2 g $KMnO_4$ per 100 ml of water). Sodium arsenite solution, 0·07 M: Dissolve 9·1 g of sodium arsenite in 100 ml of water. For use, dilute 1:10. MBTH, 2%: Dissolve 2 g of the hydrochloride in 100 ml of water. Ferric chloride–sulphamic acid solution: Dissolve 2 g of $FeCl_3 \cdot 6H_2O$ and 3 g of sulphamic acid in water and dilute to 100 ml. Standard glycol solutions: Stock standard, 500 mg l^{-1}. Immediately prior to use, prepare 5 mg l^{-1}.

Procedure. To a 10 ml volumetric flask containing 5 ml of clear test solution, add 0·5 ml of 4 N H_2SO_4 followed by 1 ml of permanganate solution. Mix and heat at 100° for exactly 5 minutes. Remove from bath and add 1 ml of sodium arsenite solution followed by 1 ml of MBTH solution. Heat at 100° for a further 6 minutes. Cool to room temp. Add 1 ml of the ferric chloride mixture to each flask and dilute to 10 ml. After 20 min, read the absorbance at 630 nm.

To compensate for natural interferences in surface waters, in addition to the reagent blank value a sample blank value should be obtained with the permanganate oxidation stage omitted.

XXII. GANGLIOSIDES

Gangliosides can also be determined as aldehyde precursors.[110] Both sphingosine and dihydrosphingosine give positive reactions in the test as do ceramide, oleic acid, and a variety of gangliosides (Table 21). It is believed that acid hydrolysis of a ganglioside yields sphingosine sulphate,[110] as occurs with sphingomyelin.[229] Sphingosine is then oxidized to an aldehyde which reacts with vanillin[230] to form the chromogen. The reaction is fairly complicated since oleic acid also reacts, but one type of aldehyde formation from sphingosine could take place as follows

Table 21. Molar colour yields of gangliosides and some of their structural components with vanillin[110]

Compound	Mol. wt.	mε
Monosialoganglioside $(G_{M2})^a$	1490	11·2
Monosialoganglioside $(G_{M1})^b$	1870	10·0
Disialoganglioside $(G_{D1a})^b$	1980	10·4
Trisialoganglioside $(G_{T1})^b$	2280	12·3
Sphingosine	298	14·5
Dihydrosphingosine	300	19·2
Ceramide	666	7·5
Oleic acid	282	15·9

^{a} This sample contains about 15% of gangliosides other than the Tay–Sachs ganglioside (G_{M2}).
^{b} These gangliosides contained 15–30% of other gangliosides.

The sulpho–phospho–vanillin reaction has been applied to the analysis of lipids present in biological fluids and tissues,[230–232] and recently has been used in the determination of total lipids present in mammalian sera.[233, 234]

Most methods commonly employed for ganglioside analysis are based either on the resorcinol reaction for N-acetylneuraminic acid[235, 236] or the orcinol reaction for carbohydrates.[237] However, the only constituents present in unimolar quantities in all gangliosides are the fatty acids, e.g. stearic acid, and the organic base sphingosine. To take advantage of this fact, a sensitive colorimetric procedure for gangliosides without prior hydrolysis has been developed; it depends on the colour produced in the reaction of the sphingosine residue with vanillin.[110] Beer's law is followed from 10–80 µg of sphingosine. Negative results are given by stearic acid, glucose, galactose, N-acetylgalactosamine and N-acetylneuraminic acid. Unsaturated fatty acids could be an interference but they are present in only small amounts in pure gangliosides.[238, 239]

There is an approx 6:1 weight relationship between a normal human ganglioside and sphingosine.[110] Thus, with the help of the resorcinol reaction the following procedure can be utilized to determine whether a purified ganglioside is a mono-, di-, or trisialoganglioside.

A. Vanillin determination of gangliosides[110]

Pipette aliquots of solutions of ganglioside (25 and 50 µg), used as standards, into 15-ml test tubes and evaporate to dryness on a 37° bath under a stream of nitrogen. Similarly evaporate a blank consisting of 0·1 ml of solvent (chloroform–methanol, 2:1, containing 1% water). To each tube add

0·05 ml water and 0·75 ml of conc H_2SO_4. Mix with a Vortex mixer and close the tubes with a Teflon-lined screw cap. Heat at 100° for 40 min and then cool to room temperature. Add 5 ml of reagent (add 800 ml of 85% phosphoric acid to 200 ml of 0·6% vanillin in water) to each tube, and mix the contents with a Vortex mixer. Develop the colour in a 37° bath for 15 minutes. Cool to room temp and read the absorbance at 525 nm.

XXIII. GLYCERIDE OILS

Secondary oxidation products form during processing of glyceride oils. These products are, to some extent, large aldehydes. The removal of these compounds during processing affects the shelf-life and quality of margarine and rapeseed and soybean oils.[112, 113] The benzidine test was introduced in 1957 to measure these carbonyl compounds, mainly aldehydic in nature.[112] Because of the carcinogenic properties of benzidine, Holm[114] introduced the p-anisidine test which was subsequently applied to a study of the oxidation and quality of soybean oil.[111] The following procedure gave better reproducibility at higher anisidine values.

A. Anisidine determination of aldehydes in glyceride oils[111]

Add 1 ml of 0·25% p-anisidine in glacial acetic acid to a solution of 1 g of soybean oil in 100 ml of isooctane. After 10 min read the absorbance at 350 nm.

The anisidine value is defined by convention as 100 times the absorbance measured in a 1 cm cell of a solution resulting from the reaction of 1 g of fat with 100 ml mixture of solvent and reagent. Since a unit peroxide value is believed to correspond to an increase of about 2 anisidine value units, the term oxidation value (OV) has been introduced by Holm to describe the degree of oxidation. And so

$$OV = \text{anisidine value} + 2(\text{peroxide value}).$$

The peroxide value measured primarily primary oxidation products and was measured analytically.[115]

Recently the benzidine method has been applied to the determination of the benzidine number in cocoa butter and chocolate goods.[116] Beer's law was followed. Essentially, the procedure consisted of the reaction of 10 ml of a solution of cocoa butter in equal volumes of chloroform and ethanol with 2 ml of the reagent (0·5% benzidine in a mixture of equal volumes of acetic acid and absolute ethanol) at 50° for one hour. Readings are made at 410 nm.

XXIV. α-GLYCOLS

α-Glycols (or *vic*-diols) are oxidized readily to aldehydes by periodate.[98, 117–134] The compounds under investigation have been carbohydrates. An excellent study of periodate oxidation of this and other types has been presented by Dryhurst.[86] Lead tetraacetate,[139] ruthenium tetroxide[140, 141] and silver carbonate[142, 143] have also been used for this purpose. One mechanism postulated for the reaction of α-glycols with periodate is shown in Fig. 20.

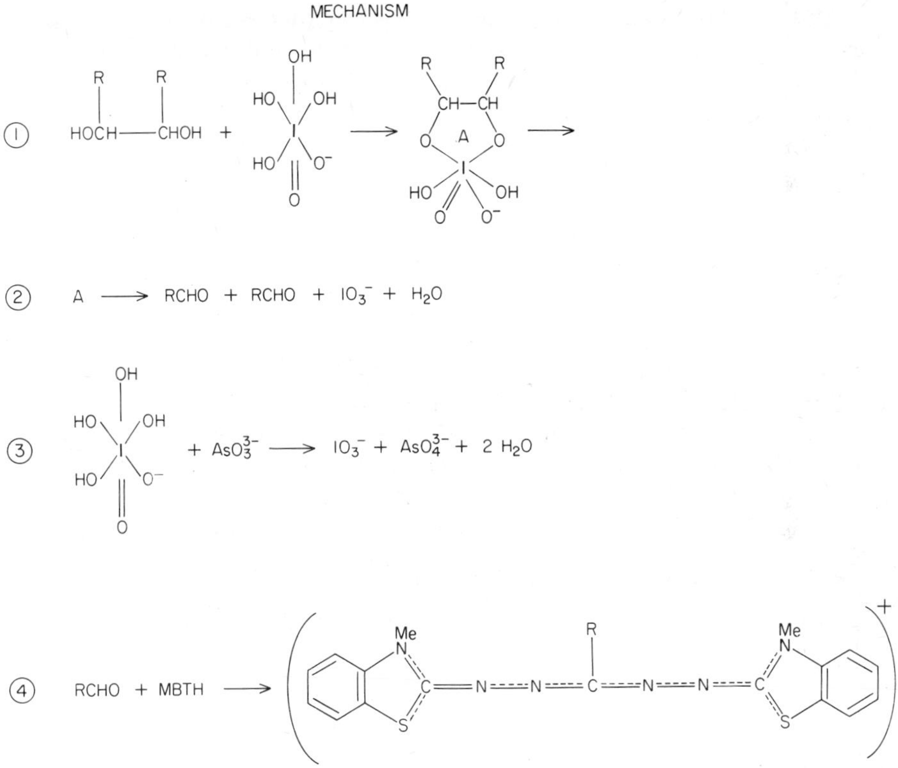

MECHANISM

Fig. 20. Mechanism for the reaction of α-glycols with periodic acid.

Procedures available for the analysis of α-glycols include the oxidative MBTH,[133] dimedone,[132] *p*-nitrophenylhydrazine[130] and DNPH[98, 131] methods. The oxidative MBTH and dimedone procedures are described and given in the section on formaldehyde precursors. The column chromatographic procedure utilizing DNPH[98] has been described for the epoxides. An alternative general procedure is the following.

A. DNPH determination of α-glycols[131]

To a 15 ml glass-stoppered centrifuge tube add 2 ml aq test solution, 1 ml of $10 \text{ N } H_2SO_4$, and 1 ml of 0·1 M sodium metaperiodate, mixing thoroughly after each addition. After 1 h add 0·5 ml 0·867 M thioacetamide and shake gently. After 5–10 min mix thoroughly with a test tube vortex mixer. Add 0·5 ml 0·1% DNPH in 2 N hydrochloric acid. After mixing let stand for 45 minutes. Add 5 ml chloroform, shake, and centrifuge at about 1000 g for 5 minutes. Transfer the chloroform extract to a cuvette and read absorbance at the wavelength maximum. The time factors are not optimal.

Although lead tetraacetate is much less specific than periodate, it complements periodate in that it will oxidize many of the diols which are inert to periodate or which are insoluble in water. With the help of both reagents, mixtures of isomeric diols could be analysed.[240]

On the other hand pyridine can be used as a solvent for the periodate oxidation of various vicinally disubstituted glycols and lipids. High yields are obtained at room temperature. Thus, oxidation of cis,cis-10,13-nonadeca-diene-1,2-diol with sodium periodate in dry pyridine results in a 71% yield of cis, cis-9,12-octadecadiene-1-al.[135]

Enzymatic methods could also be used in the formation and analysis of vic-diols.[144–146] Thus, propanediol dehydratase (EC 4.2.1.28 Propanediol hydro-lyase) catalyses the essentially irreversible dehydration of propanediol to propionaldehyde, or of ethylene glycol to acetaldehyde.[145, 146] The enzyme requires coenzyme B_{12} for activity and is inhibited by cyano- and hydroxo-cobalamin. Some of the compounds which are inactive are 2,3-butanediol, 1,2,4-butanetriol, 1,2-butylene glycol, cyclohexanediol, 1,2-dihydroxy-2-methylpropane, glycerol, ribitol, mercaptoethanol, ethanolamine, iso-propanolamine, chloroethanol, fluoroethanol, 1,2-dithiopropane and lactaldehyde.

The dehydration of a 1,2-diol can be used to determine the enzyme,[144] e.g.

$$R{-}CHOH{-}CH_2OH + NADH \xrightarrow[\text{alcohol dehydrogenase}]{\text{propanediol dehydratase}} RCH_2CHO + H_2O + NAD^+$$

The rate of oxidation of NADH can be followed spectrally at 340 nm. The method could be used to determine 1,2-diols either through NADH or the aldehydes.

XXV. GLYCOLIC COMPOUNDS

Glycolic compounds, such as phospho- and glyco-lipids can be located on thin-layer plates by the following technique.

A. Location of glycolic compounds on thin-layer plates[(241)]

Reagent (*a*) 0·5% sodium periodate, (*b*) 0·5% *p*-rosaniline, decolourized with sulphur dioxide, (*c*) 1% perchloric acid.

Procedure. Spray with (*a*), and after 5 min while still damp, expose to sulphur dioxide and then spray with (*b*). After 1 h lighten the background with (*c*). Positive results are shown by blue or purple spots on a yellow background.

XXVI. HYDRAZINES

Symmetrical and asymmetrical dialkylhydrazines decompose readily to aliphatic aldehydes (see figures in the section on formaldehyde precursors).[(90, 147)] Details are discussed in that section.

XXVII. HYDROCARBONS

Irradiation of hydrocarbon–nitrogen oxide mixtures results in aldehyde formation.[(148)] See CH_2O precursors section. Although some of the atmospheric aldehydes come directly from combustion sources, the largest portion probably comes from photooxidation reactions. Aldehydes are major products in the photooxidation of unsaturated hydrocarbons. This has been tested out with such systems as olefin–nitrogen oxides,[(149–151)] alkylbenzenes–nitrogen oxides,[(149, 150, 152)] olefin–ozone,[(153–155)] and olefin–molecular oxygen.[(156, 157)] Irradiation of air or diluted automobile exhaust[(158)] samples increases the aldehyde concentration three to five times.

Various aldehydes are derived from the combustion of *n*-paraffins, iso-paraffins, monoalkylbenzenes and polyalkylbenzenes in gasoline. The aldehydes in the exhaust gas can be determined with DNPH[(162, 163)] or MBTH.[(161)] The dinitrophenylhydrazones of formaldehyde and acetaldehyde gave mε values of 20·5 and 18·7, respectively, at 440 nm. The corresponding formazans obtained by reaction of formaldehyde and acetaldehyde with MBTH gave mε values several times higher.

XXVIII. HYDROPEROXIDES

Hydroperoxides can be formed during the autoxidation of fats. DNPH can then be used to determine these aldehyde precursors.[(166, 170)] Aldehydes can be formed from hydroperoxides by treatment with acid.[(164–166)] On this basis, hydroperoxides could be serious interferences in the determination of

aldehydes in acid solution.[167] A suggestion has been made that hydroperoxides are decomposed to carbonyl compounds during the process of
measuring carbonyl compounds in autoxidized fats.[168, 169] Hydroperoxides
of oxidized methyl oleate give good yields of aldehyde 2,4-dinitrophenyl-
hydrazones on a column of celite impregnated with DNPH.[170]

XXIX. α-HYDROXY ACIDS

Lead tetraacetate will oxidatively decarboxylate α-hydroxy acids to the
corresponding aldehyde,[171, 242–244] e.g.

$$RCHOHCOOH + Pb(OAc)_4 \rightarrow RCHO + Pb(OAc)_2 + 2HOAc + CO_2$$

In a somewhat different fashion 3α,23-dihydroxycholanic acid is oxidized
by sodium periodate in water–acetone–acetic acid to 3α-hydroxynorcholanal
in 90% yield, Fig. 21.[172]

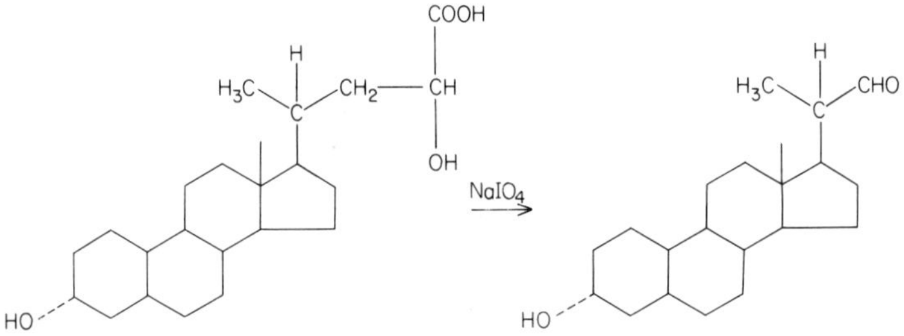

FIG. 21. Oxidation of 3α,23-dihydroxycholanic acid to 3α-hydroxynorcholanol.

XXX. 17-HYDROXY STEROIDS

Treatment of some 17-hydroxy steroids with lead tetraacetate in benzene
at 80° results in splitting of the 5-membered ring and formation of aldehydes,[173] e.g.

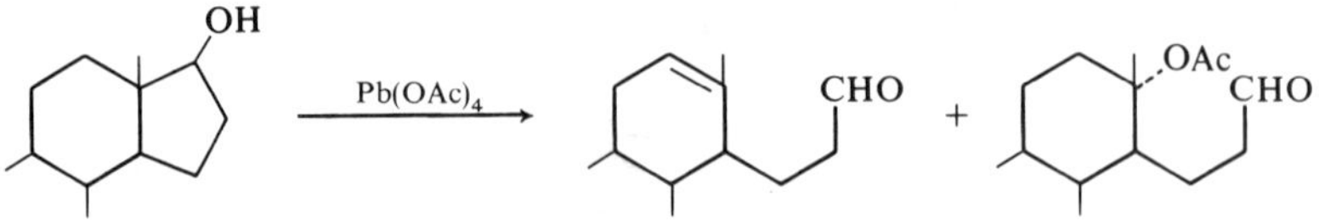

An unsaturated aldehyde is the main product (20–48% yield) and an acetoxy
aldehyde (∼6%), the minor product in this oxidation of four stereoisomeric
secondary alcohols of this type with the hydroxyl group in position 17 in
ring D.

XXXI. KETONES

With the help of alkoxymethylidenyl triphenylphosphines, ketones could be assayed through aldehydes derived from the following type of reaction.[210]

$$\phi_3P{=}CH{-}OC_4H_9 \quad + \quad R_2CO \quad \longrightarrow \quad \xrightarrow{H_2O} \quad R_2CH{-}CHO$$

XXXII. LIPIDS

Of the variety of materials formed as secondary degradation products in the autoxidation of fats, the volatile aldehydes are of special interest because of their major contribution to the off-flavour problem. Essentially these aldehydes are n-alkanals whose structures can be predicted from the cleavage of the intermediate hydroperoxides derived from unsaturated fatty acids, e.g., oleic acid, linoleic acid and linolenic acid, present in fats as triglycerides (see unsaturated fatty acids, refs 204–206). In a study of chicken fat autoxidized to various extents, a close correlation was obtained between the TBA or peroxide value (16 to 118) and the n-hexanal content (0·05–1·9 µg per g of fat).[245]

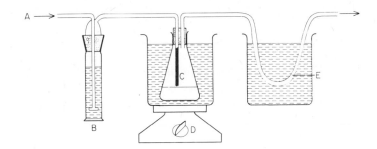

Fig. 22. Schematic diagram of the system used for trapping volatile carbonyls from fat. A = nitrogen source; B = wash bottle containing carbonyl-free water; C = Erlenmeyer flask containing fat sample immersed in a thermostatted water bath; D = magnetic stirrer; E = reaction column containing Celite impregnated with DNPH and anhydrous H_3PO_4 immersed in ice-water.[245]

The following procedure could be used to isolate the dinitrophenylhydrazones of the n-alkanals, Fig. 22.

A. The trapping of volatile aldehydes from fat[245]

Pass ultra-pure nitrogen, used as an inert stripping gas, at a flow rate of $25 \, ml \, min^{-1}$ through a sintered-glass disc into carbonyl- and oxygen-free water (B), and then into the fat sample (C) through a polyethylene tube and a fine glass capillary ending just above the surface of the fat. A magnetic stirrer (D) spreads the fat into a thin film on the walls of the flask during distillation, which is carried out at 100° for 3 hours. Vapour from C passes through a DNPH reaction column (E). Prepare the reaction column[245] as follows. Condition Celite overnight at 275° with a flow of nitrogen. Impregnate Celite with a solution containing 0·5 g of DNPH dissolved in a mixture of 6 ml of 85% H_3PO_4 and 4 ml of carbonyl-free water by immersing the powder in the solution. After filtration, dry the impregnated Celite under vacuum over phosphorus pentoxide and keep until needed. For use the material was packed in a 3 mm i.d. tube with 5 cm of material. After use GC was used but the dinitrophenylhydrazones could be eluted and assayed as total aldehydes by colorimetry or as individual derivatives by HPLC. DNPH methods for total aliphatic aldehydes have been described.[176, 246] These aldehydes have been reported in terms of a heptanal number.[176] Heptanal gives an mε of 16·6 at 358 nm and 101% recovery in the procedure. Other aliphatic aldehydes give comparable intensities and recoveries. The determination of the heptanal value is proposed as a criterion of the total carbonyl content of fat. Essentially, the fat is allowed to react directly with DNPH, excess reagent is separated by means of a cation exchange column, and the eluted chromogen solution is measured spectrophotometrically at 366 nm.

Fatty aldehydes and other lipids on a thin layer chromatogram can be stained green by spraying with 0·5% aq malachite green, drying and lightly spraying with 2% sodium bisulphite in 2 N HCl to reduce all unbound stain.[247] Spectral scanning could then be used to assay these aldehydes and their precursors.

XXXIII. METHYL OLEATE

In an attempt to understand the autoxidation of fats the oxidation of methyl oleate with 5% ammonium molybdate in 20% H_2SO_4[177] and with ozone[178] were studied. In the former study thin layer chromatography was used. In the latter, gas chromatography was used and methyl oleate was partially hydrogenated with a metal catalyst, leading to isomerization phenomena involving change of position and configuration of the double bond. Aldehydes (C_5 to C_{14}) and aldehyde esters were isolated.

XXXIV. NITROALKANES

The acid hydrolysis of the alkaline salts of nitroalkanes forms aldehydes and nitrous oxide,[179] e.g.

$$RCH_2NO_2 \xrightarrow{OH^-} RCH=NO_2{}^- \xrightarrow{H^+} RCHO$$

The salts of aliphatic nitro compounds are oxidized by weakly basic permanganate to aldehydes and ketones.[180, 248] For example, 1-nitrobutane, cyclobutylnitromethane and 2,2-dimethyl-1-nitropropane form butyraldehyde, cyclobutylcarboxaldehyde and trimethylacetaldehyde in 83–97, 91 and 69% yields, respectively.[180] The nitrite ion is also formed.

The formation of aldehydes can also be done enzymatically.[181] Nitroethane oxidase (nitroethane:oxygen oxidoreductase, EC 1.7.3.1) catalyses the following reaction for nitroethane and some aliphatic nitro compounds, e.g.

$$CH_3CH_2NO_2 + H_2O + O_2 = CH_3CHO + HONO + H_2O_2$$

Since formaldehyde and probably other aldehydes can catalyse the formation of nitrosamines from nitrites and secondary and tertiary amines under physiological conditions,[249] nitroalkanes can be precursors of the carcinogenic nitrosamines on the basis of the above reaction.

XXXV. NITROSAMINES

Many of these N,N-dialkylated compounds are carcinogens and dependent on the alkyl group can attack a large variety of animal tissues. A large variety of biologically active molecules are formed from the nitrosamines *in vivo*, such as nitrite, hydroxylamine, hydrazine, aliphatic aldehydes, nitrosamine aldehydes, nitrosamine alcohols, nitrosamine acids, azo derivatives, free radicals, etc.[182–184, 250] One of the postulated reactions involving α-C-hydroxylation of dibutylnitrosamine based on the isolation of butyraldehyde is the following[184]

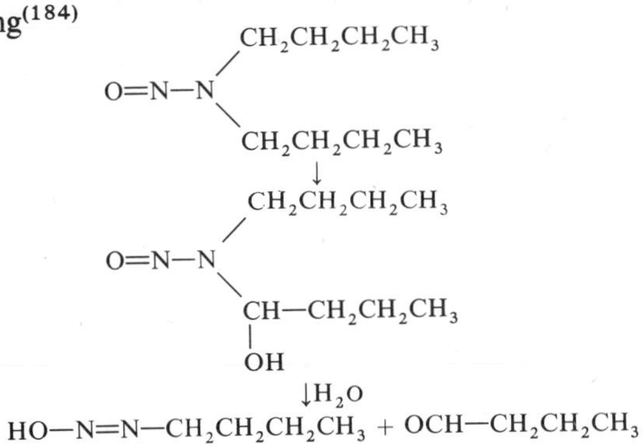

$$
O=N-N\begin{array}{l} CH_2CH_2CH_2CH_3 \\ \\ CH_2CH_2CH_2CH_3 \end{array}
$$

$$\downarrow$$

$$
O=N-N\begin{array}{l} CH_2CH_2CH_2CH_3 \\ \\ CH-CH_2CH_2CH_3 \\ | \\ OH \end{array}
$$

$$\downarrow H_2O$$

$$HO-N=N-CH_2CH_2CH_2CH_3 + OCH-CH_2CH_2CH_3$$

Nitrosamines are metabolized into potential alkyl donors and aldehydes and their carcinogenic activity has been attributed to alkylation of bio-polymers. Thus, the azo hydroxide is postulated as butylating nucleic acid.[184, 251, 252] The functional importance of the aldehyde groups has been neglected to a large extent. It is postulated that bladder carcinogenesis by N-nitrosodibutylamine and N-nitroso-4-hydroxybutyl butylamine may be the result of conversion to an active oxygenated metabolite such as a substituted 5-membered lactone, rather than alkylation.[250] The action of the cytotoxic aldehydes formed in or near high risk sites in the tissues is not known.

XXXVI. OLEFINS AND OTHER UNSATURATED COMPOUNDS

Aldehydes can be formed from olefins and ethylenic compounds through oxidation with periodate,[132, 185] ruthenium tetroxide,[11] and ozone.[187, 188] The mechanism of oxidation of methylenic compounds by periodate is shown in the CH_2O precursors chapter. In this case MBTH has been used in the analysis[185] as described in that section. Dimedone[132] or 1,3-cyclo-hexanedione can also be used in a fluorimetric determination.

Ruthenium tetroxide oxidation followed by determination with MBTH has been used in the following procedure for the determination of ethylenic and methylenic compounds, Table 22.[11]

Table 22. MBTH determination of unsaturated compounds at λ_{max} 660 nm[11]

Compound	mε
Calciferol	55
Camphene	30
7-Dehydrocholesterol	25
Ergosterol	34
Hydrocortisone	15
Prednisolone	28
Quinine	54
Secobarbital	26
Styrene	55
Testosterone	16

A. MBTH determination of unsaturated compounds[11]

To prepare the oxidizing reagent, suspend 10 mg of RuO_2 in 5 ml of carbon tetrachloride, add 5 ml of 10% aq $NaIO_4$, and shake until the organic phase becomes yellow–green; the organic phase is stable for 2 h under $NaIO_4$ solution. To 3 ml of acetic acid test solution add 0·1 ml of oxidizing reagent. Shake and after 5 min add 0·5 ml of 0·5% aq MBTH.HCl. After 10 min add 0·2 ml of 1-volume hydrogen peroxide solution. After a further 15 min, dilute with 5 ml of acetone and read at 660 nm.

Hydrocortisone and prednisolone in Table 22 also react in the procedure because they have the CO—CH_2OH group, which can form formaldehyde on oxidation.

Ozonolysis of olefins forms ozonides[253, 254] which can then be reduced to aldehydes with dimethyl sulphide,[186, 187] triphenyl phosphine[188] or sodium arsenite.[189]

Ozone adds rapidly and selectively to the electron-rich double bond of an olefin. An addition product of uncertain structure is formed, e.g.

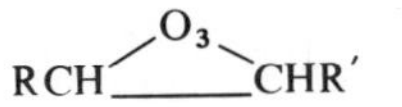

$$RCH \underset{}{\overset{O_3}{\diagup \diagdown}} CHR'$$

When ozonization of an olefin takes place in mixtures of methanol and carbon tetrachloride containing at least 50% methanol, yields of the intermediates and the aldehydes were quantitative.[186] A range of temperatures from very low to 50° did not affect the yield except for evaporation losses of olefin or aldehyde at the higher temperatures. Consequently ozonizations were performed at −65°. The following reactions took place

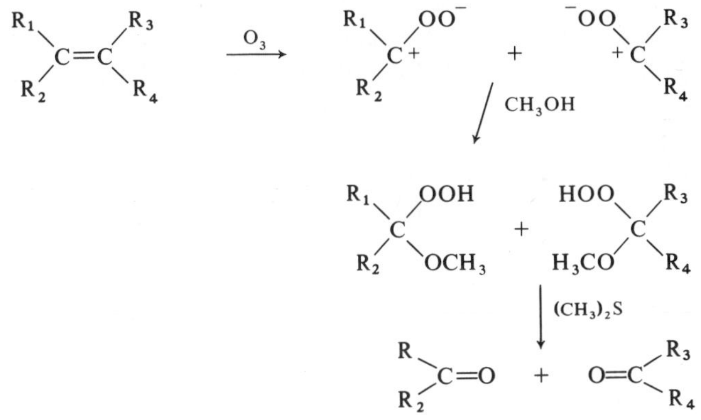

If only the low molecular weight olefins are to be analysed, the dimethylsulphide step which requires refluxing for 1 h can be substituted by treatment with DNPH. A quantitative yield of the dinitrophenylhydrazone is obtained, e.g. ozonolysis of 2-methyl-2-heptene at room temperature followed by treatment with DNPH gave the corresponding acetone and pentanal derivatives in 100% yield. Mono-olefins of different structures and chain lengths up to C_{30} gave 100% yields of carbonyl compounds. A little pyridine is added to the system prior to ozonolysis so as to prevent the formation of hemiacetals and acetals from the carbonyl compounds.

Ozonides formed from unsaturated compounds can also be treated directly with DNPH to form the hydrazone.[191–194] The ozonides can be separated on thin layer plates (or on a column) before or after formation of the dinitrophenylhydrazone.[191–195] They can be prepared in high yield in a nonpolar solvent, separated by TLC on silicic acid plates, and then treated directly with DNPH.[194] Products of the reaction can be separated by TLC on silicic acid into classes or by a partition method which separates homologous series of dinitrophenylhydrazones differing by only one carbon atom.[195]

XXXVII. OXIMES, ETC.

Aldehydes can be regenerated readily from appropriate oximes, phenylhydrazones and semicarbazones following treatment with thallic nitrate.[190]

XXXVIII. PHENOTHIAZINES

In a previous part of this section it was shown that N-alkylanilines can be oxidized to aldehydes by a wide variety of methods. N-Alkyl substituted phenothiazines can be considered to be *p*-substituted N-alkylanilines. Thus, it is not surprising that the alkyl groups in N-alkyl substituted phenothiazines can be oxidized to aldehydes by ammonium persulphate or benzoyl peroxide.[255] On this basis these types of phenothiazines can be analysed through the derived aldehyde. It is possible that many of the phenothiazine tranquilizers could be analysed in this fashion.

XXXIX. PHOSPHONOACETALDEHYDE

With the help of an enzyme which can hydrolyse C-phosphono groups, e.g. phosphonoacetaldehyde hydrolase (EC 3.11.1.1 2-phosphonoacetaldehyde phosphohydrolase), 2-phosphonoacetaldehyde is readily hydrolysed to acetaldehyde and orthophosphate.[196]

XL. PYRUVATES AND OTHER 2-KETOCARBOXYLIC ACIDS

Pyruvic acids, and probably other α-keto acids, react in the MBTH procedure to give the formazan cation.[197] The heat probably causes decarboxylation, e.g.

$$R—CO—COOH \xrightarrow{\Delta} RCHO + CO_2$$

Pyruvic acid, p-nitrobenzylpyruvate and oxalacetic acid give a millimolar absorptivity of 9·6 at λ_{max} 670 nm.

The aldehyde content of fresh orange juice increases linearly for 4 h to 130% of that in the initial juice.[174] Sodium pyruvate stimulates a 20-fold accumulation of acetaldehyde. Pyruvic acid is probably the native source of acetaldehyde in orange juice. Only pyruvic acid and to a slight extent, linoleic acid, are stimulatory to aldehyde formation. Orange juice sacs contain a linoleic oxidase (probably linoleate; oxygen oxidoreductase EC 1.13.11.12) which probably hydroperoxidizes linoleic acid.[174] This compound degrades to hexanal and octanal.[256] Heat-labile decarboxylation to acetaldehyde of added sodium pyruvate suggests that the reaction is mediated by the enzyme pyruvic decarboxylase (2-oxo acid carboxy-lyase EC 4.1.1.1).[175] Orange juice decarboxylates other 2-keto acids, Table 23.

Table 23. Substrate specificity of orange juice 2-ketodecarboxylase[174]

Acid substrate	Relative reactivity, %
Pyruvic	100
2-Ketobutyric	34
2-Ketovaleric	18
2-Ketoisovaleric	18
2-Keto-3-methylvaleric	18
2-Ketocaproic	15
2-Ketoisocaproic	15

If these keto acids are present in orange juice, their derived aldehydes would also contribute to an ADH-assayed aldehyde content.

XLI. STYRENES

Diarylacetaldehyde derivatives of MBTH can be formed by reaction of a 1,1-diarylethylene with MBTH in the presence of lead tetraacetate in acetic acid at $20°$,[211] e.g.

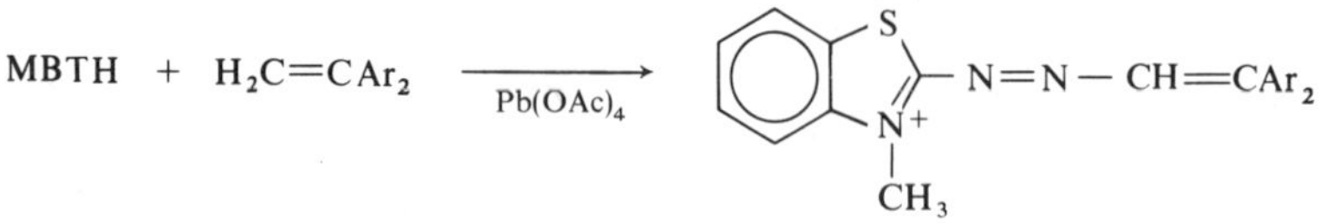

Somewhat similar reactions are the oxidation of p- and o-methoxystyrene at $20°$ with lead tetraacetate to give a 90% yield of the diacetate of p-methoxy-phenylacetaldehyde, and a 64% yield of the ortho derivative.[225] Sterically hindered enols containing a 1,1-diarylethylene structure also undergo a somewhat similar reaction, Fig. 23.[212]

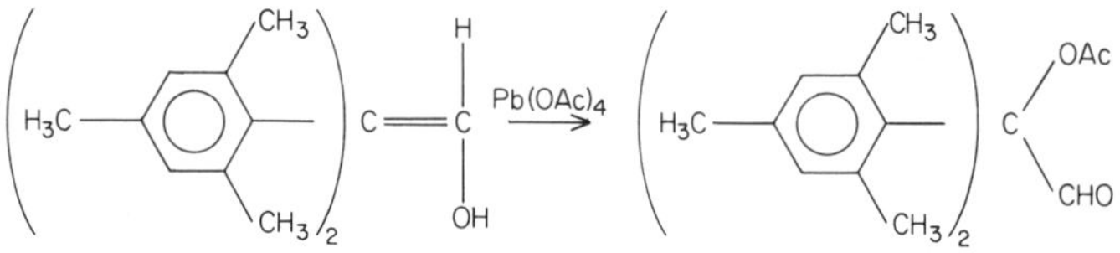

FIG. 23. Oxidation of the enol form of dimesitylenyl acetaldehyde by lead tetraacetate to an aldehyde.

A large variety of compounds containing the p-oxystyrene structure $—O—C_6H_4—CH=CH—$ react with MBTH and ferric chloride to give an intensely coloured chromogen with exactly the same visible spectrum as obtained in the reaction of aliphatic aldehydes with MBTH and ferric chloride.[257] Results are shown in Table 24. It would appear that an aliphatic aldehyde is formed from the styrene derivative.

With 4-hydroxystyrene as the test substance Beer's law was followed from 0.39 $(A = 0.1)$ to 7 µg per ml of final solution. The colour was stable for 1 h and decreased in intensity over 48 h at the rate of 0.01 absorbance units per hour.

The test is highly selective for phenols containing a p-vinyl group (and their ethers) as compared to phenols (and ethers) without a vinyl group. It is possible that phenols with an o- or m-vinyl group will react as phenols to give a red-orange colour. A p-hydroxy compound having an allyl group, i.e., where a methylene group is placed between the ethylenic double bond and the benzene ring, gives practically no reaction. Eugenol and safrole show this phenomenon, and the slight reactions observed are probably due to impurities such as isoeugenol and isosafrole. One o-hydroxystyrene compound was available, 4-(o-hydroxyphenyl)-3-buten-2-one. It reacted as a simple phenol, i.e., the reagent attacked mainly the position para to the hydroxy

Table 24. Determination of 4-hydroxystyrene derivatives

Compound	λ_{max} (nm)	mε
4-Methoxystyrene	667	62·0
	634	61·0
4-Hydroxystilbene	667	55·0
	624s	48·0
4-Methoxystilbene	667	52·0
	624s	45·6
iso-Safrole	667	65·0
	624s	60·0
iso-Eugenol	662	64·0
	624s	58·0
3-Methoxy-4-hydroxypropenylbenzene	662	62·0
	624s	57·0
4-Propenylveratrole	667	70·0
	624s	63·0
4-Hydroxybenzylideneacetophenone	667	23·2
	630	22·6
Anisalacetophenone	667	9·7
	627	9·6
4-(p-Methoxyphenyl)-3-buten-2-one	667	11·8
	630	11·7
β-Piperonylacrylic acid	667	5·2
	630s	5·0
4-(o-Hydroxyphenyl)-3-buten-2-one	664	4·9
	620s	4·3
	530	10·3

group. This was shown by the wave-length maximum at 530 nm with a milli-molar absorptivity of $10\cdot001\,\text{m}\text{M}^{-1}\,\text{cm}^{-1}$. Phenol itself reacted in the procedure to give a band at 510 nm with a millimolar absorptivity of $0\cdot561\,\text{m}\text{M}^{-1}$ cm^{-1}. A few compounds of the p-hydroxystyrene type were available with substituents on the β-carbon atom, e.g., 4-hydroxystilbene and 4-hydroxy-benzylideneacetophenone. The phenyl substituent did not appreciably affect the results; however, a benzoyl or acetyl substituent drastically decreased the intensity.

The following compounds gave essentially negative results in the procedures: phenol, anisole, 1-naphthol, 1-anthrol, 3-phenanthrol, 6-chrysenol, 7-hydroxybenz(a)anthracene, benzaldehyde, p-anisaldehyde, p-anisoin, stilbene, benzo(b)thiophene, dibenzothiophene, phenyl sulphide, and phenyl selenide.

All the diverse types of compounds which have been shown to react with MBTH could be considered as interferences.

The following procedure was used in the analyses.

A. MBTH determination of *p*-hydroxystyrenes[257]

To 1 ml methanolic test solution, add 1 ml of 0·2% aq MBTH reagent followed by 2 ml of 1·3% aq $FeCl_3$ solution. Allow the mixture to stand for 15 min and then dilute to 10 ml with methanol. Make absorbance measurements at the wavelength maxima. The blank has a light greenish-yellow colour.

XLII. THIAZOLIDINES

2-Alkyl derivatives of thiazolidine-4-carboxylic acid can be cleaved to aliphatic aldehydes by reaction with iodine.[198, 200] The aldehydes can then be determined with an MBTH procedure given in the formaldehyde precursor section. The results obtained with various thiazolidine derivatives are given in Table 25. Interferences are aliphatic aldehydes and α-keto acids. Pyruvic, oxaloacetic and 2-oxoglutaric acid give 10–20% of the millimolar absorptivity obtained with thiazolidine-4-carboxylic acids. Thiazolidine derivatives can also be readily cleaved to aldehydes by treatment with mercuric salts.

XLIII. UNSATURATED ACIDS

Unsaturated acids can be ozonized, etc., to aldehydes which are determined with DNPH,[208] or they can be treated with periodate, sodium metabisulphite followed by fuchsin,[202] or auto-oxidized to aldehydes which are reacted in the Schiff reaction.[209] The latter reaction takes place during fixation of tissue followed by the Schiff reaction for unsaturated lipids. This is called the pseudoplasmal reaction.

The procedure for the periodate method has been used to locate unsaturated monoglycerides (violet colour) and polyene acids (grey-green colour) on thin layer plates.[202]

A. Location of unsaturated acids and unsaturated monoglycerides after thin-layer chromatography[202]

Reagent. (a). 0·5 g of periodic acid in 100 ml of 90% acetic acid, (b). Mix equal volumes of cold (0°C) 30% sodium metabisulphite and 3 N hydrochloric acid, (c). 200 mg fuchsin and 5 ml of 10% sodium metabisulphite in 85 ml of water. Keep for 12 h, treat with charcoal, and filter.

Procedure. Spray lightly with (a) followed by (b) and then (c). Heat for 15 min at 90°C.

Table 25. Optimal iodine times for ring cleavage of thiazolidinecarboxylic acids and spectral characteristics of MBTH derivatives[200]

Compound of 4-carboxylic acid	Parent aldehyde	Iodine time (min)		mε		
		In water[a]	In TCA[b]	λ_{max} (mμ)	In H_2O[a]	In TCA[b]
Thiazolidine-	Formaldehyde	>180	90 (60–120)[c]	670	58	58
2-Methylthiazolidine-	Acetaldehyde	45 (30–120)[c]	45 (30–120)	670	56	58
2-Ethylthiazolidine-	Propionaldehyde	25 (20–30)	30 (20–60)	670	54	58
2-Propylthiazolidine-	n-Butyraldehyde	15 (5–60)	30 (10–120)	670	52	58
2-Hexylthiazolidine-	n-Heptanal	45 (30–90)	45 (30–90)	670	49	58
2-Isopropylthiazolidine-	Isobutyraldehyde	15 (10–30)	30 (20–90)	670	42	38
2-Hydroxymethylthiazolidine-	Glycolaldehyde	45 (30–120)	80 (60–180)	660	58	53
2-Dihydroxyethylthiazolidine-	DL-Glyceraldehyde	60 (45–180)	80 (60–180)	660	58	47
2-(1',2'-Dihydroxypropyl)thiazolidine-	L-Erythro-α,β-dihydroxy butyraldehyde	60 (30–120)	80 (60–180)	660	47	38

[a] Sample dissolved in distilled water.
[b] Sample dissolved in 5% aq TCA.
[c] Numbers in parentheses represent iodine times for which the final absorbances do not decrease by more than 2% from the maximal value.

Oxidation of fats containing C_{16}–C_{20} unsaturated acids could be expected to give C_3, C_6, C_7 and C_9 n-alkanals.[258] However, C_2, C_3, C_5, C_6 and C_7 n-alkanals were obtained.

The double bond in unsaturated acids, alcohols, aldehydes and esters is usually located through oxidation with osmium tetroxide,[259, 260] peroxy acids,[261, 262] potassium permanganate in the presence of periodic acid or its salts,[263–266] ozonolysis[267–269] and periodic acid.[203, 207, 270]

Double bonds in water-soluble substances can be determined readily with periodic acid.[270] However, a procedure involving thin-layer chromatography and absorption spectral analysis of the derived 2,4-dinitrophenylhydrazone can be even applied to water-insoluble unsaturated compounds.[203] A micro-column of periodic acid impregnated on magnesium sulphate was used to effect oxidation of ethylenic unsaturation. The aldehyde, produced on the hydrocarbon side of the double bond in 30–40% yield, was converted to a dinitrophenylhydrazone on a microderivitizing column (Celite impregnated with a phosphoric acid solution of 2,4-dinitrophenylhydrazine) and identified by thin-layer chromatography. The yield of aldehyde was determined spectrophotometrically in the products of oxidation from 25 μg of substrate. The method was applied to unsaturation in fatty acids, their methyl esters, alcohols, aldehydes, and coloured derivatives of the last two classes. The position of the double bond did not affect the results except when terminal unsaturation or unsaturation with a methyl group on either carbon of the double bond was present. The procedure could be used with 5 μg of material.

A method has been developed to determine small amounts of aldehydes in samples resulting from the ozonolysis of unsaturated mono- and di-carboxylic acids.[208] Although in this case the test mixtures were obtained from oleic and linoleic acid feed stocks, and nonanal and aldehydononanoic acid were the primary aldehydes, the method could be used for other unsaturated acids. The following method permits quantitative determination of aldehydes in samples insoluble in water or aliphatic hydrocarbons and demonstrates the advantage of the extraction method over the alkaline DNPH method with its lack of reproducibility and unstable colour complex. Peroxides, formic acid, and representative monobasic fatty acids and low molecular weight dibasic acids did not affect recoveries. Replicate analyses of a single sample over a period of 12 d gave a standard deviation of 0·0056 and a relative standard deviation of 3·4%. Good reproducibility is obtained over the concentration range from 0·025–1·8 mM g^{-1}.

B. DNPH determination of aldehydes in mixtures of mono- and dicarboxylic acids[208]

Reagents. Carbonyl-free methanol: Reflux 1 gallon of methanol with 17 g of

DNPH and 5 ml of conc HCl for 4 h. Distil through a Vigreaux column, discarding the first 100 ml, then collecting distillate until the condensate at the top of the condenser appears yellow. DNPH reagent: Prepare, fresh daily, a saturated solution of DNPH in 20% (v/v) H_3PO_4.

Procedure. In a 125 ml polyethylene stoppered flask dissolve 40 mg of test sample in exactly 5 ml of methanol. Add 25 ml of DNPH reagent, stopper flask tightly, and heat at 60° for 30 minutes. Allow to cool, add 25 ml of cyclohexane,and shake the flasks for 90 min on a mechanical shaker. After the phases have separated, transfer 5 ml aliquot of the cyclohexane solution to a 25 ml volumetric flask and dilute to the mark with cyclohexane. Read the absorbance at 339 nm.

In addition to the extraction technique various reducing agents are used to cancel the interference of excess periodate in the various colorimetric and fluorimetric methods for the determination of the derived aldehydes. The following have been the most popular—sodium arsenite,[132, 133] sodium sulphite, thioacetamide,[131] stannous chloride, etc.

One wonders what effect many years of contact of human lung and skin tissue with increased concentrations of atmospheric ozone would have on the tissue. In the case of skin, ozone in the presence of ultraviolet radiation (sunlight) could react with unsaturated compounds in the skin to form ozonides, aldehydes, etc. This reaction could be a possible factor in skin cancer.

XLIV. VINYL ETHERS AND BOUND SERUM ALDEHYDES

Vinyl ethers are readily hydrolysed to aldehydes in acid solution by the reactions shown in Table 26.

Table 26. Hydrolysis of vinyl ethers in acid solution

$$R-C=CH-ZC_2H_5 \xrightarrow{H^+} RCH-CHO$$
$$\qquad | \qquad\qquad\qquad\qquad |$$
$$\qquad X \qquad\qquad\qquad\qquad X$$

R	X	Z	Ref.
Alkyl	Br[a]	0	213
C_2H_5Se-	H	0	214
C_2H_5Se-	H	S	214
C_2H_5S-	H	0	215

[a] $CHBr=CHSC_2H_5 \xrightarrow[H_2O]{H^+} OHC-CH_2SC_2H_5$.[213]

Bound serum aldehydes can be released with arsenious oxide.[271] It is claimed that in sera of patients with early malignancy the value for bound aldehyde is lower than normal, but increases to above normal with the development of metastases. In sera of patients with malignancy who responded to treatment, the value is essentially normal. MBTH can be used in assaying for the released aldehydes.

REFERENCES

1. L. Fishbein. "Chromatography of Environmental Hazards," Vol. I, Elsevier, Amsterdam, 1972, pp. 94–134.
2. L. Fishbein, W. G. Flamm and H. L. Falk. "Chemical Mutagens," Academic Press, New York, 1970, pp. 206–214.
3. B. Holmberg and T. Malmfors. *Env. Res.* **7**, 183 (1974).
4. R. O. Martin and P. K. Stumpf. *J. Biol. Chem.* **234**, 2548 (1959).
5. M. P. Cooke. *J. Am. Chem. Soc.* **92**, 6080 (1970).
6. W. D. Siegl and J. P. Collman. *J. Am. Chem. Soc.* **94**, 2516 (1972).
7. W. A. Mosher, C. L. Kehr and L. W. Wright. *J. Org. Chem.* **26**, 1044 (1961).
8. H. Meerwein, K. Wunderlich and K. F. Zenner. *Angew. Chem.* **74**, 807 (1962).
9. M. Pesez and J. Bartos. *Bull. Soc. Chim. France* 2333 (1963).
10. J. M. Lalancette, G. Rollin and P. Dumas. *Can. J. Chem.* **50**, 3058 (1972).
11. M. Pesez and J. Bartos. *Ann. Pharm. France.* **22**, 609 (1964).
12. G. G. Guilbault and S. H. Sadar. *Anal. Letters* **2**, 41 (1969).
13. K. Dalziel. *Biochem. J.* **80**, 440 (1961).
14. H. Theorell. *Advan. Enzymol.* **20**, 31 (1958).
15. H. Sund and H. Theorell. *The Enzymes*, 2nd. ed. **7**, 25 (1963).
16. R. E. Reeves, F. E. Montalvo and T. S. Lushbaugh. *Int. J. Biochem.* **2**, 55 (1971).
17. R. DeMoss. *Bacteriol. Proc.* **81** (1953).
18. S. W. Tanenbaum. *Biochim. Biophys. Acta* **21**, 335 (1956).
19. F. W. Janssen and H. W. Ruelius. *Biochim. Biophys. Acta* **151**, 330 (1968).
20. N. H. Fidge and D. S. Goodman. *J. Biol. Chem.* **243**, 4372 (1968).
21. E. Sawicki, T. R. Hauser and F. T. Fox. *Anal. Chim. Acta* **26**, 229 (1962).
22. B. H. Kaplan and E. R. Stadtman. *J. Biol. Chem.* **243**, 1787 (1968).
23. C. Bradbeer. *J. Biol. Chem.* **240**, 4669, 4675 (1965).
24. J. S. Ellington and W. E. M. Lands. *Lipids* **3**, 111 (1968).
25. H. R. Warner and W. E. M. Lands. *J. Biol. Chem.* **236**, 2404 (1961).
26. H. R. Warner and W. E. M. Lands. *J. Lipid Res.* **4**, 216 (1963).
27. J. Y. Terner and E. R. Hayes. *Stain Technology* **30**, 265 (1961).
28. W. J. Baumann and H. K. Mangold. *Biochim. Biophys. Acta* **144**, 344 (1967).
29. H. H. O. Schmid and H. K. Mangold. *Biochem. Z.* **346**, 13 (1966).
30. H. H. O. Schmid and H. K. Mangold. *Biochim. Biophys. Acta* **125**, 182 (1966).
31. R. H. Reitsema. *Anal. Chem.* **26**, 960 (1954).
32. C. V. Viswanathan, S. P. Hoevet, W. O. Lundberg, J. M. White and G. A. Muccini. *J. Chromatog.* **40**, 225 (1969).
33. M. M. Rapport and W. T. Norton. *Ann. Rev. Biochem.* **31**, 113 (1962).
34. R. E. Anderson, R. D. Garrett, M. L. Blank and F. Snyder. *Lipids* **4**, 327 (1969).
35. W. J. Ferrell, D. M. Radloff and J. F. Radloff. *Anal. Biochem.* **37**, 227 (1970).
36. Z. L. Bandi. *Chem. Phys. Lipids* **3**, 409 (1969).

37. R. E. Flygare, S. H. Broderson and E. R. Hayes. *Stain Technol.* **45**, 149 (1970).
38. L. A. Horrocks. *Lipid Res.* **9**, 469 (1968).
39. C. V. Viswanathan, M. Basilio, S. P. Hoevet and W. ₰ Lundberg. *J. Chromatog.* **34**, 421 (1968).
40. C. V. Viswanathan, F. Phillips and W. O. Lundberg, *J. Chromatog.* **35**, 66 (1968).
41. G. Schmidt, B. Ottenstein, W. A. Spencer, C. Hackethal and S. J. Thannhauser. *Federation Proc.* **16**, 832 (1957).
42. H. K. Mangold in E. Stahl, Ed. "Thin-Layer Chromatography," Springer-Verlag, New York, 1969, p. 373.
43. W. J. W. Hanna. *U.S. Dept. Com. Office Tech. Serv. P. B. Rept.* **144, 250**, 46 pp (1959); through *Chem. Abstr.* **55**, 19740 (1961).
44. R. G. R. Bacon and W. J. W. Hanna. *Proc. Chem. Soc.* 305 (1959).
45. R. J. Baumgarten, *J. Chem. Ed.* **43**, 398 (1966).
46. K. Kahr and C. Berther. *Chem. Ber.* **93**, 132 (1960).
47. O. L. Lebedev and S. N. Kazarnovskiĭ, *Zh. Obsch. Khim.* **30**, 3105 (1960); through *Chem. Abstr.* **55**, 19740, 1473 (1961).
48. W. Lorenz, J. Kusche and E. Werle. *Z. Physiol. Chem.* **348**, 561 (1967).
49. K. F. Tipton. *Anal. Biochem.* **28**, 318 (1969).
50. A. L. Green and T. M. Haughton. *Biochem. J.* **76**, 44P (1960).
51. H. Blaschko. *The Enzymes*, 2nd. ed. **8**, 337 (1963).
52. K. F. Tipton. *Biochim. Biophys. Acta* **159**, 451 (1968).
53. E. A. Zeller. *The Enzymes*, 2nd. ed. **8**, 313 (1963).
54. H. Moehrle and W. Haug. *Arch. Pharm.* **301**, 66 (1968).
55. M. Matrka. J. Poskocil, Z. Sagner and Z. Sterba. *Coll. Czech. Chem. Commun.* **26**, 3177 (1961).
56. F. W. Neumann and C. W. Gould. *Anal. Chem.* **25**, 751 (1953).
57. L. Horner, E. Winkelmann, K. H. Knapp and W. Ludwig. *Ber.* **92**, 288 (1959).
58. L. Fieser and M. Fieser. "Reagents for Organic Syntheses," Vol. 1, Wiley-Interscience, New York, 1967, p. 817.
59. E. Aubel and J. Asselineau. *Bull. Soc. Chim. France* 114 (1947).
60. O. Frehden and L. Goldschmidt. *Mikrochim. Acta* **2**, 186 (1937).
60a. A. K. Saund and N. K. Mathur. *Microchem. J.* **18**, 300 (1973).
61. R. Saijo and T. Takeo. *Agric. Biol. Chem.* **34**, 227 (1970).
62. B. Riistow and A. Hock. *Die Pharmazie* **24**, 453 (1969).
63. D. M. Larson, D. C. Snetsinger and P. E. Waibel. *Anal. Biochem.* **39**, 395 (1971).
64. K. Soda. *Anal. Biochem.* **25**, 228 (1968).
65. R. Moubasher and W. I. Awad. *J. Biol. Chem.* **179**, 915 (1949).
66. W. I. Awad, S. Nashed, S. S. M. Hassan and R. F. Zakhary. *Talanta* **19**, 31 (1972).
67. I. R. Hunter, K. P. Dimick and J. W. Corse. *Chem. Ind.* 294 (1955).
68. A. Said, V. B. Baghos and D. H. Fleita. *Chemist-Analyst* **53**, 106 (1964).
69. S. Ruhemans. *J. Chem. Soc.* **99**, 792 (1911).
70. A. I. Virtanen and N. Rautanen. *Biochem. J.* **41**, 101 (1947).
71. A. Zlatkis and J. F. Oro. *Anal. Chem.* **30**, 1156 (1958).
72. A. Zlatkis, J. F. Oro and A. P. Kimball. *Anal. Chem.* **32**, 162 (1960).
73. M. J. Baraud. *Bull. Soc. Chim. France* 649 (1960).
74. Y. Murata and T. Takanishi. *Kogyo Kayaku Zasshi* **64**, 787 (1961).
75. S. Ruhemann. *J. Chem. Soc.* **97**, 2025 (1910).
76. A. I. Virtanen and N. Rautanen. *Acta Chem. Fenn.* **19**, 56 (1946).
77. P. Roine and N. Rautanen. *Acta Chem. Scand.* **1**, 854 (1947).

78. A. E. Parkinson and E. C. Wagner. *Ind. Eng. Chem., Anal. Ed.* **6**, 433 (1934).
79. A. I. Virtanen, T. Laine and T. Toivanen. *Z. Physiol. Chem.* **266**, 193 (1940).
80. A. Leisman and F. Turba. *Z. Physiol. Chem.* **306**, 273 (1957).
81. O. O. Blumenfeld and P. M. Gallop. *Biochemistry* **1**, 947 (1962).
82. B. H. Nicolet and L. A. Shinn. *J. Am. Chem. Soc.* **61**, 1615 (1939).
83. D. R. Kenney and J. M. Bremner. *Anal. Biochem.* **18**, 274 (1967).
84. B. H. Nicolet and L. A. Shinn. *J. Biol. Chem.* **139**, 687 (1941).
85. P. Fleury, J. Courtois and M. Grandchamp. *Bull. Soc. Chim. France* **88**, (1949).
86. G. Dryhurst. "Periodate Oxidation of Diol and Other Functional Groups." Pergamon Press, London, 1970.
87. E. Sawicki and C. R. Engel. *Chemist-Analyst* **56**, 7 (1967).
88. M. Pesez and J. Bartos. *Talanta* **14**, 1097 (1967).
89. E. Sawicki and C. R. Sawicki. *Ann. New York Acad. Sci.* **163**, 895 (1969).
90. R. Preussmann, H. Hengy, D. Lubbe and A. Von Hodenberg. *Anal. Chim. Acta* **41**, 497 (1968).
91. Z. Fialkiewicz and J. Sokolowski. *Zesz.Nauk. Mat. Fiz. Chem. Wyzsza Pedagog. Gdansku.* **8**, 235 (1968); through *Chem. Abstr.* **71**, 61721 (1969).
92. O. O. Blumenfeld, M. A. Paz, P. M. Gallop and S. Seifter. *J. Biol. Chem.* **238**, 3835 (1970).
93. G. Ohloff and W. Giersch. *Angew. Chem. Int. Ed.* **12**, 401 (1973).
94. M. Finkelstein. *Ber.* **90**, 2097 (1957).
95. P. D. Bartlett, G. L. Frazer and R. B. Woodward. *J. Am. Chem. Soc.* **63**, 495 (1941).
96. W. J. Hickinbottom and D. G. M. Wood. *J. Chem. Soc.* 1906 (1953).
97. R. Muller and H. Plieninger. *Ber.* **92**, 3009 (1959).
98. D. P. Schwartz, J. L. Weihrauch and L. H. Burgwald. *Anal. Chem.* **41**, 984 (1969).
99. F. D. Gunstone. *J. Chem. Soc.* 1611 (1954).
100. G. R. Mizuno, E. C. Ellison and J. R. Chipault. *Microchem. J.* **14**, 227 (1969).
101. G. Maerker and E. T. Haebner. *J. Am. Oil Chem. Soc.* **43**, 97 (1966).
102. B. A. Bierl, M. Beroza and M. H. Aldridge. *Anal. Chem.* **43**, 636 (1971).
103. H. E. Mishmash and C. E. Meloan. *Anal. Chem.* **44**, 835 (1972).
104. G. Maerker, E. T. Haebner and W. C. Ault. *J. Am. Oil Chem. Soc.* **43**, 100 (1966).
105. G. Maerker and E. T. Haebner. U.S. Patent 3405149 (1968); through *Chem. Abstr.* **70**, 37188 (1969).
106. R. K. Bly and R. S. Bly. *J. Org. Chem.* **28**, 3165 (1963).
107. M. P. Hartshorn, D. N. Kirk and A. F. A. Wallis. *J. Chem. Soc.* 5494 (1964).
108. J. Jadot, A. Daird and J. Kasperczyck. *Bull. Roy. Sci. Liege* **29**, 196 (1960); through *Chem. Abstr.* **55**, 11348g (1961).
109. H. W. Walborsky, R. H. Davis and D. R. Howton. *J. Am. Chem. Soc.* **73**, 2590 (1951).
109a. W. H. Evans and A. Dennis. *Analyst* **98**, 782 (1973).
110. A. Saifer and N. I. Feldman. *J. Lipid Res.* **12**, 112 (1971).
111. G. R. List, C. D. Evans, W. F. Kwolek, K. Warner and B. K. Boundy. *J. Am Oil Chemists Soc.* **51**, 17 (1974).
112. V. Holm, K. Ekbom and G. Wobe. *JAOCS* **34**, 606 (1957).
113. V. Holm. *Acta Polytech. Scand.* **21**, 320 (1962).
114. V. Holm. Abstracts, International Society for Fat Research Congress, Goteborg, Sweden, June 1972.
115. D. H. Wheeler. *Oil Soap* **9**, 89 (1932).
116. A. Popov, N. Yanishlieva and V. Antonova. *Int. Z. Lebensm. Lebensmitteltech.* **2**, 55 (1973).

117. R. D. Guthrie. "The 'Dialdehydes' from the Periodate Oxidation of Carbo-hydrates" in W. W. Pigman, Ed., "Advances in Carbohydrate Chemistry," Vol. 16, Academic Press, New York, 1961.
118. J. M. Bobbitt. "Periodate Oxidation of Carbohydrates," in W. W. Pigman, Ed. Advances in Carbohydrate Chemistry, Vol. II, Academic Press, New York, 1956.
119. J. R. Dyer. "Use of Periodate Oxidations in Biochemical Analysis," in D. Glick, Ed. "Methods of Biochemical Analysis," Vol. III, Interscience, New York—London, 1956, p. 111–152.
120. E. L. Jackson. "Periodic Acid Oxidation," in R. Adams, W. E. Backmann, L. F. Fieser, J. R. Johnson and H. R. Snyder, Eds., "Organic Reactions," Vol. II, Wiley, New York, 1944, pp. 341–375.
121. R. W. Bailey and J. B. Pridham. *Adv. Carbohydrate Chem.* **17**, 125 (1962).
122. S. A. Barker and E. J. Bourne. *Adv. Carbohydrate Chem.* **7**, 144 (1952).
123. R. D. Guthrie. *Methods in Carbohydrate Chemistry, I*, 432 (1962).
124. F. Smith and R. Montgomery. *Methods of Biochemical Analysis, III*, 153 (1956).
125. J. R. Turvey. *Adv. Carbohydrate Chem.* **20**, 194 (1965).
126. R. Mari, M. Feve and M. Dzierzinsky. *Bull. Soc. Chim. France* 1395 (1961).
127. J. F. A. McManus. "Periodate Oxidation Techniques," in J. F. Danielli, Ed., "General Cytochemical Methods," Vols. I and II, Academic Press, New York 1958 and 1961.
128. N. S. MacDonald, J. Thompsett and J. F. Mead. *Anal. Chem.* **21**, 315 (1949).
129. G. J. Buist, C. A. Bunton and J. H. Miles. *J. Chem. Soc.* 4567, 4575 (1957).
130. E. Juni and G. A. Heim. *Anal. Biochem.* **4**, 143, 159 (1962).
131. K. C. Leibman and E. Ortiz. *Anal. Chem.* **40**, 251 (1968).
132. E. Sawicki and R. A. Carnes. *Mikrochim. Acta* 602 (1968).
133. E. Sawicki, R. Schumacher and C. R. Engel. *Microchem. J.* **12**, 337 (1967).
134. P. Densuelle and M. Naudet. *Bull. Soc. Chim. France* **12**, 871 (1945).
135. W. J. Baumann, H. H. O. Schmid and H. K. Mangold. *J. Lipid Res.* **10**, 132 (1969).
136. G. de Vries and A. Schors. *Tetrahedron Letters* 5689 (1968).
137. J. S. Littler and W. A. Waters. *J. Chem. Soc.* 2767 (1960).
138. R. Criegee. *Angew. Chem.* **70**, 173 (1958).
139. A. S. Perlin, in R. L. Whistler, M. L. Wolfrom, J. N. Be Miller and F. Shafizadeh, Eds., "Methods in Carbohydrate Chemistry," Vol. I. Academic Press, New York, 1962, p. 427.
140. V. M. Parikh and J. K. N. Jones. *Can. J. Chem.* **43**, 3452 (1965).
141. P. J. Beynon, P. M. Collins, P. T. Doganges and W. G. Overend. *J. Chem. Soc.* 1131 (1966 C).
142. M. Fétizon and M. Golfier. *Compt. rend.* **276**, 900 (1968).
143. M. Fétizon, M. Golfier and J. M. Louis. *Chem. Communs.* 1118 (1969).
144. G. L. Sottocasa, N. Stagni and B. DeBernard. *Experientia* **27**, 1247 (1971).
145. R. H. Abeles and H. A. Lee, Jr. *J. Biol. Chem.* **236**, 2347 (1961).
146. H. A. Lee Jr. and R. H. Abeles. *J. Biol. Chem.* **238**, 2367 (1963).
147. R. Preussmann, H. Hengy and A. Von Hodenberg. *Anal. Chim. Acta* **42**, 95 (1968).
148. A. P. Altshuller. *Int. J. Air Water Pollut.* **10**, 713 (1966).
149. A. P. Altshuller *et al. Int. J. Air Water Poll.* **10**, 81 (1966).
150. E. R. Stephens and W. E. Scott. *Proc. Am. Petroleum Inst.* **42**, 665 (1962).
151. E. R. Stephens *et al. Int. J. Air Water Pollution* **4**, 79 (1961).

E

152. S. L. Kopczynski. *Int. J. Air Water Pollution* **8**, 107 (1964).
153. W. E. Scott *et al. Am. Petroleum Inst.* **37**, 171 (1957).
154. A. P. Altshuller and J. J. Bufalini. *Photochem. Photobiol.* **4**, 97 (1965).
155. A. P. Altshuller and I. R. Cohen. *Int. J. Air Water Poll.* **7**, 787 (1963).
156. S. Sato and R. J. Cvetanovic. *Can. J. Chem.* **36**, 1668 (1958); **37**, 953 (1959).
157. R. J. Cvetanovic. *Can. J. Chem.* **38**, 1678 (1960).
158. J. E. Sigsby, Jr., T. A. Bellar and L. J. Leng. *J. Air Poll. Control Assoc.* **12**, 522 (1962).
159. M. Feldstein. *J. Air Poll. Control Assoc.* **24**, 469 (1974).
160. B. Dimitriades. Final report of work done in FY68 under APRAC Project No. CAPE-11-68, 1968.
161. Coordinating Research Council, Oxygenates in Automatic Exhaust Gas: Part I. Techniques for determining aldehydes by the MBTH method. CRC Report 415, June 1968, 21 pp.
162. Coordinating Research Council. Oxygenates in Automotive Exhaust Gas: Part II. Techniques for determining aldehydes by the DNPH method. CRC Report 417, March 1969, 26 pp.
163. D. E. Seizinger and B. Dimitriades. *J. Air Poll. Control Assoc.* **22**, 47 (1972).
164. W. Heimann, P. Dresen and V. Klaiber. *Z. Lebensmittelunters. Forsch.* **153**, 1 (1973).
165. C. H. Lea and H. A. F. Jackson. *Chem. Ind.* 1429 (1964).
166. F. Linow, M. Roloff and K. Taufel. *Nahrung* **9**, 919 (1965).
167. G. R. Mizuno and J. R. Chipault. *J. Am. Oil Chem. Soc.* **42**, 839 (1965).
168. A. M. Gaddis, R. Ellis and G. T. Currie. *Food Res.* **25**, 495 (1960).
169. C. H. Lea and P. A. T. Swoboda. *J. Sci. Food Agric.* **13**, 148 (1962).
170. M. M. Horikx. *J. Appl. Chem.* **14**, 50 (1964).
171. R. Criegee and E. Buchner. *Ber.* **73**, 563 (1940).
172. Y. Yanuka, R. Katz and S. Sarel. *Tetrahedron Letters* 1725 (1968).
173. M. Amorosa *et al. Helv. Chim. Acta* **45**, 2674 (1962).
174. B. Roe and J. H. Bruemmer. *J. Agric. Food Chem.* **22**, 285 (1974).
175. T. P. Singer and J. Pensky. *J. Biol. Chem.* **196**, 375 (1952).
176. C. Franzke and F. Baumgardt. *Die Nahrung* **17**, 209 (1973).
177. J. Sliwiok and W. J. Kowalski. *Microchem. J.* **17**, 576 (1972).
178. P. Van Der Plank. *J. Am. Oil Chemists' Soc.* **49**, 489 (1972).
179. W. E. Noland. *Chem. Revs.* **55**, 137 (1955).
180. H. Schechter and F. T. Williams, Jr. *J. Org. Chem.* **27**, 3699 (1962).
181. H. N. Little. *J. Biol. Chem.* **193**, 347 (1951).
182. P. N. Magee. *Annals N. Y. Acad. Sci.* **163**, 717 (1969).
183. L. Blattmann, N. Joswig and R. Preussmann. *Z. Krebsforsch.* **81**, 71 (1974).
184. L. Blattmann and R. Preussmann. *Z. Krebsforsch.* **81**, 75 (1974).
185. E. Sawicki, C. R. Engel and M. Guyer. *Anal. Chim. Acta* **39**, 505 (1967).
186. M. M. Smits and D. Hoefman. *Z. Anal. Chem.* **264**, 297 (1973).
187. J. J. Pappas, W. P. Keaveney, E. Gaucher and M. G. Berger. *Tetrahedron Letters* **36**, 4273 (1966).
188. M. Beroza and B. A. Bierl. *Anal. Chem.* **38**, 1976 (1966).
189. J. E. Hoff and E. D. Feit. *Anal. Chem.* **36**, 1002 (1964).
190. A. McKillop, J. D. Hunt, R. D. Naylor and E. C. Taylor. *J. Am. Chem. Soc.* **93**, 4918 (1971).
191. O. S. Privett, M. L. Blank, D. W. Codding and E. C. Nickell. *J. Am. Oil Soc.* **42**, 381 (1965).

192. W. A. Bonner. *J. Chem. Educ.* **30**, 452 (1953).
193. P. W. Haagman and J. P. Wibault. *Res. Trav. Chem.* **60**, 842 (1941).
194. O. S. Privett and E. C. Nickell. *J. Am. Oil Chem. Soc.* **39**, 414 (1962); **40**, 189 (1963).
195. G. Urbach. *J. Chromatog.* **12**, 196 (1963).
196. J. M. La Nauze and H. Rosenberg. *Biochim. Biophys. Acta* **165**, 438 (1968).
197. M. A. Paz, O. O. Blumenfeld, M. Rojkind, E. Henson, C. Furfine and P. M. Gallop. *Arch. Biochem. Biophys.* **109**, 548 (1965).
198. G. G. Guidotti, A. F. Borghetti and L. Loreti. *Anal. Biochem.* **17**, 513 (1966).
199. L. J. Altman and S. L. Richheimer. *Tetrahedron Letters* 4709 (1971).
200. S. Ratner and H. T. Clarke. *J. Am. Chem. Soc.* **59**, 200 (1937).
201. A. I. Meyers, R. Munavu and J. Durandetta. *Tetrahedron Letters* 3929 (1972).
202. H. Jatzkewitz and E. Mehl. *Z. Physiol. Chem.* **320**, 251 (1960).
203. J. L. Weihrauch and D. P. Schwartz. *Microchem. J.* **17**, 234 (1972).
204. A. M. Gaddis, R. Ellis and G. T. Currie. *J. Am. Oil Chem. Soc.* **38**, 371 (1961).
205. R. Ellis, A. M. Gaddis and G. T. Currie. *J. Food Sci.* **31**, 191 (1966).
206. R. Ellis, A. M. Gaddis, G. T. Currie and S. L. Powell. *J. Am. Oil Chem. Soc.* **45**, 553 (1968).
207. K. Kusamran and N. Polgar. *Lipids* **6**, 961 (1971).
208. E. P. Crowell and B. B. Burnett. *J. Am. Oil Chem. Soc.* **47**, 281 (1970).
209. W. D. Belt and E. R. Hayes. *Stain Technology* **31**, 117 (1956).
210. G. Wittig, W. Böll and K. H. Krück. *Chem. Ber.* **95**, 2514 (1962).
211. S. Hunig and K. H. Fritsch. *Ann.* **609**, 143 (1957).
212. R. C. Fuson, E. W. Maynert, T. Tan, R. E. Trumbull and F. W. Wassmundt. *J. Am. Chem. Soc.* **79**, 1938 (1957).
213. J. F. Arens and T. Doornbos. *Rec. Trav. Chim.* **75**, 482 (1956).
214. H. C. Volger and J. F. Arens. *Rec. Trav. Chim.* **77**, 1170 (1958).
215. J. F. Arens, A. C. Hermans and J. F. S. Weiland. *Proc. Koninkl. Ned. Akad. Welenschap.* **B58**, 78 (1955).
216. O. W. Parks, M. Keeney and D. P. Schwartz. *J. Dairy Sci.* **44**, 1940 (1961).
217. O. W. Parks, M. Keeney and D. P. Schwartz. *J. Dairy Sci.* **46**, 295 (1963).
218. D. P. Schwartz and J. L. Weihrauch. *Microchem. J.* **18**, 249 (1973).
219. E. Sawicki, T. R. Hauser, T. W. Stanley, W. C. Elbert and F. T. Fox. *Anal. Chem.* **33**, 1574 (1961).
220. E. Sawicki, T. W. Stanley, T. R. Hauser, W. C. Elbert and J. L. Noe. *Anal. Chem.* **33**, 722 (1961).
221. P. F. Collins, N. M. Sarji, W. W. Laurence and J. F. Williams. *Tobacco Sci.* **14**, 182 (1970).
222. P. F. Collins, N. M. Sarji and J. F. Williams. *Beitrag. Tabakforsch.* **7**, 73 (1973).
223. M. Lavas. *Ann. Chim. (Paris)* **7**, 697 (1952).
224. H. O. L. Fischer, E. Baer and L. Feldmann. *Ber.* **63**, 1732 (1930).
225. R. Criegee, P. Dimroth, K. Noll, R. Simon and C. Weis. *Ber.* **90**, 1070 (1957).
226. Y. Yukawa and M. Sakai. *Bull. Chem. Soc. Japan* **36**, 761 (1963).
227. L. Malaprade. *Bull. Soc. Chim. France* **43**, 683 (1954).
228. J. C. Speck and A. A. Forist. *Anal. Chem.* **26**, 1942 (1954).
229. G. Rouser, J. F. Berry, G. Marinetti and E. Stotz. *J. Am. Chem. Soc.* **75**, 310 (1953).
230. E. Chabrol and R. Charonnat. *Presse Med.* **54**, 1713 (1937).
231. E. Chabrol, M. Boszormenyi and P. Fallot. *Semaine d. Hop.* **25**, 3437 (1949).
232. E. Chabrol, M. Boszormenyi and P. Fallot. *Paris Med.* **40**, 225 (1950).
233. B. Drevon and J. M. Schmit. *Compt. Rend. Soc. Biol.* **158**, 778 (1964).

234. C. S. Frings and R. T. Dunn. *Am. J. Clin. Pathol.* **53**, 89 (1970).
235. L. Svennerholm. *Biochem. Biophys. Acta* **24**, 604 (1957).
236. T. Miettinen and I. T. Takki-Luukkainen. *Acta Chem. Scand.* **13**, 856 (1959).
237. L. Svennerholm, in L. van Bogaert, J. N. Cumings and Lowenthal, Eds., "Cerebral Lipidoses", Charles C. Thomas, Springfield, Ill., 1957, pp. 122–138.
238. Y. Kishimoto and N. S. Redin. *J. Lipid Res.* **7**, 141 (1966).
239. L. Svennerholm. *J. Lipid Res.* **5**, 145 (1964).
240. C. A. Bunton and M. D. Carr. *J. Chem. Soc.* 770 (1963).
241. M. Lepage. *J. Chromatog.* **13**, 99 (1964).
242. E. Baer, R. Grosheintz and H. O. L. Fischer. *J. Am. Chem. Soc.* **61**, 2607 (1939).
243. L. K. Dyall and K. H. Pausacker. *J. Chem. Soc.* 3950 (1958).
244. J. P. Cordner and K. H. Pausacker. *J. Chem. Soc.* 102 (1953).
245. D. P. Schwartz and O. W. Parks. *Anal. Chem.* **33**, 1396 (1961).
246. F. Linow, M. Roloff and K. Taufel. *Fette, Seifen, Anstrichmittel* **68**, 866 (1966).
247. R. J. Teichman, G. H. Takei and J. M. Cummins. *J. Chromatog.* **88**, 425 (1974).
248. S. Nametkin and A. Zabrodina, *Ber.* **69**, 1789 (1936) and earlier papers.
249. L. K. Keefer and P. P. Roller. *Science* **181**, 1245 (1973).
250. G. F. Kolar, *Brit. J. Cancer* **26**, 515 (1972).
251. F. W. Krüger in W. Nakahara *et al*, Eds. "Topics in Chemical Carcinogenesis," Univ. of Tokyo Press, 1972 pp. 213–232.
252. F. W. Krüger. *Z. Krebsforsch.* **76**, 145 (1971).
253. S. Fliszar, J. Renard and D. Z. Simon. *J. Am. Chem. Soc.* **93**, 6953 (1971).
254. P. S. Bailey, *Chem. Rev.* **58**, 925 (1958).
255. T. Beyrich. *Pharm. Zentralhalle. Dtl.* **108**, 837 (1969).
256. M. Keeney in H. W. Schultz, E. A. Day and R. O. Sinnhuber, Eds. "Lipids and Their Oxidation", Avi Publishing Co., Westport, Conn., 1962, p. 79.
257. E. Sawicki, T. R. Hauser and S. McPherson. *Chemist-Analyst* **50**, 68 (1961).
258. H. Halvarson. *J. Chromatog.* **76**, 125 (1973).
259. J. A. McCloskey and M. J. McClelland. *J. Am. Chem. Soc.* **87**, 5090 (1965).
260. E. G. Perkin and C. J. Argoudelis. *Lipids* **4**, 619 (1969).
261. G. W. Kenner and E. Stenhagen. *Acta Chem. Scand.* **18**, 1551 (1964).
262. M. J. Vacherow, G. Michel and R. Guilluy. *Bull. Soc. Chim. Biol.* **51**, 177 (1969).
263. L. D. Bergelson, E. V. Dyatlovitskaya and V. V. Voronkova. *J. Chromatog.* **15**, 191 (1964).
264. D. T. Downing and R. S. Greene. *Lipids* **3**, 95 (1968).
265. G. Grimmer and J. Jacob. *Z. Naturforsch.* **24b**, 565 (1969).
266. E. von Rudloff. *J. Am. Oil Chem. Soc.* **33**, 126 (1956).
267. M. Beroza and B. Bierl. *Anal. Chem.* **39**, 1131 (1967).
268. V. L. Davison and H. J. Dutton. *Anal. Chem.* **38**, 1302 (1966).
269. H. M. Edwards. *Lipids*, **1**, 1 (1966).
270. A. Chatterjee and S. G. Majumdar. *Anal. Chem.* **28**, 878 (1956).
271. G. Quash and K. Maharaj. *Clin. Chim. Acta* **39**, 13 (1970).

8. ALDEHYDES, TOTAL, PRECURSORS

This section discusses a few reactions which have analytical potential. A very large number of precursors could be listed. Many of these will be discussed in other sections. Reactions that are applicable to the formation of the various types of aldehydes will be discussed in this section.

I. ACYL DERIVATIVES

Acids, acyl chlorides and acyl phosphonates can give aldehydes in fairly good yield as shown by the following reactions.[1]

$$RCOCl + P(OR')_3 \rightarrow RCO-P(O)(OR')_2 + R'Cl$$

$$RCOP(O)(OR')_2 \xrightarrow{NaBH_4} RCH(OH)-P(O)(OR')_2$$

$$RCH(OH)-P(O)(OR')_2 \underset{H^+}{\overset{OH^-}{\rightleftharpoons}} RCHO + HP(O)OR')_2$$

By use of these reactions, these aldehyde precursors could be assayed through the aldehyde.

Aldehydes can also be formed from acyl halides and acyl hydrazides by reaction with o-nitrophenylsulphenyl chloride in tetrahydrofuran at room temperature followed by decomposition of the product o-nitrophenylsulphenyl hydrazide by treatment with 4 N NaOH solution or solid Na_2CO_3 or NaH at room temperature,[2] e.g.

$$RCONHNH_2 + 2-O_2N-C_6H_4SCl \rightarrow RCONHNH-S-C_6H_4-NO_2(2)$$

$$RCONHNHS-C_6H_4-NO_2(2) + OH^- \rightarrow RCHO + N_2 + {}^-S-C_6H_4-NO_2 + H_2O$$

Yields of 40–60% benzaldehyde, 40–50% o-chlorobenzaldehyde, and 20–30% p-anisaldehyde were obtained from the corresponding acid hydrazides.

II. ALCOHOLS, PRIMARY

Another interesting reaction which has analytical possibilities is the selective oxidation of primary alcohols and 1,2-diols to aldehydes with chromium trioxide intercalated in graphite. Good yields are obtained, but at this stage reflux periods of 24 h in toluene are necessary.[3] Secondary and tertiary alcohols are not affected.

Primary alcohols have been oxidized to the corresponding aldehyde with reagents[4] such as chromium(VI) in sulphuric acid or pyridine, specially prepared manganese dioxide in pentane, aluminium isopropoxide in acetone, or lead tetraacetate in pyridine. A much milder method which shows considerable potential for analytical work is the oxidation of primary alcohols and amines with potassium ferrate[5] at room temperature in water and mixed solvents.[6, 7] Secondary alcohols are converted to ketones. Unsaturation in the molecule as well as aldehyde, tertiary alcohol and tertiary amine functional groups are resistant to oxidation under the conditions employed.[6] Since ferrate reacts slowly in neutral solution and is very unstable in acid media, reactions were carried out at room temperature in water at an initial pH of approx 11·5. Tertiary alcohols and amines are unreactive. Although reaction does not proceed in dry dimethylformamide or dioxane, addition of water initiates the reaction, so mixed solvents can be used. The following reaction pathway is postulated.[6]

$$RCH_2OH + OH^- \rightleftarrows RCH_2O^- + H_2O \tag{1}$$

$$RCH\text{---}\overset{\frown}{O}^- + FeO_4^{2-} \rightarrow RCH{=}O + HFeO_4^{3-} \tag{2}$$
$$\quad\ \ |$$
$$\quad\ \ H$$

$$FeO_4^{2-} + HFeO_4^{3-} + OH^- \rightarrow H_2O + 2FeO_4^{3-} \tag{3}$$

$$FeO_4^{3-} + RCH_2O^- \rightarrow HFeO_4^{4-} + RCHO \tag{4}$$

$$HFeO_4^{4-} + 3H_2O \rightarrow Fe(OH)_3\downarrow + 4OH^- \tag{5}$$

The intermediate for the amine oxidation could be an imine which is rapidly hydrolysed by water to a carbonyl compound.

The following procedure is used in the syntheses to obtain the yields of aldehydes shown in Table 27. The procedure would have to be modified for trace analytical investigations.

A. Oxidation of primary alcohols or amines to aldehydes[6]

Add 0·002 mol of K_2FeO_4 to 0·003 mol of the alcohol or amine in 10 ml of water. Shake vigorously until the purple colour disappears. Aldehydes can be extracted with ether or benzene.

Some of the general synthetic methods which have been useful for the preparation of aldehydes from primary alcohols are shown in Table 28. The methods could be applied analytically. The analytical methods should be

Table 27. Formation of carbonyl compounds from alcohols and amines[6]

Reactant	Product	Approximate Yield (%)	Time for Complete Reaction (min)
Ethanol	Acetaldehyde	20–30	45
n-Heptanol	n-Heptaldehyde	30	70
Benzyl alcohol	Benzaldehyde	80	4
1-Phenylethanol	Acetophenone	90	18
2-Phenylethanol	α-Phenylacetaldehyde	20	6
Cyclohexanol	Cyclohexanone	20–30	90
Cinnamyl alcohol	Cinnamaldehyde	75	7
Benzyl amine	Benzaldehyde	70	1
1-Methylbenzylamine	Acetophenone	70	4

capable of higher yields than the synthetic methods. In addition, the methods should be capable of simplification. The t-butyl chromate method looks particularly promising.

Although many methods are known for the oxidation of alcohols to aldehydes, few of them are useful in trace analysis. One interesting method involves the formation of an aldehyde from RX (which can form a Grignard reagent) or from p-RCH(OH)-C_6H_4-N(CH$_3$)$_2$.[38] The reaction takes place as shown in Fig. 24. The second half of this reaction resembles the reaction involved in the determination with MBTH of 4-dimethylaminobenzaldehyde, 4-dimethylaminobenzyl alcohol, and analogous compounds.[39] Thus, compounds such as 4-(CH$_3$)$_2$N-C_6H_4CH(OH)R could be expected to be determinable by the reaction shown in Fig. 25. RCHO would probably react further with MBTH to form the formazan cation.

Other methods for the conversion of primary alcohols to aldehydes involve the use of dimethylsulphoxide as an oxidizing agent.[40] The first to be considered involves the reaction of dimethylsulphoxide, dicyclohexylcarbodiimide and alcohol, with phosphoric acid or pyridinium trifluoroacetate

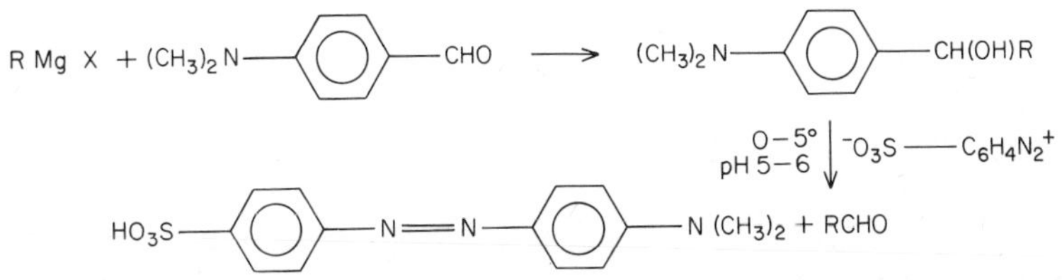

FIG. 24. Formation of aldehydes from p-dimethylaminobenzaldehyde.

Table 28. Preparation of aldehydes from primary alcohols

Alcohol	Reagent	Product	Yield (%)	Ref.
Ethanol	Chromate	Acetaldehyde	72	8
n-Propanol	Chromate	Propionaldehyde	49	9
Allyl alcohol	Dichromate in CH$_3$COOH	Acrolein	100[a]	10
2-Methylpropanol	Chromate	2-Methylpropanal	64	11
n-Pentanol	Chromate	Pentanal	50	12
n-Pentanol	Dichromate in CH$_3$COOH	Pentanal	65[a]	10
2-Methylbutanol	Chromate	2-Methylbutanal	52	13, 14
3-Methylbutanol	Chromate	3-Methylbutanal	60	15, 16
3-Methylbutanol	Dichromate in CH$_3$COOH	3-Methylbutanal	63[a]	10
4-Chloro-1-butanol	Dichromate in CH$_3$COOH	4-Chloro-1-butanal	62[a]	10
1-Heptanol	Pyridine-CrO$_3$(PyC)[b]	1-Heptanal	10	17
1-Dodecanol	PyC	1-Dodecanal	18	17
1-Dodecanol	Dichromate in CH$_3$COOH	1-Dodecanal	84[a]	10
2-Ethyl-1-hexanol	Dichromate in CH$_3$COOH	2-Ethyl-1-hexanal	68[a]	10
1-Dodecanol	Dichromate in CH$_3$COOH	1-Dodecanal	84[a]	10
1-Tetradecanol	Dichromate in CH$_3$COOH	1-Tetradecanal	42	10
1-Hexadecanol	Dichromate in CH$_3$COOH	1-Hexadecanal	68[a]	10
1-Hexadecanol	t-Butyl chromate	1-Hexadecanal	83	18
1-Octadecanol	Dichromate in CH$_3$COOH	1-Octadecanal	65	10
2-Chlorobutanol	Chromate	2-Chlorocrotonaldehyde		19
2-Penten-1-ol	Chromate	2-Pentenal	50	20, 21
2-Hexen-1-ol	Chromate	2-Hexenal	50	20, 21
2-Hepten-1-ol	Chromate	2-Heptenal	75	20, 21
2-Octen-1-ol	Chromate	2-Octenal	35	22
2-Nonen-1-ol	Chromate	2-Nonenal	50	20, 21
2-Propyn-1-ol	Chromate	2-Propyn-1-al	46	23, 24
3,3,3-Trifluoro-1-propanol	Chromate	3,3,3-Trifluoropropanal	57	25
2-Methoxyethanol	Chromate	Methoxyacetaldehyde	17	26
2-Ethoxyethanol	Chromate	Ethoxyacetaldehyde	10	26
2-Phenoxyethanol	Chromate	Phenoxyacetaldehyde	20	27

Substrate	Reagent	Product	Yield	Reference
3,7-Dimethyl-2,6-octadien-1-ol	Chromate	Citral	42	28
Geraniol	t-Butyl chromate	Geranial	85	18
Cyclopropylmethanol	Chromate	Cyclopropanecarboxaldehyde	35	29
Cyclohexanemethanol	Chromate	Cyclohexanecarboxaldehyde	94	30
Benzyl alcohol (BA)[c]	t-Butyl chromate	Benzaldehyde (B)[d]		18
BA	Lead tetraacetate	B	70	31, 32
BA	PyC	B	63	17
p-Isopropyl BA	PyC	p-Isopropyl B	83	17
o-Methoxy BA	PyC	o-Methoxy B	89	17
m-Methoxy BA	PyC	m-Methoxy B	60	17
p-Methoxy BA	PyC	p-Methoxy B	76	17
o-Hydroxy BA	PyC	o-Hydroxy B	17	17
m-Hydroxy BA	PyC	m-Hydroxy B	75	17
p-Hydroxy BA	PyC	p-Hydroxy B	50	17
o-Nitro BA	PyC	o-Nitro B	30	17
m-Nitro BA	PyC	m-Nitro B	50	17
p-Nitro BA	PyC	p-Nitro B	28	17
3,4-Methylenedioxy BA	PyC	Piperonal	85	17
Veratryl alcohol	PyC	Veratraldehyde	41	17
2-Chloro-6-nitro BA	Chromate	2-Chloro-6-nitro B	87	33
Citronellol	PyC	Citronellal	25	17
1-Naphthylmethanol	Chromate	1-Naphthaldehyde	42	34
4-Methyl-1-naphthylmethanol	Chromate	4-Methyl-1-naphthaldehyde	84	35
2-Thiophenemethanol	Chromate	2-Thiophenecarboxaldehyde	65	36
2-Pyridylmethanol	Lead tetraacetate–pyridine	2-Formylpyridine	60–80	37
3-Pyridylmethanol	Lead tetraacetate–pyridine	3-Formylpyridine	60–80	37
4-Pyridylmethanol	Lead tetraacetate–pyridine	4-Formylpyridine	60–80	37

[a] Yield as determined with DNPH
[b] PyC = Pyridine–chromium trioxide
[c] BA = Benzyl alcohol
[d] B = Benzaldehyde

E*

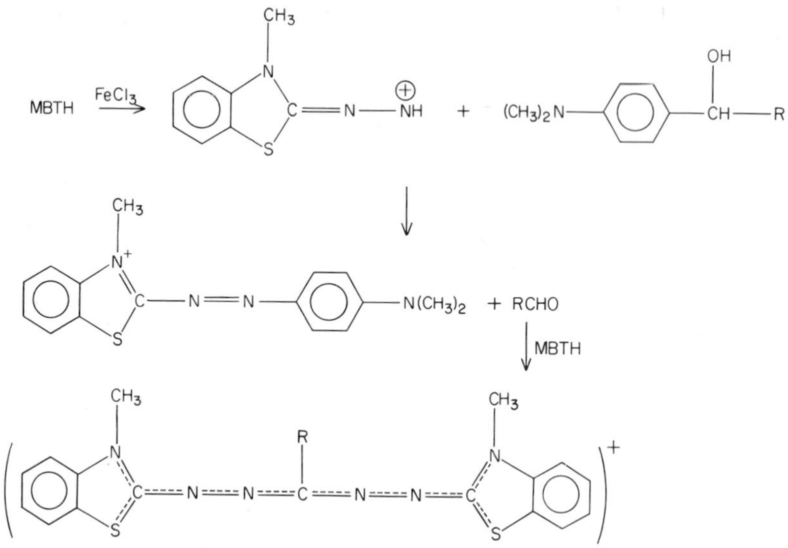

FIG. 25. Determination of 4-dimethylaminophenylcarbinols with MBTH through the derived aldehydes. Formazan cation formed readily if R is alkyl group.

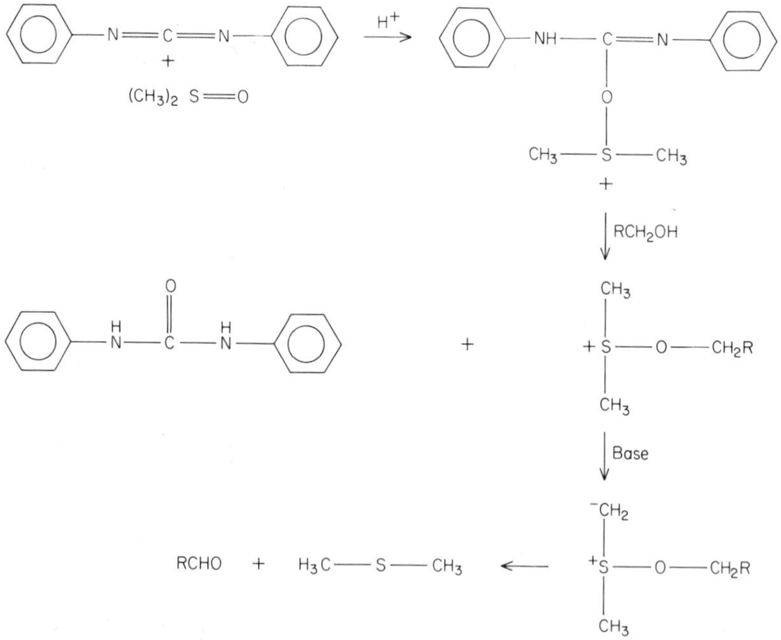

FIG. 26. Reaction of dimethylsulphoxide, dicyclohexylcarbodiimide and a primary alcohol to give an aldehyde.

present as a proton source.[41-43] The following reaction is postulated, Fig. 26.

Alternatively the acetic anhydride method can form aldehydes from primary alcohols[44, 45] in the following fashion

$$(CH_3)_2SO + CH_3-\overset{\overset{O}{\|}}{C}-O-\overset{\overset{O}{\|}}{C}-CH_3$$

$$\downarrow$$

$$(CH_3)_2\overset{+}{S}-O-\overset{\overset{O}{\|}}{C}-CH_3 + {}^-O-\overset{\overset{O}{\|}}{C}-CH_3$$

$$\downarrow RCH_2OH$$

$$(CH_3)_2\overset{+}{S}-O-CH_2R \xrightarrow{\text{base}} (CH_3)_2S + RCHO$$

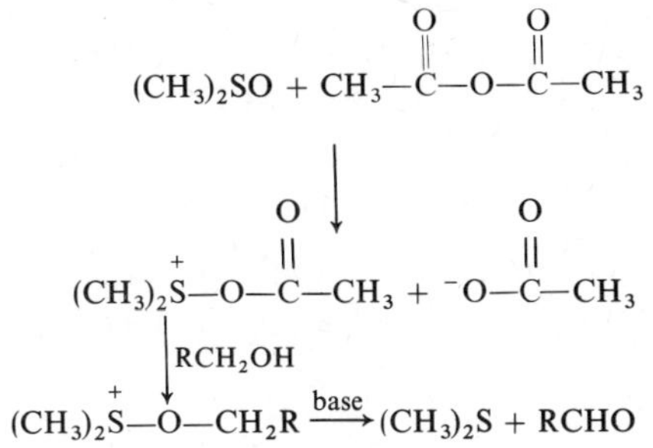

Another approach to the oxidation of alcohols involves conversion of the alcohol to a chloroformate which reacts with dimethylsulphoxide at room temp. or below in the presence of a base, e.g. triethylamine, to give the corresponding aldehyde.[46]

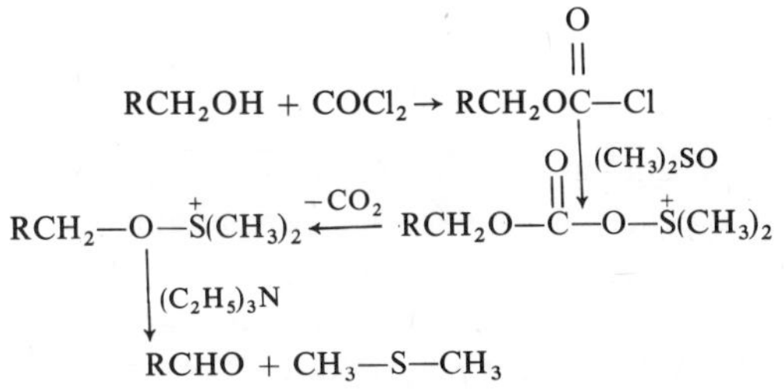

$$RCH_2OH + COCl_2 \rightarrow RCH_2O\overset{\overset{O}{\|}}{C}-Cl$$

$$\downarrow (CH_3)_2SO$$

$$RCH_2-O-\overset{+}{S}(CH_3)_2 \xleftarrow{-CO_2} RCH_2O-\overset{\overset{O}{\|}}{C}-O-\overset{+}{S}(CH_3)_2$$

$$\downarrow (C_2H_5)_3N$$

$$RCHO + CH_3-S-CH_3$$

III. ALKYL HALIDES

Active halides, such as n-alkyl iodides[47] and tosylates,[48-50] α-halo esters or acids,[51] phenacyl halides,[52,53] benzyl halides,[54,55] chlorides, bromides[55] and primary and secondary sulphonates,[48,49,54-56] can be oxidized to aldehydes with dimethylsulphoxide in the following fashion

$$(CH_3)_2\overset{+}{S}O + RCH_2X \rightarrow (CH_3)_2=\overset{+}{S}-O-CH_2R$$

$$\downarrow \text{base}$$

$$(CH_3)_2S + RCHO$$

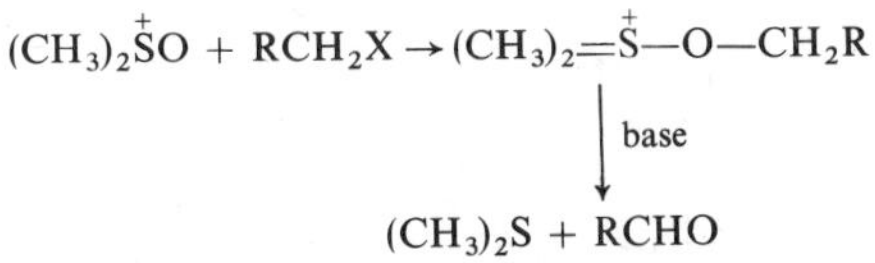

Alkyl chlorides and bromides are not readily oxidized, but they may be converted *in situ* to the corresponding tosylate and oxidized to the aldehyde without prior purification.[55]

IV. ALKYLARYLAMINES

The oxidation of N-alkylarylamines can give aldehydes in yields up to 37%.[57] Aliphatic amines are not oxidized under these conditions.

V. AMINES, ALIPHATIC

A. Chemical oxidation

In a somewhat similar reaction aliphatic amines are treated with 2,4-dinitrochlorobenzene. The derived amine is then degraded by oxidation, Fig. 27.[58]

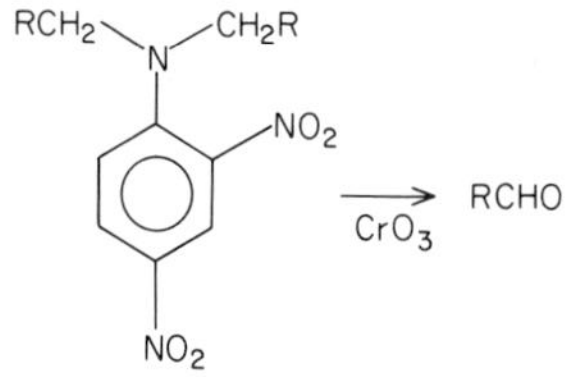

FIG. 27. Formation of aldehydes from the oxidation of N,N-dialkyl-2,4-dinitroanilines.

Amines can be degraded oxidatively to aldehydes and other carbonyl compounds with the help of potassium permanganate,[59, 60] manganese dioxide,[61] lead tetraacetate,[62] N-bromosuccinimide,[63] osmium tetroxide,[64] mercuric acetate,[65] 2,3-dichloro-1,4-naphthoquinone,[66] silver persulphate,[67] ozone,[68] chlorine dioxide,[69] oxygen,[70] benzoyl peroxide,[71] alkyl hydroperoxides,[72] peroxymonosulphuric acid,[73] nitrous acid,[74] and photolytically with benzophenones.[75]

As an example, let us consider the permanganate oxidation. Primary, secondary and tertiary amines containing two hydrogens on the carbon α to nitrogen are oxidatively hydrolysed to the corresponding aldehyde(s) by warm aq t-butyl alcohol.[60] The following equations illustrate the possibilities of the procedure

$$RCH_2N(CH_2R')CH_2R'' \xrightarrow[H_2O]{MnO_4^-} RCHO + R'CH_2NHCH_2R''$$

$$R'CH_2NHCH_2R'' \xrightarrow[H_2O]{MnO_4^-} R'CHO + R''CH_2NH_2$$

$$R''CH_2NH_2 \xrightarrow[H_2O]{MnO_4^-} RCHO + NH_3$$

Intermediate products are postulated as shown for the oxidation of ethylamine

$$CH_3CH_2NH_2 \xrightarrow{MnO_4^-} CH_2\text{=}CHNH_2 + CH_3CH\text{=}NH \xrightarrow{H_2O}$$

$$CH_3CH\text{—}NH_2 \rightarrow CH_3CHO + NH_3$$
$$\underset{\displaystyle OH}{|}$$

Rapid removal of the aldehydes from the reaction mixture by distillation, steam distillation, or extraction is essential, especially if the aldehydes are particularly susceptible to oxidation.

Primary amines containing the structure, RCH_2NH_2, are oxidized by ninhydrin, perinaphthindantriones, or analogous compounds to the aldehyde.[76] The reaction shown in Fig. 28 is postulated. Acetaldehyde, butyraldehyde, and benzaldehyde were obtained from ethylamine, butylamine, and benzylamine respectively.

Aldehydes can also be formed by hydrolysis of 2-hydroxy-1-naphthylmethylamines, Fig. 29.[77] The velocity sequence is

$$R = C_6H_5CH_2CH_2 < C_6H_5 < p\text{-}CH_3C_6H_4 < p\text{-}CH_3O\text{—}C_6H_4.$$

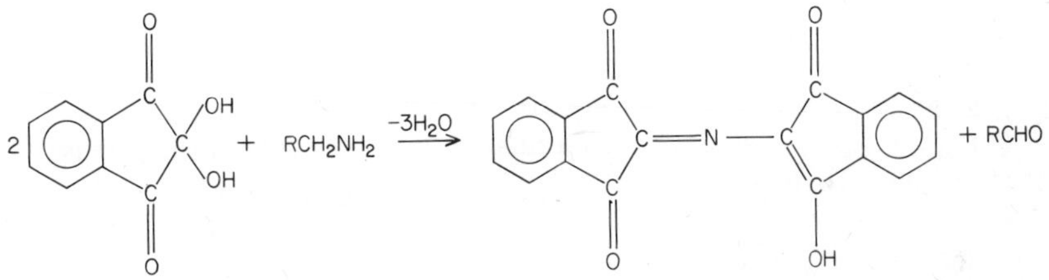

FIG. 28. Reaction of ninhydrin with primary aliphatic amines.

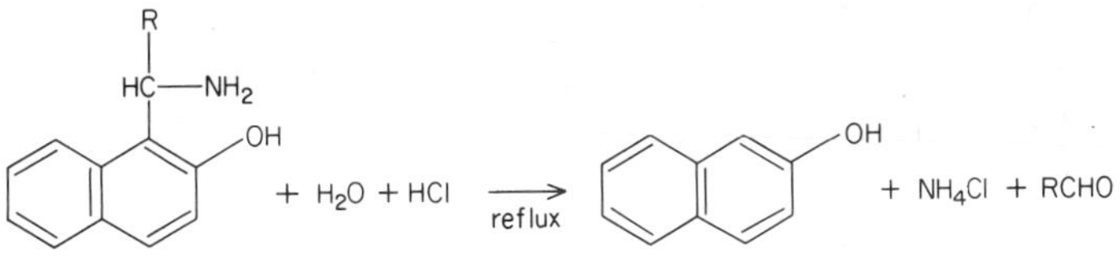

FIG. 29. Hydrolysis of 2-hydroxy-1-naphthylmethylamines.

B. Enzymatic oxidation

Amine oxidases can also be used to catalyse the oxidation of aliphatic primary amines to aldehydes, e.g.

$$RCH_2NH_2 + H_2O + O_2 \rightarrow RCHO + NH_3 + H_2O_2$$

Amine oxidases are a group of widely distributed enzymes of great metabolic importance, and some source of confusion. Thus, there are monoamine oxidase (MAO), diamine oxidase, mitochondrial monoamine oxidase. The substrates may include aliphatic monoamines (e.g. octylamine), aliphatic diamines (e.g. 1,4-diaminobutane), aromatic monoamines (e.g. benzylamine), aromatic diamines (e.g. bis (aminomethyl benzenes), and a miscellaneous group including histamine, tryptamine, dopamine, spermidine, spermine, mescaline, and others. Of equal fascination is the plasma amine oxidase (beef plasma) that seems to have activity primarily on spermine and spermidine, but not the other physiological amines. The enzyme appears to play a protective role in some animals, because the products of the oxidation of spermine and spermidine, which include hydrogen peroxide, amine aldehydes, dialdehydes (some unstable), and putrescine, plus some acrolein, have been shown to be inhibitory or toxic to bacteria, viruses, and higher cells. For that matter, so are spermine and spermidine! The best known of these enzymes are amine oxidase (flavin-containing) (EC 1.4.3.4)[78-80] and amine oxidase (pyridoxal-containing).[80-85] In these reactions primary amines could be determined by the appropriate aldehyde reagent.

The amine oxidase (EC 1.4.3.4) is considered to be of some importance in mental health. It may eventually give a clue to the existence of a possible specific genetic marker for schizophrenia. It is important in the metabolism of amines to aldehydes and is present in blood platelets. It is implicated in a number of psychiatric conditions and is reduced in quantity in schizophrenics, the size of reduction being related to the severity of the disease.[86] Strangely enough, in identical twins of which one is a schizophrenic the level of the enzyme is lowered in both. It would appear that the reduction is not a consequence of the disease but indicates a predisposition to it.

VI. AMINO ACIDS

Aldehydes are produced from amino acids in roasted cocoa by a Strecker degradation.[87] Thus, from leucine and L-3-phenylalanine, isovaleraldehyde and phenylacetaldehyde are the major products, respectively. Also, as shown in other sections, amino acids can be oxidatively deaminated and decarboxylated to aldehydes with the help of ninhydrin.

VII. DINITROPHENYLHYDRAZONES

Aldehydes (and other carbonyl compounds) can be regenerated from 2,4-dinitrophenylhydrazones by a variety of procedures, e.g. treatment with

pyruvic acid as regenerator-acceptor,[88] reduction of the nitro groups of
DNPH with stannous chloride followed by treatment with hydrochloric
acid and acetone for cleavage and acceptance,[89, 90] treatment with 80%
formic acid and copper carbonate,[91] reduction of the nitro groups with
chromous chloride simultaneously with cleavage by HCl,[92] cleavage with
levulinic and hydrochloric acids,[93, 94] heating with α-ketoglutaric acid,[95]
treatment with conc H_2SO_4 and water,[96] regeneration in the injection port
of a gas chromatograph,[97] and cleavage on a periodic–sulphuric acid
column.[98]

Table 29. Regeneration of aldehydes from dinitrophenylhydrazones on a periodic
acid–sulphuric acid column[98]

Dinitrophenylhydrazone	Flow rate (min/0·5 ml)	Amount over column μmols	Recovery of aldehyde (%)
Formaldehyde	15	0·29	0
Acetaldehyde	20	0·34	96
Butanal	15	0·35	98
Tridecanal	18	0·05	101
Octadecanal	18	0·08	102
Phenylacetaldehyde	17	0·27	82
Benzaldehyde	18	0·06	99

The regeneration of aldehydes (and other carbonyl compounds) *via*
treatment on a periodic acid column is readily applicable. Table 29 sum-
marizes the results obtained for aldehyde dinitrophenylhydrazones. Although
formaldehyde 2,4-dinitrophenylhydrazone is regenerated, free formaldehyde
is not detected in the effluent. Similarly no formaldehyde is detected in the
effluent when terminal glycols are oxidized on a periodic acid column.[99]

The following procedure can be modified to regenerate microgram quantities of dinitrophenylhydrazones on microcolumns in melting point capillaries.

A. Regeneration of aldehydes from dinitrophenylhydrazones[98]

Column preparation. Grind 1 ml of a saturated solution of periodic acid,
1 ml of 2 N H_2SO_4 and 8 g of magnesium sulphate in a mortar with a pestle
until homogeneous. Sieve through an 80-mesh screen, and store sieved
material at 0°. Prepare a column of this material.

Regeneration procedure. Dissolve less than 1 μmol of the dinitrophenylhydrazone in carbon tetrachloride and pipette 0·5 ml (max.) on the column.

The yellow dinitrophenylhydrazine accumulates at the top of the column. Collect the colourless effluent with a column volume of carbon tetrachloride.

Analysis. Position the exit tip of the periodic acid column on top of a small column of Celite impregnated with a 60% H_3PO_4 solution of DNPH.[100] Following derivitization, pass the carbon tetrachloride effluent directly over a 400 mg column of Dowex 50 × 8 (H^+) to remove 2,4-dinitrophenylhydrazine. Absorb the coloured effluent on alumina,[100] and elute the dinitrophenylhydrazones with benzene. Evaporate the benzene, and dissolve the residue in chloroform and read absorbance at wavelength maximum.

VIII. 1,3-DITHIANES

1,3-Dithianes can be hydrolysed readily to the corresponding aldehydes, as shown in Table 30, with the help of red mercuric oxide and boron trifluoride etherate in aq tetrahydrofuran[101] or with mercuric acetate plus boron trifluoride in dry *t*-butyl alcohol.[101, 102]

Table 30. Formation of aldehydes from 1,3-dithianes[101]

$$RCH(OAc)_2 \xleftarrow[BF_3]{Hg(OAc)_2} \quad \xrightarrow{HgO-BF_3} RCHO$$

R	acetaldiacetate	Yield aldehyde
C_6H_5—	76	90
$C_6H_5CH{=}CH$—	73	86
i-C_3H_7	78	78
n-C_6H_{13}—		60
$(C_2H_5O)_2CH.CHOAc.CH_2$—		80
$C_6H_5OCOC_6H_{10}$—		84[a]

[a] 1-Benzoyloxycyclohexanecarboxaldehyde

By these reactions, substituted acroleins can be prepared from dithianes and epoxides, Fig. 30.

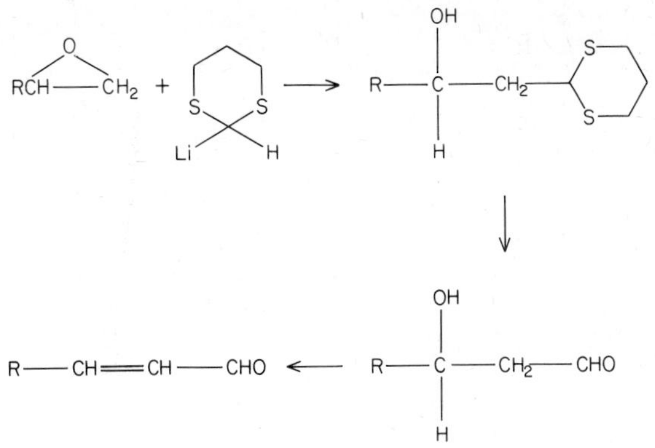

FIG. 30. Preparation of α,β-unsaturated aldehydes from the reaction between dithianes and epoxides.

IX. EPOXIDES, GLYCOLS AND α-HYDROXY ACIDS

A. Water-soluble compounds

Epoxides, *vic*-glycols and α-hydroxy acids in natural product mixtures can be isolated, characterized and determined with the help of a periodic acid column procedure.[99] Pertinent data is given in Table 31. No attempt was made to improve yields.

B. Analysis of epoxides, *vic*-glycols, and α-hydroxy acids[99]

Preparation of periodic acid columns. Grind 5 g of $CaSO_4$ with 1 ml of a saturated aq solution of periodic acid. This is stable for up to 6 months in a closed container at room temperature. Wet a column (0·8 × 15 cm) containing 0·5 g of the powder with 1 ml of hexane. Tamp the column tight enough so that 1 ml of solvent will flow completely into the column in 9–11 minutes. Wash the column with one column-volume of benzene. The column is now ready for sample.

Preparation of dinitrophenylhydrazine column. Transfer 2·5 g of impregnated Celite[103] to a column (1·7 cm i.d. × 17 cm), tamping so that the flow-rate of hexane through the column will be 40–50 ml h^{-1}. Wash the column with 2 column-volumes of benzene, and then with hexane until the effluent emerges colourless.

Oxidation and derivitization procedure. Position the periodic acid column in the DNPH column so that the tip of the former is just above the top of the

Table 31. Periodic acid column oxidation of glycols, epoxides, and α-hydroxy acids[99]

Substrate[a]	Average yield (%)	Identity of 2,4-dinitrophenylhydrazones	Max (nm) CHCl$_3$	mε
Benzoin	100	Benzaldehyde	378	28
Benzopinacol	0	—	—	—
Threo-9,10-dihydroxymethyl stearate	99	Nonanal, methyl azelaldehydate	355 / 355	22·5 / 22·5
DL-1,2-Diphenyl-1,2-ethanediol	102	Benzaldehyde	378	28
Meso-1,2-diphenyl-1,2-ethanediol	103	Benzaldehyde	378	28
9,10-Epiminooctadecane	0	—	—	—
1,2-Epoxybutane	79	Propanal	355	22·5
1,2-Epoxyoctane	90	Heptanal	355	22·5
9,10-Epoxy methyl stearate	63	Nonanal, methyl azelaldehydate	355 / 355	22·5 / 22·5
Glyceryl-1-hexadecyl ether	93	Hexadecoxy acetaldehyde	355	22·5
Glyceryl-1-octadecyl ether	95	Octadecoxy acetaldehyde	355	22·5
α-Hydroxylauric acid	72	Undecanal	355	22·5
2-Hydroxy-2-methyl-3-butanone	100	Acetone	362	22·5
2-Hydroxy-2-methyl butyric acid	73	2-Butanone	362	22·5
α-Hydroxy-methyl eicosanoate	0	—	—	—
α-Hydroxy-myristic acid	74	Tridecanal	355	22·5
DL-Lactic acid	38	Acetaldehyde	362	22·5
DL-Mandelic acid	102	Benzaldehyde	378	28
Methyl mandelate	0	—	—	—
1-Monopalmitin	95	Glycolaldehyde palmitate	350	20
1-Monostearin	91	Glycolaldehyde stearate	350	20
1-Phenyl-1,2-ethanediol	105	Benzaldehyde	378	28
Pinacol	87	Acetone	362	22·5
1,2-Propanediol	56	Acetaldehyde	355	22·5
trans-Stilbene oxide	83	Benzaldehyde	378	28
Styrene oxide	97	Benzaldehyde	378	28

bed. By pipette add 0·25–1 ml of the benzene test solution (methylene chloride can also be used) to the periodic acid column and, when drained, wash the sides of the column with 1 ml of benzene. When this has drained, wash the periodic acid column with 1 ml benzene. Permit all washings to drain into the bed of DNPH and add 5 ml of benzene. When this has percolated into the column, add hexane until the effluent emerges colourless.

Isolation and analysis of derivatives. Mix effluent and transfer to a 5-g column of alumina contained in a chromatographic tube (0·8 × 15 cm). Elute the simple aliphatic carbonyls with hexane-benzene (1:1); aromatic and polyfunctional carbonyls are removed with benzene. Evaporate the solvent, dissolve the residue in chloroform, and read the absorbance at the wavelength maximum, making use of the mε values in Table 31.

C. Water-insoluble compounds

As shown in this and subsequent volumes, periodate is an extremely useful reagent for the analysis of a large variety of aldehyde precursors through their derived aldehydes. One of the difficulties in utilizing periodate or periodic acid in analysing many types of organic compounds through their derived aldehydes is the insolubility of these compounds in water. Three organic periodates recently introduced for the analysis of linear *vic*-diols are hexadecyl pyridinium periodate (I), benzylhexadecyldimethylammonium periodate (II), and hexadecyltrimethylammonium periodate (III).[104, 105]

$$CH_3-(CH_2)_{15}-\overset{+}{N}\diagup\hspace{-0.3em}\bigcirc\hspace{-0.8em}\diagdown\ IO_4^-$$

I

$$CH_3-(CH_2)_{15}-\overset{+}{N}\underset{CH_3}{\overset{CH_3}{\diagdown}}CH_2-C_6H_5\ IO_4^-$$

II

$$CH_3-(CH_2)_{15}-\overset{+}{N}\underset{CH_3}{\overset{CH_3}{\diagdown}}CH_3\ IO_4^-$$

III

These periodates are only slightly soluble in water, but very soluble in acetic acid, alcohol, and chloroform. The relative reactivities of primary, secondary and tertiary diols in 100% acetic acid at 20° and in 70% acetic acid at 0° have been investigated. Oxidation is more rapid in the aqueous medium.

X. ESTERS

Esters can be reduced to aldehydes in high yields with sodium bis(2-methoxyethoxy)aluminium hydride (Vitride*) at -50 to $-70°$ in ether,[106] e.g.

$$2RCOOR' + NaAlH_2(OCH_2CH_2OCH_3)_2 \rightarrow 2RCHO + NaAl(OR')_2(OCH_2CH_2OCH_3)_2$$

The aldehyde carbonyl group is practically non-reactive below $-50°$, whereas the reactivity of the ester is still quite high. Better solubility in ether of the larger carboxylates is often obtained with methoxyethyl esters.

XI. HYDROCARBONS

Olefins can be converted through ozonolysis to aldehydes.[107–117] The procedure has been applied to the determination of atmospheric ozone. Thus, with 4,4'-dimethoxystilbene as the substrate[118] the resultant p-anisaldehyde is determined by the fluoranthene test,[119] and with 1,2-di-(4-pyridyl)ethylene as the substrate the resultant 4-pyridinealdehyde can be determined colorimetrically with MBTH[120, 121] or fluorimetrically with 2-diphenylacetyl-1, 3-indandione-1-hydrazone.[122]

The conversion of olefins to aldehydes by ozonolysis followed by reduction of the ozonolysis product with dimethylsulphide results in excellent yields under very mild conditions.[116] Dimethyl sulphide has the virtues of reducing hydroperoxides at low temperatures under neutral conditions, of being highly selective in that nitro and carbonyl groups are not reduced, and of being readily removed by evaporation (b.pt. 37°). The following reactions are postulated, Fig. 31.[116, 123]

Aliphatic and aromatic aldehydes are derived from the incomplete oxidation of hydrocarbons in internal combustion engines, incinerators, and other sources.[124, 125] They are also formed in the photochemical oxidation of olefinic and aromatic hydrocarbons in smog chambers and in the atmosphere.[126–128] Some typical analytical data obtained during the irradiation of automotive exhaust gas–air mixtures in a smog chamber is shown in Fig. 32.[129–131] The increase in total aldehydes over three hours is fairly dramatic.

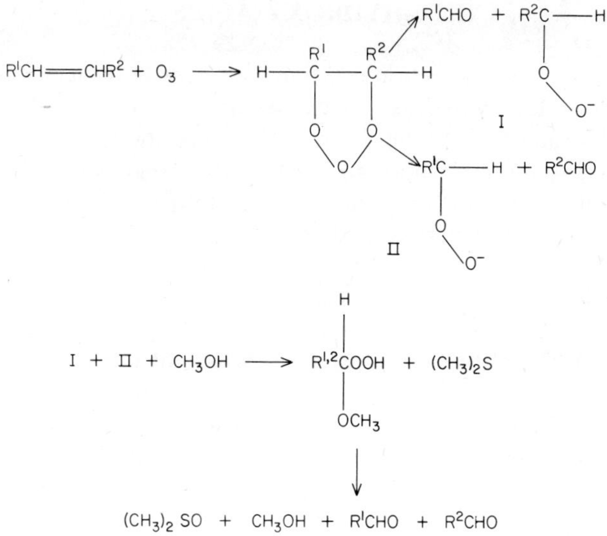

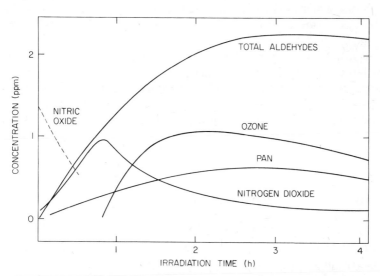

FIG. 31. Conversion of olefins to hydroperoxides by ozonolysis followed by reduction of the product with dimethylsulphide to an aldehyde.

FIG. 32. Variation of concentration in components of auto exhaust irradiated with ultraviolet light. PAN is peroxyacetyl nitrate.

XII. α-HYDROXY ACIDS

In a previous part of this section mention was made of the use of periodic acid to decarboxylate α-hydroxy acids oxidatively to aldehydes. Other oxidizing agents can be used. Thus, lactic acid can be converted to acetaldehyde in aqueous solution[132] and p-methylmandelic acid to terephthalaldehyde tetraacetate by chromyl acetate in acetic anhydride.[133] Lead tetraacetate will also cleave α-hydroxy acids,[134, 135] e.g.

$$RCH(OH)COOH + Pb(OAc)_4 \rightarrow RCHO + Pb(OAc)_2 + HOAc + CO_2$$

XIII. MISCELLANEOUS PRECURSORS

Many of the aldehydes found in plant or animal tissue are probably to some extent (or completely) present as a readily hydrolysable precursor. Thus, for example, a large number of aliphatic and aromatic aldehydes have been found in cotton plant buds through chromatography of their dinitrophenylhydrazones.[136] Many of these aldehydes are probably part of a precursor structure. This possibility must be kept in mind in any investigation of tissue aldehydes. In many of the analytical tests aldehydes are formed from readily hydrolysed or oxidized precursors during the analytical procedure.

Another fact that needs emphasis is that many of the methods described for aldehydes in Part 1 of this treatise can be used with slight modification for the analysis of many of the precursors. Thus, for example, o-aminothiophenol can be used in the analysis of aliphatic and aromatic aldehydes.[137] Most aromatic aldehydes give a blue or green fluorescence after heating for 20 min with the reagent in sulphuric acid. Hydroxy derivatives of benzaldehyde give a weak fluorescence in acid medium and strong fluorescence in basic medium.

Similarly 4-amino-5-hydrazino-1,2,4-triazole-3-thiol[138] can be used for the analysis of the precursors of aliphatic and aromatic aldehydes.

Following the formation of aldehydes from their precursors, a sodium bisulphite–Celite column can be used to extract microgram amounts of saturated and unsaturated normal chain aliphatic and aromatic aldehydes from hexane or carbon tetrachloride solution.[139] A capillary tube packed with Celite impregnated with sodium bisulphite can be used for microlitre amounts of solution. Several recoveries of carbonyl compounds from the adducts formed on the column were described.

Another possibility in the analysis of aldehydes and their precursors is the use of porous glass beads with a covalently attached aliphatic extension arm, terminating in a group which can bind aldehydes. Such a material has been described by the Pierce Chemical Co., e.g. Porous glass-$CH_2CH_2CH_2NH$—CO—$C_6H_4NHNH_2$.

From the various precursors and reactions described in these volumes, standard aldehydes could be prepared by passing the precursor through an appropriate aldehyde-forming column. For example, aldehydes could be generated as needed by passing the 2,4-dinitrophenylhydrazone of the aldehyde[98] or an appropriate primary aliphatic alcohol[99] over a periodic acid column. For example, octadecoxyacetaldehyde and 2-hexadecanoyl-oxyacetaldehyde can be prepared from batyl alcohol and 1-monopalmitin, respectively.

REFERENCES

1. L. Horner and H. Röder. *Chem. Ber.* **103**, 2984 (1970).
2. S. Cacchi and G. Paolucci. *Gazz. Chim. Ital.* **104**, 221 (1974).
3. J. M. Lalancette. As reported by Ventron Corp., Alfa Products, 8 Congress St., Beverly, Mass.
4. K. B. Wiberg. "Oxidation in Organic Chemistry." Academic Press, New York, 1965.
5. G. W. Thompson, L. T. Ockerman and J. M. Schreyer. *J. Am. Chem. Soc.* **73**, 1379 (1951).
6. R. J. Audette, J. W. Quail and P. J. Smith. Presented at 54th Canadian Chemical Conference and Exhibition, Halifax, Nova Scotia, June 2, 1971.
7. Y. A. Zhdanov and O. A. Pustovarova. *Zhur. Obshch Khim.* **37**, 2780 (1967).
8. E. Wertheim. *J. Am. Chem. Soc.* **44**, 2658 (1922).
9. C. D. Hurd and R. N. Meinert. Org. Synth. Coll. Vol. II, 541 (1943).
10. M. I. Bowman, C. E. Moore, H. R. Deutsch and J. C. Hartman. *Trans. Kentucky Acad. Sci.* **14**, 33 (1953).
11. W. Fossek. *Monatsh.* **2**, 614 (1881); **4**, 660 (1883).
12. R. Kuhn and C. Grundmann. *Ber.* **70**, 1894 (1937).
13. V. Neustädter. *Monatsh.* **27**, 879 (1906).
14. E. J. Badin and E. Pacsu. *J. Am. Chem. Soc.* **67**, 1352 (1945).
15. L. Boureault and L. Rousset, *Bull. Soc. Chim. France*, **11**, 300 (1894).
16. C. Weygand. "Organic Preparations", Wiley, New York, 1945, p. 143.
17. J. R. Holum. *J. Org. Chem.* **26**, 4814 (1961).
18. R. V. Oppenauer and H. Oberrauch. *Anales Asoc. Quim. Arg.* **37**, 246 (1949).
19. M. Julia. *Comp. Rend. Acad. Sci.* **234**, 2615 (1952).
20. R. Delaby and S. Guillot-Allegre. *Bull. Soc. Chim. France* **53**, 301 (1933).
21. C. J. Martin, A. I. Schepartz and B. F. Daubert. *J. Am. Chem. Soc.* **70**, 2601 (1948).
22. M. Jacobson. *J. Am. Chem. Soc.* **72**, 1489 (1950).
23. F. Wille and L. Saffer. *Ann.* **568**, 34 (1950).
24. J. Sauer. Org. Synth., Coll. Vol. IV, 813 (1963).
25. A. L. Henne, R. L. Pelley and R. M. Alm. *J. Am. Chem. Soc.* **72**, 3370 (1950).
26. C. D. Hurd and J. L. Abernethy. *J. Am. Chem. Soc.* **63**, 1966 (1941).
27. A. Halasz. *Bull. Soc. Chim. France* **8**, 170 (1941).
28. M. Stoll and A. Commarmont. *Helv. Chim. Acta* **32**, 1355 (1949).
29. N. J. Demjanow and K. Fortunatov. *Ber.* **40**, 4397 (1907).
30. N. Zelinsky and J. Gutt. *Ber.* **40**, 3050 (1907).
31. R. Criegee, L. Kraft and B. Rank. *Ann.* **507**, 159 (1933).

32. R. E. Partch. *Tetrahedron Letters* 3071 (1964).
33. L. Gindraux. *Helv. Chim. Acta* **12**, 921 (1929).
34. B. L. West. *J. Am. Chem. Soc.* **42**, 1656 (1920).
35. K. Ziegler and P. Tiemann. *Ber.* **55**, 3406 (1932).
36. W. S. Emerson and T. M. Patrick, Jr. *J. Org. Chem.* **14**, 790 (1949).
37. V. M. Micovic and M. L. Mihailovic. *Rec. Trav. Chim.* **71**, 970 (1952).
38. M. Stiles and A. J. Sisti. *J. Org. Chem.* **25**, 1691 (1960).
39. E. Sawicki, T. W. Stanley, T. R. Hauser, W. C. Elbert and J. L. Noe. *Anal. Chem.* **33**, 722 (1961).
40. W. W. Epstein and F. W. Sweat. *Chem. Revs.* **67**, 247 (1967).
41. K. E. Pfitzner and J. G. Moffatt. *J. Am. Chem. Soc.* **85**, 3027 (1963).
42. K. E. Pfitzner and J. G. Moffatt. *J. Am. Chem. Soc.* **87**, 5661 (1965).
43. K. E. Pfitzner and J. G. Moffatt. *J. Am. Chem. Soc.* **87**, 5670 (1965).
44. J. D. Albright and L. Goldman. *J. Am. Chem. Soc.* **87**, 4214 (1965).
45. J. D. Albright and L. Goldman. *J. Org. Chem.* **30**, 1107 (1965).
46. D. H. R. Barton, B. J. Gardner and R. H. Wightman. *J. Chem. Soc.* 1855 (1964).
47. A. P. Johnson and A. Pelter. *J. Chem. Soc.* 520 (1964).
48. F. X. Jarreau, M. B. Tchoubar and R. Goutarel. *Bull. Soc. Chim. France* 887 (1962).
49. D. N. Jones and M. A. Saeed. *J. Chem. Soc.* 4657 (1963).
50. M. M. Robinson, W. G. Pierson, R. A. Lucas, I. Hsui and R. L. Dziemian. *J. Org. Chem.* **28**, 768 (1963).
51. I. M. Hunsberger and J. M. Tien. *Chem. Ind. London* 88 (1959).
52. N. Kornblum, J. W. Powers, G. J. Anderson, W. J. Jones, H. O. Larson, O. Levand and W. M. Wearer. *J. Am. Chem. Soc.* **79**, 6562 (1957).
53. R. T. Major and H. J. Hess. *J. Org. Chem.* **23**, 1563 (1958).
54. H. R. Nace and J. J. Monagle. *J. Org. Chem.* **24**, 1792 (1959).
55. N. Kornblum, W. J. Jones and G. J. Anderson, *J. Am. Chem. Soc.* **81**, 4113 (1959).
56. V. Mahadevan. *J. Am. Oil Chem. Soc.* **41**, 520 (1964).
57. F. W. Neumann and C. W. Gould. *Anal. Chem.* **25**, 751 (1953).
58. A. T. Boltini and R. E. Olsen. *J. Org. Chem.* **27**, 452 (1962).
59. H. Shechter, S. S. Rawalay and M. Tubis, *J. Am. Chem. Soc.* **86**, 1701 (1964).
60. S. S. Rawalay and H. Shechter. *J. Org. Chem.* **32**, 3129 (1967).
61. E. F. Curragh, H. B. Henbest and A. Thomas. *J. Chem. Soc.* 3559 (1960).
62. L. Horner, E. Winkelmann, K. H. Knapp and W. Ludwig. *Ber.* **92**, 288 (1959).
63. S. Dunstan and H. B. Henbest. *J. Chem. Soc.* 4905 (1957).
64. N. Y. Dem'yanov and Z. I. Shuikina. *J. Gen. Chem. USSR* **6**, 350 (1936).
65. N. J. Leonard and D. F. Morrow. *J. Am. Chem. Soc.* **80**, 371 (1958).
66. H. B. Henbest and P. Slade. *J. Chem. Soc.* 1558 (1960).
67. R. G. R. Bacon and W. J. W. Hanna. *Proc. Chem. Soc.* (London) 305 (1959).
68. W. Strecker and M. Baltes. *Ber.* **54**, 2693 (1921).
69. L. A. Hull, G. T. Davis, D. H. Rosenblatt, H. K. R. Williams and R. C. Weglein *J. Am. Chem. Soc.* **89**, 1163 (1967).
70. Z. I. Shuikina. *J. Gen. Chem., USSR* **7**, 983 (1937).
71. D. Buckley, S. Dunstan and H. B. Henbest. *J. Chem. Soc.* 4901 (1957).
72. H. E. De La Mare. *J. Org. Chem.* **25**, 2114 (1960).
73. R. J. Kennedy and A. M. Stock. *J. Org. Chem.* **25**, 1901 (1960).
74. P. A. S. Smith and R. N. Loeppky. *J. Am. Chem. Soc.* **89**, 1147 (1967).
75. S. G. Cohen and R. J. Baumgarten. *J. Am. Chem. Soc.* **87**, 2996 (1965).

76. R. Moubasher and A. M. Othman. *J. Am. Chem. Soc.* **72**, 2666 (1950).
77. M. Kharasch and L. B. Howard. *J. Am. Chem. Soc.* **56**, 1370 (1934).
78. P. D. Boyer, H. Lardy and K. Myrback. "The Enzymes", 2nd ed. 1963, p. 313.
79. V. G. Erwin and L. Hellerman. *J. Biol. Chem.* **242**, 4230 (1967).
80. H. Blaschko. "The Enzymes", 2nd ed., Vol. 8, Academic Press, New York, 1963, p. 337.
81. H. Blaschko and F. Buffoni. *Proc. Roy. Soc. Ser. B.* **163**, 45 (1965).
82. F. Buffoni and H. Blaschko. *Proc. Roy. Soc., Ser. B.* **161**, 153 (1964).
83. C. M. McEwen, Jr. *J. Biol. Chem.* **240**, 2003 (1965).
84. B. Mondivi, M. T. Costa, A. F. Agro and G. Rotilio. *Arch. Biochem. Biophys.* **119**, 373 (1967).
85. H. Yamada, O. Adachi, and K. Ogata. *Agric. Biol. Chem.* (Tokyo) **29**, 649, 863, 912 (1965).
86. R. J. Wyatt, D. L. Murphy, R. Belmaker, S. Cohen, C. H. Donnelly and W. Pollin. *Science* **179**, 916 (1973).
87. R. R. Darsley and V. C. Quensel. *J. Sci. Food. Agric.* **23**, 215 (1972).
88. J. B. Conant and P. B. Bartlett. *J. Am. Chem. Soc.* **54**, 2881 (1932).
89. N. M. Cullinane and B. F. R. Edwards. *J. Chem. Soc.* 1311 (1958).
90. J. Demaecker and R. H. Martin. *Nature* **173**, 266 (1954).
91. R. Robinson. *Nature* **173**, 541 (1954).
92. J. Elks and J. F. Oughton. *J. Chem. Soc.* 4729 (1962).
93. C. H. DePuy and B. W. Pender. *J. Am. Chem. Soc.* **81**, 4629 (1959).
94. M. Keeney. *Anal. Chem.* **29**, 1489 (1957).
95. J. W. Ralls. *Anal. Chem.* **32**, 332 (1960).
96. R. Bassette and E. A. Day. *J. Am. Oil Chem. Soc.* **37**, 482 (1960).
97. N. P. Wong and D. P. Schwartz. *J. Chromatog. Sci.* **7**, 569 (1969).
98. D. P. Schwartz and C. R. Brewington. *Microchem. J.* **17**, 63 (1972).
99. D. P. Schwartz, J. L. Weihrauch and L. H. Burgwald. *Anal. Chem.* **41**, 984 (1969).
100. D. P. Schwartz and O. W. Parks. *Anal. Chem.* **33**, 1396 (1961).
101. E. Vedejs and P. L. Fuchs. *J. Org. Chem.* **36**, 366 (1971).
102. E. Spath. *Monatsh. Chem.* **36**, 29 (1915).
103. D. P. Schwartz and O. W. Parks. *Anal. Chem.* **33**, 1386 (1961).
104. M. Guernet and E. Espinassou. *Analusis* **2**, 348 (1973).
105. M. Guernet, E. Espinassou and M. Hamon. *Annales Pharm. Franc.* **31**, 343 (1973).
106. J. Vit. *Eastman Org. Chem. Bull.* 42, No. 3, 8 (1970).
107. S. Fliszár, D. Gravel and E. Cavalieri. *Can. J. Chem.* **44**, 1013 (1966).
108. S. Fliszár and M. Granger. *J. Am. Chem. Soc.* **92**, 3361 (1970).
109. P. S. Bailey, S. B. Mainthia and C. J. Abshire. *J. Am. Chem. Soc.* **82**, 6136 (1960).
110. S. Fliszár, Cz. Belzecki and J. B. Chylińska. *Can. J. Chem.* **45**, 221 (1967).
111. S. Fliszár. *Can. J. Chem.* **44**, 2351 (1966).
112. W. P. Keaveney, M. G. Berger and J. J. Pappas. *J. Org. Chem.* **32**, 1537 (1967).
113. S. Fliszár and J. Renard. *Can. J. Chem.* **45**, 533 (1967).
114. S. Fliszár. *Tetrahedron Letters* 6083 (1966).
115. S. Fliszár and M. Granger. *J. Am. Chem. Soc.* **91**, 3330 (1969).
116. J. J. Pappas, W. P. Keaveney, E. Gancher and M. G. Berger. *Tetrahedron Letters* 4273 (1966).
117. D. A. Cronin and J. Gilbert. *J. Chromatog.* **87**, 387 (1973).

118. J. P. Lodge and H. A. Bravo. *Anal. Chem.* **36**, 671 (1964).
119. E. Sawicki, T. Stanley and T. Hauser. *Chemist-Analyst* **47**, 31 (1958).
120. T. R. Hauser and D. W. Bradley. *Anal. Chem.* **38**, 1529 (1966).
121. T. R. Hauser and D. W. Bradley. *Anal. Chem.* **39**, 1184 (1967).
122. D. Amos. *Anal. Chem.* **42**, 842 (1970).
123. R. Criegee. *Record of Chemical Progress* **18**, 111 (1957).
124. A. P. Altshuller, I. R. Cohen, M. E. Meyer and A. F. Wartburg, *Anal. Chim. Acta* **25**, 101 (1961).
125. B. Dimitriades and T. C. Wesson, *J. Air Poll. Control Assoc.* **22**, 33 (1972).
126. N. A. Renzetti and R. J. Bryan. *J. Air Poll. Control Assoc.* **11**, 421 (1961).
127. J. E. Sigsby, T. A. Bellar and L. J. Leng. *J. Air Poll. Control Assoc.* **12**, 522 (1962).
128. A. P. Altshuller and J. J. Bufalini. *J. Photochem. Photobiol.* **4**, 97 (1965).
129. E. A. Schuck, H. W. Ford and E. R. Stephens. 'Air Pollution Effects of Irradiated Automobile Exhaust as related to Fuel Consumption', Report No. 26, San Marino, California, Air Pollution Foundation, 1958.
130. P. A. Leighton. "The Photochemistry of Air Pollution", Academic Press, New York, 1962.
131. J. N. Pitts, Jr. *Advances Env. Sci. Technol.* **1**, 289 (1969).
132. E. T. Chapman and M. H. Smith. *J. Chem. Soc.* **20**, 173 (1867).
133. L. Dyksterhuis and D. E. A. Rivett. *J. S. African Chem. Inst.* **15**, 20 (1962).
134. E. Baer, R. Grosheintz and H. O. L. Fischer. *J. Am. Chem. Soc.* **61**, 2607 (1939).
135. R. Criegee. *Angew. Chem.* **70**, 173 (1958), and previous work.
136. J. P. Minyard, J. H. Tumlinson, A. C. Thompson, and P. A. Hedin, *J. Agric. Food Chem.* **15**, 517 (1967).
137. T. Uno and H. Taniguchi. *Japan Analyst* **21**, 76 (1972).
138. C. H. Rahn and H. Schlenk. *Lipids* **8**, 612 (1973).
139. D. P. Schwartz and J. L. Weihrauch. *Microchem. J.* **18**, 249 (1973).

9. ALDOGLUCOSE, PRECURSORS

I. INTRODUCTION

The history of analytical chemistry is the story of precise definition and resultant search for specific interference-free quantitative methods applicable to the mixture under investigation. The development of methods for analysis of body-fluid glucose provides a prime example[1] and in some of the more highly selective of these methods aldoglucose plays an important role.

Aldoglucose is defined as the free aldehyde form of glucose. Important precursors of this aldehyde include various types of glucose derivatives (see Table 32).

II. ENZYMATIC METHODS

A. Introduction

Enzymatic methods have been developed for the specific determination of glucose and several are now available using a variety of enzyme systems, e.g. glucose oxidase and peroxidase,[2–63] glucose oxidase and molybdate,[64–67] glucose oxidase and vanadate,[68] hexokinase and glucose-6-phosphate dehydrogenase,[69–85] D-glucokinase and glucose-6-phosphate dehydrogenase,[74] hexokinase, phosphokinase and lactic dehydrogenase,[70] and glucose oxidase and catalase,[86–88] acyl phosphate: D-hexose phosphotransferase,[89–90] and glucose transferase, acyl phosphate and glucose-6-phosphate dehydrogenase.[91]

Where human health is concerned, fast, reliable and inexpensive procedures are necessary to monitor the problems involved. For example, there is a need for a simple and accurate screening procedure for detecting hypo-, eu-, and hyperglycaemic states quantitatively. Application of rapid but accurate tests for determining serum glucose levels in night and emergency work and in many acute diagnostic situations would be especially useful in

(a) emergency room differentiation of coma due to hypoglycaemic shock, diabetic coma, or coma of other etiology,

(b) bedside monitoring of patients in diabetic acidosis and/or coma,

(c) screening and monitoring for hypoglycaemia in the newborn.

Table 32. Glucose derivatives

Family	Examples
O-Glucosides	Digitonin
	Lanatosides
	Methylglucosides
	Salicin
	Scillaren A
	Solanine
	Strophantin
N-Glucosides	Amygdalin
	Hesperidin
	Indican
Disaccharides	Cellobiose
	Gentiobiose
	Isomaltose
	Lactose
	Maltose
	Palatinose
	Sucrose
	Trehalose
	Turinose
Oligosaccharides	Raffinose
Polysaccharides	Cellulose
	Glycogen
	Starch

(d) mobile multiphasic screening for diabetes in the ambulant population,

(e) screening programmes for diabetics—one or two hour procedures following carbohydrate challenge.[92]

Procedures are described in this chapter, and in Chapter 14 (also in the literature cited) which could be modified and utilized in this fashion. Tests can be run on a chromatogram or on paper, and the colour quantified with a reflectance meter.[92] Similarly a fluorescence method could be used and the test quantified on paper or other solid surfaces with a filter fluorimeter.[93]

B. Glucose oxidase

Glucose oxidase, (β-D-glucose; oxygen oxidoreductase, 1.1.3.4), specifically oxidizes β-D-glucopyranose.[94–97] One of the difficult factors in the analysis of glucose with this method is the 150-fold slower rate of oxidation at 20° of α-D glucose compared with the β-anomer.[97] However, the total glucose can be determined since even highly purified glucose oxidase contains an enzyme which completely catalyses mutarotation of α → β during an appropriate incubation period.[97] These two isomeric forms exist in solution in equilibrium with the chain form, usually 36% in α-form, 64% in β-form, and only a trace in the chain form. The shift from one form to the other in solution is called mutarotation and is catalysed by aldose mutarotase (aldose 1-epimerase, 5.1.3.3)[98, 99] as shown in Fig 33. Mutarotation is accelerated by the presence of buffer and increased temperature.[100]

The specificity of the oxidation has been investigated, Table 33.

C. Glucose Oxidase–Peroxidase

One of the main methods of analysis for glucose involves the following reactions

$$\alpha\text{-D-Glucose} \underset{}{\overset{\text{Mutarotase}}{\rightleftharpoons}} \beta\text{-D-Glucose}$$

$$\beta\text{-D-Glucose} + H_2O + O_2 \underset{}{\overset{\text{Glucose oxidase}}{\rightleftharpoons}} H_2O_2 + \text{D-Glucono-}\delta\text{-lactone}$$
$$\downarrow$$
$$\text{D-Gluconic acid}$$

$$H_2O_2 + DH_2 \underset{}{\overset{\text{Peroxidase}}{\rightleftharpoons}} 2H_2O + D$$

DH_2 is the hydrogen donor while D is the final chromogen measured in the reaction. Some of the hydrogen donors that have been used in these analytical procedures including o-tolidine,[3, 10, 43 – 45] o-dianisidine,[2, 7, 19, 22 – 24, 26 – 42, 101,102] 2,6-dichlorophenolindophenol,[20] 4-hydroxyphenylacetic acid,[25,46] homovanillic acid,[46–48] resazurin,[25] 4-aminophenazone and a phenol,[103] 4-aminophenazone and sulphonated 2,4-dichlorophenol,[104] and 2,2'-azino-di-(3-ethylbenzothiazoline-6-sulphonic acid).[105]

1. *Benzidine derivatives.*

The benzidine type molecule has been used as the hydrogen-donor or chromogen-precursor. Thus, with o-dianisidine as the reagent, 3,3'-dimethoxy-4,4'-diiminodiphenoquinone, **I**, has been postulated as the chromogen.[113] However, in the presence of an excess of reagent one would expect free radicals to be formed in these reactions. With *N* atoms as resonance terminals and proton acceptors, pH should affect the long wavelength bands of these

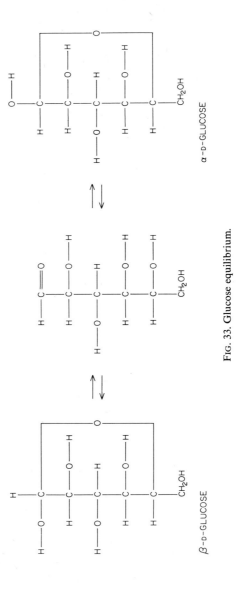

Fig. 33. Glucose equilibrium.

Table 33. Rates of oxidation by glucose oxidase.
(Glucose taken as 100)

Sugar	Rate	Ref.
β-D-Glucose	100	
α-D-Glucose	0·6	97
2-Deoxy-D-glucose	12, 25	106–108
6-Deoxy-6-fluoro-D-glucose	3	107, 108
6-Methyl-D-glucose	2	107
4,6-Dimethylglucose	1·2	107
Mannose	1	2, 96, 97
D-Xylose	1	96, 108
Trehalose	0·3	107
Galactose	0·1	2, 97
Altrose	0·1	109, 110
Talose	0·02	109, 110
Idose	0·02	109 ,110
D- and L-Arabinose	0·00[a]	111
Allose	0·00	109, 110
Gulose	0·00	109, 110
D-Fructose	0·00	111
Glucose-1-phosphate	0·00	2
Glucose-6-phosphate	0·00	2

[a]About 75 other sugars are not attacked.[107] Comparison of specificity with other methods.[112]

types of molecules. For example, in the determination of glucose in the presence of sucrose the chromogen from o-dianisidine absorbs in the following solutions at the following wavelengths; pH 1, 390; pH 2, 410; pH 4–7, 450; and 33% aq sulphuric acid, 540 nm.[114] Similar groups of free radical cations have been described[115] and will be discussed.

The colour obtained in the o-anisidine procedure can be stabilized for at least 3 h either by dissolving the final chromogen in a dilute acid at pH 1·55–1·7, such as 1% sulphamic or 10% citric acid,[38] or by the addition of gum ghatti.[33] Extraction of the chromogen into isobutanol improves the sensitivity and the colour stability considerably.[33]

The method has been adapted to the Auto Analyser.[101] The sample solution, diluted with sodium sulphate solution is dialysed and the dialysate, after mixing with the glucose oxidase–peroxidase enzyme system and with

o-dianisidine, is incubated at 37° to develop the colour and the absorbance is measured at 440 nm against standards. Since the glucose–enzyme system forms a colloidal complex which, in time, results in a deposit on the surface of the cell, the procedure is modified by the addition of 20% H_2SO_4 immediately after contact of the glucose with the enzyme system.

The method has also been used to determine skin sugar.[102] Essentially 10 mg of sample is defatted, extracted with physiological saline, the sugar in the clarified extract reacts to produce the hydrogen peroxide, which is then measured at 535 nm by a procedure involving peroxidase and dianisidine. With o-tolidine as the reagent a blue chromogen is obtained which is reported to absorb at 382 and 635 nm[45] or 365 and 635 nm.[10] The narrow band at 365 nm is about 68% higher than the broad band at 635 nm. Five micrograms of glucose can be determined with this procedure. The sensitivity and the colour stability of the procedure can be improved by the use of a secondary alkylaryl sulphonate and a polyethylene glycol.[45]

A simple procedure for the determination of glucose with glucose oxidase, peroxidase and o-tolidine is available.

Glucose oxidase-o-tolidine determination of glucose in blood[10]

To 1·8 ml of water, add 0·2 ml of blood, 1 ml of 1·8% zinc sulphate heptahydrate solution, and 1 ml of 0·4% sodium hydroxide solution (or 1 ml of 0·85% barium hydroxide solution). Centrifuge briefly at high speed, and transfer 2 ml and 0·5 ml portions of the supernatant liquid to tubes of about 18 mm diameter.

To prepare the o-tolidine dihydrochloride, add conc hydrochloric acid to a solution of free base in ethanol. Filter the precipitated salt by suction, wash with ethanol and ether and dry over sodium hydroxide *in vacuo*. Prepare a buffer of pH 4·1–4·2 by mixing 1 + 9 acetic acid and 16% sodium acetate solution to the proper pH. To prepare the composite reagent, add 150 ml of buffer to 700 mg of o-tolidine dihydrochloride dissolved in a few drops of water. Dissolve 200 mg of glucose oxidase and 15 mg of horseradish peroxidase in several ml of buffer, add to the o-tolidine mixture, and dilute to 300 ml with buffer and filter. Reagent blanks made with freshly prepared reagent should have an absorbance of less than 0·01 at 635 nm.

To the sample solution, add 1·5 ml of the reagent, incubate at 25° for 1 h and read at 365 nm or 635 nm.

Urine. Mix equal parts by weight of reconditioned air-dried Amberlite IR-120 (acid form) and Amberlite IR-45 (basic form). Slowly add a diluted sample to the resin in a 15 mm tube held in a slanting position to prevent entrapment of air until the liquid rises above the level of the resin. Refrigerate for 1 h to prevent bacterial action and separate the urine from the resin. Develop as described for blood from "To prepare the o-tolidine . . .".

On the other hand, several workers have made a comparative study of various enzymic and colorimetric methods for glucose and have reached the conclusion that the glucose oxidase-peroxidase-o-dianisidine method produced the best results.[36, 37] Two procedures which have seen some use are described in this section. In the second method maximum colour production was reached in 20 min, the colour was stable for at least 18 h and Beer's law was obeyed from 10–75 µg of glucose.[40] Impure glucose oxidase preparations can liberate glucose from 1 → 4-linked α-glucans. The presence of tris inhibits this undesirable activity.[116]

Glucose oxidase-o-dianisidine determination of glucose in blood[19]
Reagents. (1) Sodium dihydrogen phosphate solution, 0·5 M. Dissolve 69 g of $NaH_2PO_4.H_2O$ in water, make up to 1 litre and saturate with chloroform. (2) Standard glucose solutions. 100 mg per 100 ml in 0·3 % (w/v) benzoic acid. (3) Perchloric acid. Dilute 2·85 ml of 72% perchloric acid AnalaR to 100 ml. (4) Blood glucose reagent. Dissolve 0·625 g glucose oxidase, 0·025 g of peroxidase, and 0·036 g of o-dianisidine dihydrochloride, in 0·5 M sodium dihydrogen phosphate solution, make up to 500 ml with the same solution, and adjust to pH 7·0 (by addition of approximately 8·5 ml of 40% sodium hydroxide solution.) Filter and store in a dark glass bottle in the refrigerator.

Method. Pipette 0·1 ml of patient's whole blood into 1 ml of dilute perchloric acid contained in a centrifuge tube and spin in the centrifuge. At the same time add 0·1 ml of standard glucose solution to 1·0 ml of dilute perchloric acid in another similar tube. Take three test tubes, into each pipette exactly 5·0 ml of glucose reagent and allow to attain room temperature. Into one test tube pipette accurately 0·2 ml of supernatant fluid from the blood sample. Into a second tube pipette accurately 0·2 ml of distilled water. Into the third test tube pipette accurately 0·2 ml of the standard glucose/perchloric acid solution. Stand in room temperature away from direct light for 45 min or place in an incubator at 37° for 20 minutes. Read the absorption of the standard and test solutions at 436 nm with the blank solution in the reference cell.

Glucose oxidase-o-dianisidine determination of glucose in the presence of maltose[40]
Reagents. (1) tris-Phosphate–glycerol buffer. Dissolve 36·3 gm tris and 50 gm $NaH_2PO_4.H_2O$ in water. Add 400 ml glycerol and water to 1000 ml. Adjust to pH 7·0 by addition of solid $NaH_2PO_4.H_2O$. (2) Glucose oxidase reagent. Dissolve the following in 100 ml of tris-phosphate–glycerol buffer: glucose oxidase, 30 mg; horseradish peroxidase, 3 mg; o-dianisidine dihydrochloride, 10 mg.

F

Procedure. To 1 ml of test solution containing 0–75 μg glucose, add 2 ml glucose oxidase reagent. Mix well, and incubate at 37° for 30 mins. Add 4 ml of 5 N HCl, mix well, and read absorbance at 525 nm.

Although the glucose oxidase procedure provided the first method for the specific determination of glucose in body fluids, Henry[117] stated in 1964 that it was not used extensively because of inhibitors, while Richterich[118] stated (in 1968) that the glucose oxidase–peroxidase method is the best method for the exact determination of blood sugar.

In the more recent methods attempts have been made to cancel or decrease interferences. In one method glucose can be determined manually in 25 μl samples of capillary blood.[54] Modifications have been introduced to shorten the assay time and eliminate possible interferences.

These include dilution of the blood sample with isotonic sodium fluoride (1·76–1·78 %) to eliminate protein precipitation (except in the case of elevated bilirubin), removal of cells by centrifugation, and increasing the enzyme concentration so the incubation period can be shortened to 20 minutes. Interference from bilirubin and uric acid has been eliminated or minimized. Bilirubin is removed from samples with high levels of co-precipitation with protein using barium hydroxide and zinc sulphate. Uric acid is added to all standards to decrease its interference.

Modified glucose oxidase method for determination of glucose in whole blood[54]

Add 25 μl of whole blood, standard, or control to 2·00 ml of isotonic sodium fluoride and centrifuge. Combine 1·00 ml of the supernatant and 1·00 ml of the enzyme reagent (500 mg glucose oxidase, 20 mg peroxidase, and 2·0 ml 1 % o-dianisidine in 100 ml). Incubate at 37° for 20 minutes. Add 4·0 ml of 3·8 M sulphuric acid to stop the reaction. Read the absorbance at 540 nm within two hours.

In an alternative method,[119] where only small amounts of blood are available from small animals, only 2 μl of whole blood are necessary for an assay. In this case protein is precipitated with 2 % perchloric acid, the centrifuged supernate reacted with the o-dianisidine reagent, and the absorbance read at 436 nm.

Automated methods utilizing the glucose oxidase–peroxidase–dianisidine procedure are also available which claim to give "true glucose" values.[57] Although uric acid inhibition of glucose recovery in glucose oxidase procedures[5, 59] has discouraged the application of glucose oxidase–peroxidase techniques to second generation continuous-flow systems, recent reports of glucose oxidase methods in which there is no inhibition by uric acid[52] or interference in uremic states[60] has prompted a re-evaluation of this technique.[57] The glucose value in the method is unaffected by the presence of 16 mg of uric acid per deciliter, and the system is highly resistant to interference from L-cysteine, glutathione, acetylsalicylic acid and phenol. At the extremely high concentration of 10 mg/dl, ascorbic acid, gentisic acid and L-dopa cause decreases in the value for glucose of 17, 29 and 51 % respectively, for the glucose oxidase–peroxidase–MBTH–dimethylaniline technique[52, 57] (to be discussed). The practical ascorbic acid effect was determined in three subjects who were ingesting 3 g of ascorbic acid per day for several months for cold (coryza) prevention. The glucose values from the dianisidine method were identical to those from the glucose oxidase–neocuproine procedure.

Both the dianisidine and the MBTH–dimethylaniline procedures appear to give "true glucose" values for normal, hyperuricemic, and uremic subjects. These methods are recommended for use in second generation continuous-flow systems.[57] These various methods have been compared as shown by the data in Table 34. The flow diagram is shown in Fig. 34 for the dianisidine method.

Table 34. Comparison of serum glucose values in fasting normal subjects[57]

Method	No. of sera	Mean ± SD (mg dl^{-1})	Normal range (M ± 2·5 × SD)
Glucose oxidase–neocuproin	58	89 ± 9	67–112
Glucose oxidase–peroxidase–dianisidine	58	88 ± 9	66–111
Glucose oxidase–peroxidase–MBTH–DMA	58	92 ± 9	70–115
Hexokinase	28	93 ± 9	71–116
Toluidine	58	95 ± 10	70–120
Ferricyanide	58	99 ± 12	69–129
SMA 12/60 neocuproine	26	95 ± 10	70–120

2. p-*Diphenylamine sulphonate*.

The glucose oxidase–peroxidase (β-D-glucose; oxygen oxidoreductase (EC 1.1.3.4); and hydrogen peroxide oxidoreductase (EC 1.11.1.7) for determining glucose in plasma serum has been modified by changing the assay pH to 5·5, altering the ratio of glucose oxidase to peroxidase, and using a soluble reagent, p-diphenylamine sulphonate, to prepare a single complete reagent mixture that develops stable colour within two minutes without deproteinization.[56] 2,2'-Azino-di-[3-ethylbenzothiazoline-6-sulphonate][119–121] could probably be substituted in the procedure.

Examination of the method showed that measurements are linear to 350 mg dl^{-1}, and a representative standard curve is expressed by the equation $y = 0·0018x$, where y is absorbance and x is the glucose concentration in

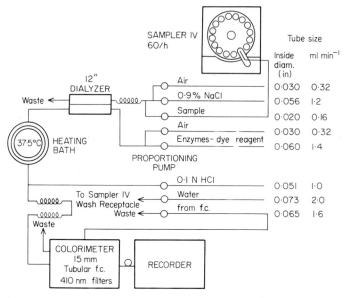

FIG. 34. Flow diagram for determination of glucose with the glucose oxidase–peroxidase–
dianisidine system.[57]

milligrams per decilitre. Reference sera containing 75, 150, and 300 mg of
added glucose gave mean results ($\pm$ SD) of 75($\pm$ 2), 150($\pm$ 2) and 300($\pm$ 3)
mg dl^{-1}. The coefficient of variation for 120 determinations was 1·3%.
Day-to-day precision was checked with 20 replicate assays each, six times over
a six-month period. The coefficient of variation for all 360 determinations was
3·3%. Recoveries from 96%–100%, averaging 99%, were obtained with 20
serial additions of 20 mg of glucose per decilitre to a glucose-free dialysed
serum base. A close correlation was obtained with a copper–neocuproine
procedure[122, 123] for 60 sera from a general hospital population. The regression equation was $y = 0.98x - 12.57$, $Syx = 3.4$, $r^2 = 0.98$.

   Possible interferences in this procedure were extensively investigated. Use
of isotonic sodium fluoride (1·78 g dl^{-1}) produced a 32% depression in
values which was attributed to diminished glucose oxidase activity. If the
cells can be separated from the plasma or serum within 2 h, the sample
refrigerated, and the test performed within 24 h, there is no need for an inhibitor or fluoride. If an inhibitor is necessary, then sodium iodoacetate (2 mg
ml^{-1} of blood) can be used. Routine anticoagulants such as oxalate, citrate,
ethylenediaminetetraacetate and heparin salts do not interfere. Chemicals
and maximal concentrations in mg dl^{-1} for 100 mg of glucose at which there
is no interference are as follows: bilirubin, 8; uric acid, 12; ascorbic acid, 10;

and haemoglobin, 200. Above these concentrations the apparent glucose values will increase gradually with increase in the concentration of the inhibitor. Creatinine (20 mg dl^{-1}), reduced glutathione (500 mg dl^{-1}), gentisic acid (10 mg fl^{-1}), or acetylsalicylic acid (10 mg dl^{-1}) do not interfere. To remove the inhibitor from haemoglobin and bilirubin, clearly icteric or hemolytic serum should be Somogyi-precipitated.

Two-minute determination of serum glucose with p-*diphenylamine sulphonate*[56]

Reagent. 60 mg of glucose oxidase (19000 u/g), 30 mg of peroxidase (160 Purpurogallin units/mg), and 90 mg of reduced sodium p-diphenylamine sulphonate in 100 ml of citrate buffer (0·1 mol l^{-1}, pH 5·5). The mixture is stable for at least 3 months in a refrigerator; at room temp, it is stable for about 4 hours. Stock glucose standard—1% anhydrous primary standard dextrose in distilled water containing 0·1 g of benzoic acid per decilitre. Make appropriate dilutions with distilled water. Store refrigerated.

Procedure. Add 50 μl of serum to 2·5 ml of reagent (prewarmed to room temp), mix, and after 2 min read the absorbance at 465 nm. The colour is stable for more than 8 minutes.

3. *Difficulties.*

Difficulties arise when some of these methods are applied directly to serum or plasma because of the presence of inhibitors.[23, 53, 58, 59, 124] Some of the inhibitors are vitamin C (>5 mg/100 ml),[55, 125] catechols, glutathione and cysteine,[126] bilirubin,[31] uric acid,[5] ergothioneine and reduced glutathione.[44] The interferences by icterus, haemolysis and uric acid can be avoided by a zinc hydroxide (Somogyi) filtrate.[23] When properly diluted, physiological concentrations of uric acid, ergothioneine, ascorbic acid and glutathione in the blood of either rabbit, guinea-pig or rat do not interfere seriously.[44] Trichloroacetic acid should be avoided as a deproteinizing agent since peroxides may be released.[126] Oxidizing agents on glassware, fluorides, chlorides, thymol and fungistatic agents should be avoided.

In the analysis of urine for glucose, reducing compounds, such as ascorbic acid, creatinine, glutathione and uric acid must be removed. Anion and cation exchange resins[10, 14] and charcoal and Lloyd's reagent[8, 9, 127] have been used for this purpose. Thus, ascorbic acid can be removed by passage of urine samples through a 5 mm × 10 mm column prepared from a slurry of an anion exchange resin (Bio-Rad AGl-x4 chloride form, 200–400 mesh) in a Pasteur pipette with a cotton plug.[55]

Hydrazine derivatives, such as tolazamide and isoniazide, depressed the result for blood glucose by differing amounts, the effect being enhanced by the presence of a benzene nucleus in close proximity to the active group.[53]

Another serious potential interference is the presence of substantial amounts of β-glucosidase (β-D-glucoside glucohydrolase, EC 3.2.1.21) in commercial peroxidase–glucose oxidase preparations used in routine glucose assays. This contaminant can result in excessively high and incorrect glucose measurements if oligosaccharides containing β-(1 → 4) linkages are also present.[128], [129] However, glucose can be assayed by a peroxidase–glucose oxidase method in the presence of cellobiose, and perhaps in the presence of other short chain cello-oligosaccharides, if the peroxidase–glucose oxidase is preincubated with 0·1 M D-glucono-δ-lactone.[62]

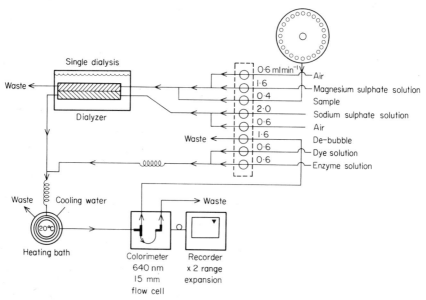

FIG. 35. Flow diagram for the automated micro determination of blood glucose.[44]

4. *Automation and test mixtures.*

These methods have been automated or semi-automated.[4, 5, 12–14, 21, 39, 44, 130] A flow diagram for the determination of blood glucose with an Auto-Analyser is shown in Fig. 35.[44] An *in vivo* technique is available using a glucose oxidase–peroxidase–*o*-tolidine procedure wherein the patient is connected directly to the Auto-Analyser by an implanted catheter in an ante-cubital vein, Fig. 36.

Some of the mixtures which have been analysed for glucose by the glucose oxidase–peroxidase methods include blood,[10, 19, 31, 32, 38, 39, 43–45] urine,[6–14] corn syrup,[15] hydrolysates of polysaccharides,[16] fermentation liquors[17] and plant materials.[41]

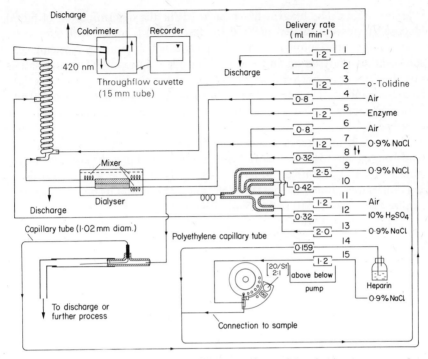

FIG. 36. Flow diagram for *in vivo* glucose determination.

5. *Free radical precursors.*

In the glucose oxidase–peroxidase procedures free radical precursors are usually used as reagents to react with the hydrogen peroxide. An example is the reagent 2,2'-azino-di-(3-ethylbenzothiazoline-6-sulphonic acid).[49–51, 105,119–121,128] The free radical cation, **II**, is formed.

Its most intense band is at 420 nm (mε 19) with a shoulder at 400 nm and longer wavelength bands at about 650, 720 and 830 nm. The reagent absorbs near 340 nm with mε 42. The advantages of this method are that the method is four times more sensitive than the *o*-dianisidine procedures and the test solution including all reagents necessary for the determination of the glucose is highly stable. The reagent has been used for the determination of blood glucose. In one automated method the test serum is mixed with a solution containing copper sulphate and neocuproine, which removes reducing substances, then dialysed against sodium chloride solution.[50] The dialysate is mixed with a glucose oxidase–peroxidase–2,2'-azinobis–(3-ethylbenzothiazoline-6-sulphonate) reagent, the colour produced being measured at 420 nm. Reducing substances, such as ascorbic and uric acids, and creatinine, did not interfere.

Many such precursors are known which react with trace amounts of oxidizing agents to form free radical cations absorbing at very long wavelength.[115] For example, 3-methyl-2-benzothiazolinone azine absorbs at 334 nm, its free radical cation, **III**, at 388 and 735 nm, and its more completely oxidized dication at 510 and 825 nm, Figure 37.

III

Other free radical precursors which can be substituted for the benzidine type of reagent in these oxidative analyses are given in Table 35 with the wavelength maxima of the final free radical cation.[115] Any of these derivatives or their sulphonated forms could be used in the analysis of glucose in the presence of glucose oxidase or as reagents in other similar types of assays

Table 35. Free radical precursor reagents and their free radical cations[115]

Compound	Free radical cation, main λ_{max}
N,N'-Diphenyl-p-phenylenediamine	386, 705 or 720
Glyoxal bis(N,N-diphenylhydrazone)	540, 1152
3-Methyl-2-benzothiazolinone azine	735
3-Methyl-2-benzothiazolinone picrylhydrazone	406
1-Methyl-2-quinolone azine	520
Phenoselenazine	517
Phenothiazine	518
Phenoxazine	530
N,N,N',N'-Tetramethylbenzidine	473, 1018
N,N,N',N'-Tetramethyl-4,4'-diaminostilbene	514
·N,N,N',N'-Tetramethyl-p-phenylenediamine	565, 614
N,N,N'-Trimethyl-p-phenylenediamine	577

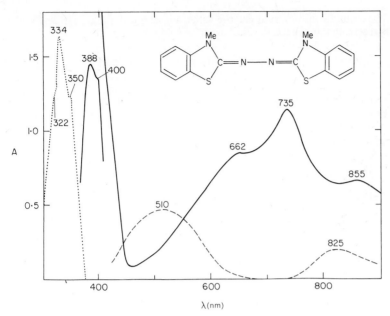

FIG. 37. Visible absorption spectra obtained with 3-methyl-2-benzothiazolinone azine.[115]
Procedure for nitrite determination: ——— 0·92 µg nitrite, λ_{max} 388 nm, A = 2·45.
– – – – – To 1 ml of aq 1 % sodium nitrite add 8 ml of 2 × 10^{-5} M azine in acetic acid
followed by 0·5 ml of 70 % aq perchloric acid. Read immediately.
· · · · · · · · 4 × 10^{-5} M azine in 2-methoxyethanol or acetic acid.

where hydrogen peroxide or some other oxidizing agent is one of the products of a reaction.

Because of the carcinogenic activity of benzidine, o-dianisidine and o-tolidine, some alternative reagents are discussed in this section.

6. *MBTH methods.*

In addition, a reagent couple can be used which on oxidation combines to form a highly coloured chromogen or a highly fluorescent fluorogen. For example, such a couple could be acetaldehyde 3-methyl-2-benzothiazolinone azine and 3-methyl-2-benzothiazolinone hydrazone. In the presence of an oxidizing agent such as hydrogen peroxide the formazan cation absorbing at about 630 and 760 nm would be formed.

One reagent couple that has been introduced recently is dimethylaniline plus MBTH.[52,57,131] The postulated reaction is shown in Fig. 38. Aldoglucose or its enediol form is probably involved in the reaction. Day-to-day reproducibility of the automated glucose procedure[52] gave coefficients of

F*

Table 36. Comparisons of serum glucose values for icteric patients receiving therapeutic doses of ascorbic acid[131]

Method[a]	Mean glucose (mg dl^{-1})	
	Icteric[b]	Ascorbate[c]
GOD/POD/MBTH/DMA (52)	88·2	113·1
GOD/POD/ABTS (105)	87·0	111·4
Neocuproine (132)	95·0	114·7
O-Toluidine (133)	104·2	113·4
Alkaline ferricyanide	99·7	117·6
Hexokinase	73·4	109·7

[a]GOD = glucose oxidase, POD = peroxidase, MBTH = 3-Methyl-2-benzothiazolinone hydrazone, DMA = N,N-dimethylaniline, ABTS = 2,2′-azinodiethylbenzothiazoline-6-sulfonate.
[b]13 patients; total bilirubin range: 10–35 mg dl^{-1}; mean, 20 mg dl^{-1}.
[c]17 patients; ascorbic acid dosage, 1 g per day or less.

variation of about 2–3% for 33 daily analyses. The accuracy of the new procedures for plasma glucose was determined by comparison with the spectrophotometric hexokinase (ATP: D-hexose 6-phosphotransferase, E.C. 2.7.1.1.)/glucose-6-phosphate dehydrogenase (D-glucose-6-phosphate: NADP oxidoreductase, E.C. 1.1.1.49) method.[69,75] Excellent agreement was obtained over a wide range of plasma glucose values ($y = 1·01 x = 1, r = 0·998, N = 307$). No interferences were found except greater than physiological concentrations of ascorbic acid.

This automated method was further evaluated and found to be acceptable [131]. Added bilirubin, creatinine, dextrans and uric acid did not interfere. The method was compared with various other methods in terms of interferences and practical results obtained with sera, Table 36, and urine, Table 37.[131–133]

Table 37. Mean glucose values for urine samples[131]

Method	Mean glucose (mg dl^{-1})	
	Group 1 ($n = 29$)[a]	Group 2 ($n = 16$)[b]
GOD/POD/MBTH/DMA	7	127
GOD/POD/ABTS	0	68
Hexokinase	27	128
o-Toluidine	20	139
Neocuproine	107	175
Ferricyanide	201	242

[a]Measurable glucose present in urine.
[b]Urines to which glucose standard (100 mg dl^{-1}) was added.

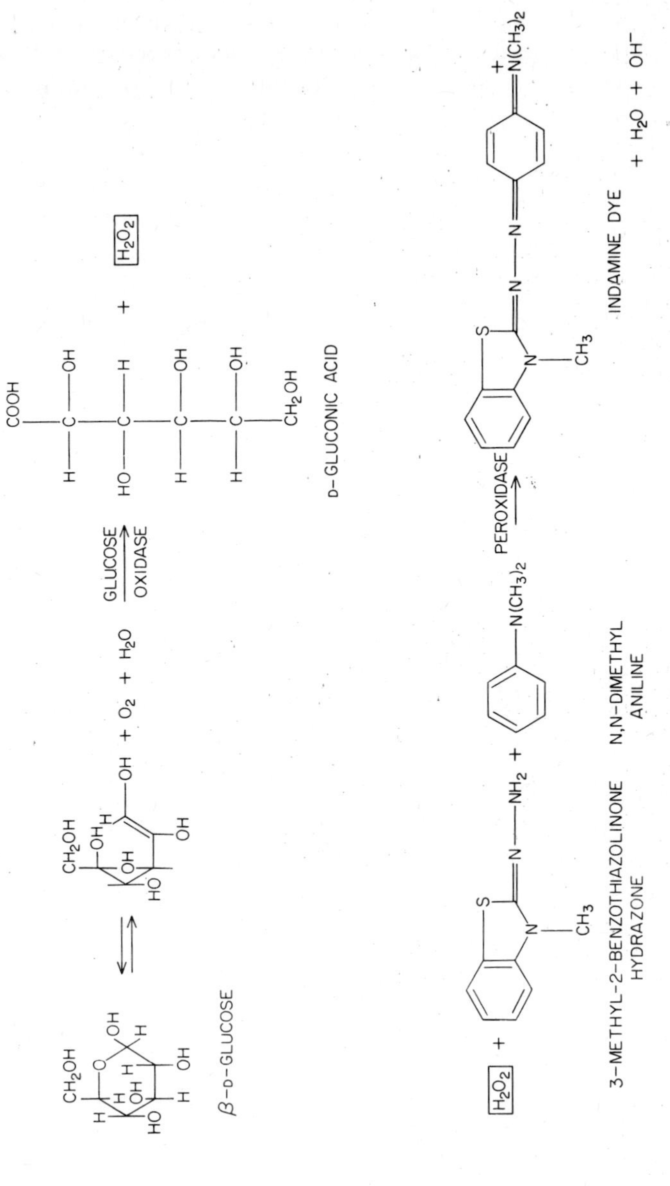

FIG. 38. Determination of glucose with the help of MBTH and dimethylaniline.

Essentially these reactions are between oxidized MBTH and dimethyl-aniline. This reaction of MBTH with dimethylaniline and a large number of aromatic amines has been studied.[134] With dimethylaniline an $m\varepsilon$ of 84 is obtained at λ_{max} 598 nm. The spectra obtained in the reactions between MBTH and aniline, N-methylaniline and N,N-dimethylaniline are shown in Fig. 39.

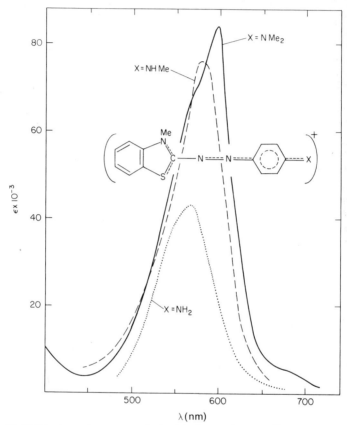

FIG. 39. Visible absorption spectra obtained in the reaction of aniline (······), N-methylaniline (- - - -), and N,N-dimethylaniline (——) with MBTH.[134]

Replacing dimethylaniline with N,N-dibenzylaniline gave a chromogen absorbing at λ 614 nm with $m\varepsilon$ 103. Diphenylamine and N-methyldiphenyl-amine give bands at λ 606 $m\varepsilon$ 78 and λ 610 $m\varepsilon$ 87, respectively. p-Diphenyl-amine-sulphonic acid could also be used in place of dimethylaniline. The sensitivities obtained in the reaction between oxidized MBTH and these amines or the heterocyclic imines could be considerably improved. If necessary, their sulphonic acid derivatives could be used. The reaction of oxidized MBTH with additional aromatic amines and nitrogen heterocyclic compounds to give highly coloured azo dyes has been studied.[135]

Other possible reagent couples which can be used to determine the hydrogen peroxide formed in the determination of glucose with glucose oxidase and peroxidase include MBTH plus azulene, HBT plus azulene, and MBTH plus a p-hydroxystyryl compound. In line with this is the reaction of oxidized MBTH with azulene to give the chromogen absorbing at λ 588 with mε 52,[136] HBT with azulene to give the chromogen absorbing at λ 583 with mε 50,[136] and MBTH with isosafrole to give the chromogen absorbing at λ 667 nm with mε 65.[137]

7. 4-Aminophenazones.

Another reagent couple useful in the determination of glucose in blood by both manual and automated techniques is phenol plus 4-aminophenazone which forms the purple chromogen, **IV**, in the presence of hydrogen peroxide and peroxidase.[103]

IV

In acid solution this type of structure would add a proton to the phenolic oxygen which would result in a shift of the long wavelength maximum to shorter wavelength.

The 4-aminophenazone:phenol method has been improved by utilizing two reagent solutions, one containing protein precipitants and phenol and the other containing the aminophenazone, glucose oxidase, peroxidase and sodium azide as a preservative.[63] In addition, enzymes were used that contained a low catalase level, which helped to ensure maximum colour development. With these modifications colour stability was good up to 25 minutes.

Although this method is adequate in routine application, a more sensitive modification has been developed for use when an adequate amount of blood is difficult to obtain, or when samples containing low concentratins of glucose are required for analysis. As compared with the phenol:4-aminophenazone method where an mε of 5·1 is obtained, the method using sulphonated 2,4-dichlorophenol-4-aminophenazone gives an mε of 20.[104]

Since crude glucose oxidase extracts contain relatively large amounts of catalase which could destroy the hydrogen peroxide necessary in the analytical determination, sodium azide has been added to the reagent to inhibit the catalase. Quantitative recoveries of glucose were obtained when it was added to whole blood from which all the glucose had been removed by dialysis.

Oxidizing reagents can interfere in the non-specific reaction but peroxides liberated from erythrocytes by mineral acids would be the only oxidants found in blood. However, under the weakly acid conditions there is no interference from erythrocyte peroxides. The most likely interfering reducing substances in protein-free blood filtrates are uric acid and creatinine, but in concentrations up to 30 mg per 100 ml they had no effect on the results. Ascorbic acid interferes with colour development, but since its concentration in blood is less than 1 mg per 100 ml of whole blood, its interference is negligible. Large amounts of fluoride and potassium oxalate have no effect on the results. Twenty successive analyses gave a mean result of 149·8 mg of glucose per 100 ml with a range from 148·0 to 151·0 mg per 100 ml and a standard deviation of 0·91 mg per 100 ml.

Determination of blood glucose by the glucose oxidase–peroxidase–sulphonated 2,4-dichlorophenol plus 4-aminophenazone system[104]
Reagents. Glucose standards: 0–400 mg per 100 ml in 0·2% (w/v) benzoic acid solution. Sulphonated 2,4-dichlorophenol, 2%: To 10 g of distilled 2,4-dichlorophenol add 20 ml of conc H_2SO_4 and heat at 100° for 5 hours. Cool, add 400 ml of distilled water and neutralize with 10 N NaOH. Add 10 ml of 1 N H_2SO_4 and dilute to 500 ml with water; this solution keeps indefinitely. Protein precipitant solution: Dissolve 5 g of sodium tungstate, $Na_2WO_4.2H_2O$, 5 g of disodium hydrogen orthophosphate, Na_2HPO_4, and 4·5 g of sodium chloride in sufficient water to make 200 ml of solution. Add 250 ml of the 2% sulphonated 2,4-dichlorophenol solution and adjust the pH to 3 by adding 1 N HCl. Dilute to 500 ml with water; this solution is stable for at least two months. Colour reagent: Dissolve 3 g of dipotassium hydrogen orthophosphate, and 0·3 g of sodium azide in 290 ml of water. Add 5 ml of a glucose oxidase solution (*e.g.* Fermcozyme 653 AM from Hughes and Hughes Ltd., Brentwood, Essex) and 5 ml of 0·1% peroxidase (type 1, RZ approximately 0·6, Sigma Chemical Co.). Finally add 100 mg of 4-aminophenazone and stir until it has dissolved; this solution is stable for at least two months at 4°.

Procedure. Add 0·05 ml of blood to 4·95 ml of protein precipitant solution. After 5 mins, centrifuge the solution. To 1 ml of the clear liquid, 1 ml of the protein precipitant solution and 1 ml of standard (0·05 ml of 0·15% glucose and 4·95 ml of protein precipitant solution) in separate tubes add 3 ml of colour reagent and incubate all tubes at 37° for 15 minutes. Read the absorbance of S and U against B at 515 nm using 10 mm cells.

$$\text{Blood glucose in mg per 100 ml} = \frac{AU \times 150}{A_S}$$

The absorbance of the 150 mg per 100 ml standard is about 0·45. The colour is stable for 30 min and subsequently fades by 10% per hour.

8. Fluorescent methods.

Fluorescent glucose oxidase methods have also been developed for the determination of glucose.[46–48] The best of many compounds tested were *p*-hydroxyphenylacetic acid, homovanillic acid and tyramine.[46] The *p*-hydroxyphenylacetic acid was believed to be the best substrate for peroxidase, because it permits the determination of lower concentrations of sugars as a result of its very low blank. β-D(+) Glucose, 2-deoxy-D-glucose, and sucrose could be determined with an average relative error of ±3%. Non-fluorescent *p*-hydroxyphenylacetic acid and homovanillic acids form the fluorogens **Va** and **Vb**, respectively.

	X	$F_{exc/em}$
a.	H	317/414
b.	OCH$_3$	315/425

V

Glucose oxidase, the reagent generally conceded to be the most specific, is little used in routine laboratories.[47] The following is a method which does not require removal of protein, and in which uric acid and bilirubin do not interfere even at elevated levels. As little as 1 µl of plasma may be used.

Homovanillic acid determination of blood sugar[47]

Reagents. (1) Phosphate buffer (0·1 M, pH 7). Dissolve 13·9 g of NaH_2PO_4 and 26·8 g of $Na_2HPO_4 \cdot 7H_2O$ (analytical reagent) separately in deionized water and dilute each to 1 litre. Mix together in the ratio 2 : 3, and adjust as necessary with the appropriate solution to give pH 7 ± 0·1.

(2) Reagent solution: Dissolve 50 mg of homovanillic acid (4-hydroxy-3-methoxy-phenylacetic acid, 20 mg of horseradish peroxidase, and 0·15 ml of glucose oxidase in 0·1 M phosphate buffer, pH 7, to a volume of 50 ml.

(3) Sodium hydroxide (0·1 N). Dissolve 4·0 gm of reagent grade NaOH in deionized water and dilute to one litre. Store in polyethylene or polypropylene.

(4) Glucose standards. Prepare a stock standard containing 1000 mg per 100 ml by dissolving anhydrous analytical reagent grade dextrose in 0·1 % aq benzoic acid. Prepare working standards of 100, 200, and 300 mg per 100 ml by appropriate dilution of stock standard with 0·1 % benzoic acid. The stock standard, stored in convenient aliquots at −20°, is stable for several years. The working standards are stable for at least one month at 4°.

Procedure. (1) Prepare 40-fold dilutions of plasma and standards with phosphate buffer (reagent 1) using any convenient volumes.

(2) For each sample, standard, or blank, pipette 0·2 ml of reagent solution (reagent 2) into an appropriately marked 12 × 75 mm cuvette. Pipette 50 µl of diluted sample, standard or blank (phosphate buffer) into appropriate tubes.

(3) Incubate all tubes in a water bath at 37° for 15 minutes.

(4) Add 4·5 ml of 0·1 N NaOH (reagent 3) to each tube.

(5) Adjust fluorimeter to read zero with the dummy cuvette and 80–100 divisions with the high standard. The samples may be read immediately or at any time within 30 minutes.

Calculation. Plot on rectilinear coordinate paper the fluorescence (in dial divisions) of the standards and of the reagent blank *versus* the glucose concentrations; draw the best straight line through the points. Read the value of each unknown from this standard curve.

p-Hydroxyphenylacetic acid can be substituted for the homovanillic acid. Somewhat similar procedures have been reported for the determination of glucose or sucrose with homovanillic acid or *p*-hydroxyphenylacetic acid using the initial rate of reaction as affected by the concentration of glucose.[46, 48]

p-*Hydroxyphenylacetic acid determination of glucose*[46]

To 2 ml of 0·1 N tris(hydroxymethyl)aminomethane (pH 8·5) add 0·1 ml of the test solution, 0·1 ml *p*-hydroxyphenylacetic acid (3·7 mg per ml), 0·1 ml of horseradish peroxidase (1 mg per ml) and 0·1 ml of fungal glucose oxidase (2 mg per ml). The latter is added at zero time and the initial rate of reaction (ΔF/min) is recorded. From calibration plots of ΔF/min versus glucose concentration, the amount of carbohydrate can be calculated.

D. Glucose oxidase plus molybdate or vanadate

In the enzymatic estimations of glucose utilizing glucose oxidase, peroxidase and an oxygen acceptor, the peroxidase can be substituted by molybdate[64–66] or vanadate.[68] For example, in the reaction of iodide with peroxide in the presence of molybdate, the triiodide ion can be measured[66] or the iodine can be reacted with o-tolidine[65] or starch.[64] The starch reaction is postulated as taking place in the following manner:

$$\text{RCHO} + O_2 + 2I^- + 2H^+ \underset{\text{molybdic acid}}{\overset{\text{Glucose oxidase}}{\rightleftharpoons}} \text{RCOOH} + H_2O + I_2$$

$$I_2 + \text{Starch} \rightleftharpoons \text{Starch-Iodine chromogen}$$

In these iodometric methods it is possible that free radical precursors,[115] p-hydroxyphenylacetic acid,[46] or acetophenone plus p-nitrobenzylpyridine or an appropriate hydrazone[138] could be used as oxygen acceptors.

The two molybdate procedures compare very well. The recovery of added glucose is nearly 100% and a mean and standard deviation of 121 ± 1.1 mg per ml is obtained.[64] Beer's law is obeyed from about 40–320 mg glucose per 100 ml of blood.

Glucose oxidase-molybdate-o-tolidine determination of blood sugar[65]

For glucose levels up to 100 mg/100 ml blood. To a centrifuge tube containing 3 ml of 0.9% NaCl add 0.2 ml blood preserved with an oxalate fluoride mixture. Deproteinize by adding 0.4 ml of 5% $ZnSO_4$ solution and 0.4 ml of 0.3 N Ba $(OH)_2$ solution, mixing gently after each addition. Centrifuge and pipette 1 ml of the supernatant into test tubes (in cases of low blood glucose levels use 2 ml of the supernatant).

Standards. Pipette 0.5 and 1 ml of dilute glucose solution (40 µg/ml saturated benzoic acid).

Blank. 1 ml water.

Bring the volume in each tube to 3 ml with water. Add 0.5 ml 0.5% KI solution, 0.5 ml ammonium molybdate solution, and 2 ml buffer-enzyme-o-tolidine reagent, mixing after each addition.

[Make the latter reagent (stable for 1 week in the cold) by mixing the components in the ratio of 1 ml acetate buffer (100 ml N acetic acid and 70 ml N NaOH diluted to 100 ml with water and store cold, pH 5.0), 0.05 ml of 1% o-tolidine in ethanol and 20 units of glucose oxidase diluted to 2 ml with water. The mixed reagent is stable for one week in the cold.]

After the mixture has stood for 60 min at room temp, measure the absorbance at 620 nm.

Starch-iodide determination of blood glucose[64]

Reagents. (1) 0·5 M Acetate buffer, pH 5·5.

(2) Glucose standard: 100 mg glucose (dried in a desiccator) in 100 ml saturated benzoic acid solution. Dilute 1 to 10 with saturated benzoic acid to give working standard of 100 μg per ml solution.

(3) Buffered starch solution: add 0·6 g soluble starch to 80 ml of gently boiling 0·05 M acetate buffer. Cool and dilute to 100 ml with buffer. Filter through Whatman No. 54 and store at 4°. Keeps for one week.

(4) Glucose oxidase, free of carbohydrases and catalase. Contains about 2 units of activity per ml (one unit will oxidize 1 μmole of glucose per min at pH 5·1 at 35°).

(5) Combined reagent. One part 10% KI solution, 5 parts of saturated molybdic acid and 6 parts of buffered starch, freshly prepared.

Procedure. To 6·2 ml of 1·32% anhydrous Na_2SO_4 add 0·2 ml heparinized blood, plasma, or serum followed by 0·8 ml of 5% $ZnSO_4$, and 0·8 ml of 0·3 N barium hydroxide, mixing after each addition. Centrifuge or filter. Pipette into separate tubes 1 ml of supernatant, 1 ml of glucose standard (100 μg), and 1 ml of buffer.

To each tube add, in order, 1 ml buffer, 2 ml combined reagent and 2 ml glucose oxidase solution. Mix and let stand for 20 min. Read the absorbance at 600 nm in a spectrophotometer or use a suitable filter in a colorimeter.

Calculation

$$\text{Blood glucose (mg/100 ml)} = \frac{\text{Test} \times 400}{\text{Standard}}$$

E. Hexokinase methods

The demand for a reliable, specific, automated method for the determination of glucose, free from interferences, has prompted the development of a large number of different methods. Among them have been the hexokinase methods. One of these is the hexokinase glucose-6-phosphate dehydrogenase method.[42, 69–85, 139, 140] The following reactions take place:

$$\text{Glucose + ATP} \xrightleftharpoons{\text{Hexokinase}} \text{Glucose-6-phosphate + ADP}$$

$$\text{Glucose-6-phosphate + NADP} \xrightleftharpoons{\text{G-6-P·DH}} \text{6-Phosphogluconate + NADPH}$$

where ATP is adenosine-5-triphosphate, ADP is adenosine-5-diphosphate,

NADP is nicotinamide-adenine dinucleotide phosphate, NADPH is reduced nicotinamide-adenine dinucleotide phosphate and G-6-P·DH is glucose-6-phosphate dehydrogenase.

The stoichiometric generation of reduced nicotinamide-adenine dinucleotide phosphate (NADPH) from its oxidized form (NADP) serves as a measure of glucose. Since NADPH is the only fluorescent component of the above reactions and absorbs at much longer wavelength than any of the other components, it can be measured fluorimetrically at $F350/450$[69, 76, 81, 84] or at or near its wavelength maximum at 340 nm, mε 6·2.[42, 75, 77, 80, 82, 85]

The hexokinase method is said to lack specificity[74] and to be highly specific and interference-free.[85, 140]

In one method, light-sensitive phenazinium methosulphate was replaced by lipoamide dehydrogenase (NADH: lipoamide oxidoreductase, EC 1.6.4.3) resulting in a simplified one-reagent system.[82] In the colorimetric automated method it is claimed that lipemia, hemolysis, bilirubin, fructose and mannose do not interfere.[85] With controlled constant volumes, times and temperatures, absolute determinations can be performed over eight months without calibration. Beer's law is followed up to 500 mg/100 ml, and precision is excellent.

The fluorimetric method is about 20 times more sensitive.[84] By precipitation with zinc hydroxide, hemoglobin, protein, bilirubin, lipids, uric acid, and a host of other possible interferences are removed, leaving a clear supernatant. The method can be used to determine glucose in 3 µl of serum or plasma.

An alternative method utilizes the reduction of a tetrazolium salt by the NADPH to a coloured formazan cation, Fig 40. The method involves incubation of the sample at 37° for 10 min with a reagent containing hexokinase, glucose-6-phosphate dehydrogenase, ATP, NADP, a magnesium salt, 2-p-iodophenyl-3-p-nitrophenyl-5-phenyl-tetrazolium chloride, N-methylphenazinium methosulphate, EDTA and tris buffer solution of pH 7·8.[83] The reaction is then stopped by adding 0·1 N HCl and the colour measured at 520 nm.

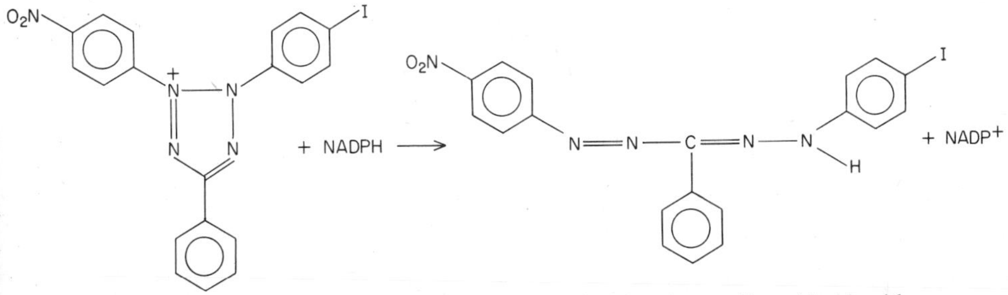

FIG. 40. Reduction of 2-p-iodophenyl-3-p-nitrophenyl-5-phenyltetrazolium chloride with NADPH.

F. Glucokinase

To bypass the alleged interferences in the glucose oxidase and hexokinase methods a highly stereospecific D-glucokinase (purified from *Aerobacter aerogenes*)[141] has been substituted for the hexokinase in that method.[74] The same reactions take place as shown in the hexokinase equations except that D-glucokinase (ATP: D-glucose 6-phosphotransferase, 2.7.1.2) is substituted for hexokinase (ATP: D-hexose 6-phosphotransferase, 2.7.1.1).

D-*Glucokinase determination of glucose*[74]

Add the following components to a final volume of 0·15 ml: 8 μmoles of glycylglycine buffer (pH 7·5), 0·2 μmole of NADP, 0·5 μmol of ATP, 1 μmole of $MgCl_2$, D-glucose, and excess D-glucokinase and glucose-6-phosphate dehydrogenase. Initiate reaction by addition of the D-glucokinase.

With 0·1 unit of each of the enzymes, the reaction was normally complete in 15 min (1 unit = 1 μmol of substrate reacted per min). The difference in the initial and final absorbance at 340 nm times 0·0242 gives the amount (μmol) of D-glucose in the cuvette.

G. Glucose oxidase plus catalase

1. *Chromotropic acid*

Because of the difficulties of reproducibility in the glucose oxidase peroxidase methods, some glucose oxidase–catalase methods have been developed.[86,87] The chromotropic acid method is stated to have increased specificity, greater precision, reliability and suitability for routine use than the various copper and ferricyanide reduction methods.[87] Fluoride poses no problem. By use of volumes one-fifth of those described for the microadaptation, ultra-micro analysis may be performed on 4 μl of blood, with a final volume for spectrophotometry of 1·1 ml. Advantage is taken of the contamination of glucose oxidase with catalase.

Glucose oxidase-catalase-chromotropic acid determination of glucose[87]

Reagents. (1) Glucose-stock, 0·3% glucose in 0·25% (w/v) benzoic acid, stable for several months in refrigerator; working standard, dilute stock 1:100 with 0·25% benzoic acid, 30 μg per ml. Prepare every 2 weeks. (2) Citrate-phosphate buffer (pH 5·6 ± 0·2). Dilute 290 ml of 0·2 M Na_2HPO_4 (28·396 g/l) with 0·1 M citric acid (21·014 g $C_6H_8O_7.H_2O$ per l) to 500 ml. (3) Glucose oxidase reagent. Approximately 25 mg of pure glucose oxidase dissolved in 100 ml of citrate-phosphate buffer. Optimal concentration should be determined. (4) Chromotropic acid reagent. Dissolve 0·5 g of disodium salt in few millilitres of water. Add 175 ml conc sulphuric acid cautiously with cooling and dilute to 250 ml with distilled water; this solution is stable for several weeks in the refrigerator.

Procedure. To 0·1 ml of whole blood, serum or plasma in a centrifuge tube add 2 ml of 0·3% $Ba(OH)_2$ followed by 1·9 ml of 0·5% $ZnSO_4.7H_2O$. Mix and centrifuge.

Transfer 0·5 ml of protein-free filtrate, glucose working standard, and distilled water into three separate large pyrex tubes (18 by 150 mm labelled "unknown", "standard" and "blank". To each unstoppered tube, add 0·5 ml reagent grade methanol and 0·5 ml glucose oxidase reagent, and incubate at 37° for 60 min or at 47° for 40 minutes.

Add 4 ml chromotropic acid reagent, cap the tubes with large marbles, and heat in a boiling water bath for 6 minutes. Cool to room temp and read the absorbance at 575 nm.

Calculation

$$\text{Glucose (mg/100 ml blood)} = \frac{A \text{ unknown} \times 120}{A \text{ standard}}$$

2. *MBTH.*

A simpler and more sensitive method for glucose utilizing the glucose oxidase-catalase enzyme system has been described.[86] MBTH was treated with the formaldehyde generated by the action of catalase on methanol at the optimal pH of 5·6.

Glucose oxidase–catalase–MBTH determination of glucose[86]

Reagents. (1) Enzyme: 0·4% of glucose oxidase in 20% methanol. (2) Phosphate buffer, pH 5·6. (3) 0·5% aq MBTH.HCl. (4) 0·83% of $FeCl_3.6H_2O$ in 10% aq $KHSO_4$.

Procedure. To 1 ml of test solution containing 1–20 μg glucose add 1 ml of enzyme reagent and 2 ml of phosphate buffer. Incubate at 37–38° for 90 minutes. Add 1 ml of 0·5% MBTH reagent and allow the mixture to stand for 60 minutes. Add 1 ml of ferric chloride reagent. After 60 min read at 620 nm.

Beer's law is obeyed from 1 μg–20 μg per ml of test solution. Approx 100% recovery of added glucose was obtained.

The glucose oxidase–catalase reactions are shown in Fig. 41. As depicted, colorimetric methods could also be developed with 2-hydrazinobenzothiazole, 2,4-pentanedione, 1,3-cyclohexanedione, dimedone, ethyl acetoacetate and acetoacetaldehyde dimethylacetal. Fluorimetric methods could be developed with J-acid, 2,4-pentanedione, 1,3-cyclohexanedione, and 2-nitro-1,3-indandione. Other reagents which could be used are discussed in Chapter 23.

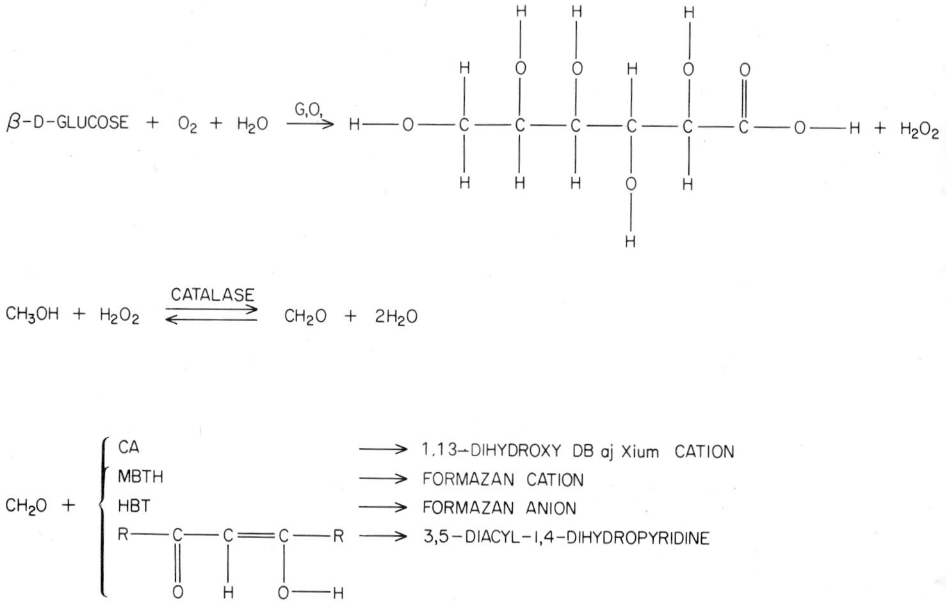

Fig. 41. Glucose oxidase catalase determination of glucose through indirectly formed formaldehyde.

H. Glycogen and other glucose polymers

Di-, oligo- and polysaccharides containing glucose units and glucosides can be analysed following chemical or enzymatic hydrolysis by the methods described in this section. The following substances have been hydrolysed to glucose and in some cases the glucose is then determined enzymatically, e.g. sucrose,[22,41,142] glycoproteins,[78] glycogen,[25,143–155] starch,[156,157] cellulose,[158] cellobiose,[25,159] lactose,[25,160,161] maltose,[25] and salicin.[25] Intestinal disaccharidases readily hydrolyse disaccharides.[162]

One of the procedures for the analysis of glycogen is of some interest since it involves the analysis of glucose by a procedure not yet discussed here. The glycogen is hydrolysed to D-glucose with hot dilute sulphuric acid.[151] The following reactions then take place.[143]

$$\text{D-Glucose} + \text{ATP} \xrightarrow{\text{Hexokinase}} \text{D-Glucose-6-phosphate} + \text{ADP}$$

$$\text{ADP} + \text{Phosphoenol pyruvate} \xrightarrow{\substack{\text{Pyruvic} \\ \text{kinase}}} \text{ATP} + \text{Pyruvate}$$

$$\text{Pyruvate} + \text{NADPH} + \text{H}^+ \underset{}{\overset{\text{Lactic dehydrogenase}}{\rightleftharpoons}} \text{Lactate} + \text{NADP}^+$$

The concentration of the glucose is then determined by the loss in absorbance at 340 nm.

The usual type of enzymatic method for glycogen can also have a high degree of selectivity and can be applied to crude homogenates. For example, in the estimation of glycogen in very small tissue samples, an o-dianisidine method can be used.[144] The glycogen is hydrolysed to glucose by the addition of α-glucosidase and pancreatic α-amylase in acetate buffer solution of pH 4·8 and incubation for 1 h at 30°. The glucose is then determined by the addition of a reagent containing glucose oxidase, peroxidase, and o-dianisidine hydrochloride in tris-phosphate-glycerol buffer solution of pH 7·0.

The accuracy of the glycogen methods depends upon the complete extraction of glycogen from tissue without destruction, complete recovery of the precipitated glycogen, hydrolysis, and accurate determination of the released glucose. A method has been proposed to measure glycogen content in liver homogenates without extraction and acid hydrolysis of tissue glycogen.[148] Homogenates are treated with amyloglucosidase (EC 3.2.1.33), which degrades glycogen to glucose, which is then determined with glucose oxidase and peroxidase. The glucose oxidase and peroxidase must not be contaminated with hydrolytic enzymes, such as polysaccharidases, maltase, isomaltase and sucrase. The method gave 99% recoveries of standard glycogen. Beer's law was followed from 5–80 µg of glycogen. Only 1 mg of tissue is needed for assay.

Enzymatic determination of glycogen[148]

Hydrolysis of standard glycogen. Preincubate aliquots of a glycogen standard solution containing 5–80 µg of pure rabbit liver glycogen for 10 min at 55° with 0·1 ml of 9·05 M acetate buffer, pH 4·5, 3·5 units of amyloglucosidase and water to make 0·5 ml. The test sample is then ready for assay.

Hydrolysis of liver glycogen. Maintain male Sprague–Dawley rats on a high glucose (58%), low fat (2%) diet *ad libitum.* Divide the rats into two groups, one of which continues to receive food and water and the other only water for 72 h before being killed by decapitation. Freeze a portion of liver *in situ* by the liquid-nitrogen–freeze-clamp technique.[163] Prepare a 10% homogenate of the frozen liver by homogenizing a weighed portion of the frozen liver in ice-cold water using a Potter–Elvehjem homogenizer. Assay a 10 µl aliquot of the homogenate for glycogen by incubation with amyloglucosidase and assay for glucose.

Determination of glucose. Prior to assay, premix the following reagents: 125 units of glucose oxidase, 410 purpurogallin units of peroxidase, 2·5 ml of *o*-dianisidine (2·5 mg per ml), and 100 ml of 0·1 M phosphate buffer, ph 6·0. Add 4 ml of this premix to each sample, and bring volume to 4·5 ml with water. Incubate for 37 min at 37°, and read the absorbance at 500 nm.

III. NON-ENZYMATIC METHODS

Redox methods are briefly discussed in the aldose precursors section. There is such a wide variety and such a large number of modifications of these methods that only a small representative selection will be discussed.

In the following methods the reagents react with the aldehyde derived from glucose to form a highly coloured chromogen.

A. MBTH

It has been shown that aldose precursors can be determined with MBTH. [164, 165] The method has been applied to the determination of glucose in 0·01 ml or 0·1 ml of serum or plasma. [166] A blue formazan cation was formed. Beer's law was followed from 30–600 mg of glucose per 100 ml with a correlation coefficient of 0·999. Repeatability was excellent, and reproducibility over 8 d

Table 38. In vitro effects of reducing substances, drugs, anticoagulants, sugars, and pigments in solutions containing 100 mg of glucose per millilitre[166].

Added substance	Amount present (mg/100 ml)	Apparent glucose concn. by MBTH method (mg/100 ml)
Ascorbic Acid	5	104
Creatinine	15	102
Uric Acid	10	100
L-Dopa	10	100
Tetracycline	10	108
Dextran-75	1020	104
Sodium Fluoride	200	100
Potassium Oxalate	200	100
EDTA, Disodium Salt	200	100
Galactose	100	198
Mannose	100	201
Bilirubin	20	100
Haemoglobin	200	100

was good. The MBTH method was compared with three methods widely used for glucose, an automated hexokinase,[80] an indirect *o*-toluidine,[167] and an Auto Analyzer II neocuproine method #AA II–02, Nov. 1970 (Technicon Instruments Corp., Tarrytown, N.Y. 10591). Excellent correlation was obtained with these methods.

Interferences were investigated, Table 38.[166] Only reducing sugars exhibited marked interference, but significant amounts of these sugars are rarely present.

MBTH determination of serum or plasma glucose[166]

Reagents. MBTH-0·1% in 0·01 N HCl; this is stable in a refrigerator for 1 month. Base reagent: 12 ml of 1 N NaOH diluted to 100 ml. TCA reagent: 3% trichloroacetic acid. Oxidizing reagent: 0·4% $FeCl_3 \cdot 6H_2O$ in water containing 28 ml of 1 N HCl. Glucose standards: prepare in 50 mg/100 ml increments in 0·25% benzoic acid solution.

Procedure. Add 0·01 ml of test sample to 0·1 ml of TCA reagent, or alternatively 0·1 ml of sample to 1 ml of TCA reagent. Mix, let stand for 3 min, and then centrifuge for 3 min at 2400 rev min^{-1}. Add 0·05 ml of supernatant to 3 ml of MBTH reagent. Add 1 ml of base reagent to each tube, mix, place a marble on the top of each tube, incubate for 12 min at 97°, and then place in cool water for 5 minutes. In timed 20 s intervals, starting with the blank, add 1 ml of oxidizing reagent to each tube, mix thoroughly on vortex, and let stand at

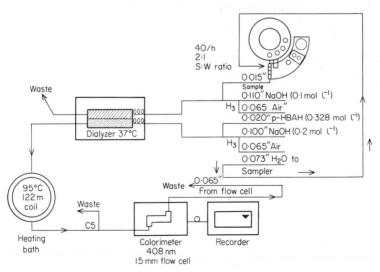

FIG. 42. Flow diagram for *p*-hydroxybenzoylhydrazide procedure for glucose.[168]

room temp for 20 minutes. Read the absorbances in consecutive order at 20 s intervals at 625 nm.

As compared to the o-toluidine method with an mε of 3 to 5, MBTH gave an mε of 57 at 625 nm. The fasting normal range in 28 serum specimens for the MBTH method averaged 72–106 mg/100 ml.

B. p-Hydroxybenzoyl Hydrazide

An automated method for serum glucose has been developed, based on the reaction between glucose and p-hydroxybenzoyl hydrazide in alkaline solution.[168] The use of this reagent in the determination of aldose precursors,[169, 170] has been described. The method is believed to be unaffected by non-glucose reducing substances in body fluids and is more specific than either the ferricyanide or the copper–neocuproine methods for glucose. Beer's law is followed from 0.2–$2 \, g \, l^{-1}$ of glucose. The flow diagram for the procedure is given in Fig. 42.[168]

C. o-Toluidine

The mechanism for this reaction has not been completely elucidated. With this reagent aldohexoses give bands at 620, 480 and 380 nm, ketoses give a band in the ultraviolet, and pentoses a band at 480 nm.

Before discussion of the mechanism of the reaction of glucose with o-toluidine, it should be mentioned that there are a large number of manual[171–184] and automated[183–185] methods for the determination of glucose with o-toluidine; only a selection of these will be discussed here.

Spectrophotometric and thin layer chromatographic evidence indicates a complex series of reactions with the Schiff base of aldoglucose and o-toluidine as an intermediate and with at least 4 chromogens as the final products.[171] Citric acid was found to be the most effective acidic catalyst, thiourea and borate the best non-acidic catalysts.

Because of the simplicity of the o-toluidine method many attempts have been made to improve it. The modifications have consisted mainly of the replacement of corrosive glacial acetic acid with another solvent or the use of additives and stabilizers which produce an increase in the colour development or a better sensitivity in determining minimal amounts of glucose. Some of the mixtures used with o-toluidine include thiourea and glycolic acid,[179] thiourea, glycolic acid, hexamethylphosphoric triamide and benzyl alcohol,[178] thiourea, glycolic acid and propylene glycol,[172] benzyl alcohol, acetic acid, thiocarbamide and sodium tetraborate,[181] aq acetic acid, thiourea, boric acid and Cremophor EL (Badische Anilin und Soda Fabrik, Ludwigshafen am Rein, West Germany; a derivative of castor oil and ethylene oxide),[182] etc. Two examples are given below.

In one method the reagent is stable for at least one year in the refrigerator.[172] The calibration curve is linear up to 500 mg per 100 ml. The method gave close agreement over a wide range of glucose concentrations with a hexokinase plus glucose-6-phosphate dehydrogenase procedure. Dextran gave no interference.

Determination of serum glucose with o-toluidine in propylene glycol[172]

Reagent. Disolve 0·25 g thiourea and 5 g glycolic acid in 10 ml water. Cool, and add 5 ml o-toluidine followed by 70 ml of propylene glycol with mixing. Keep at 4° in a brown bottle.

Procedure. Add 0·2 ml serum to 3 ml of reagent, mix, heat at 100° for 10 min, cool, and read the absorbance at 640 nm.

In the benzyl alcohol procedures the wavelength maximum is at 655 nm; in the aq acetic acid methods it is at 630 nm.

In the second procedure the colour is stable for longer than 24 hours.[182] Haemolysis, high bilirubin content, or turbidity do not affect the reaction adversely. Recoveries of $101 \pm 2 \cdot 1 \%$ were obtained. The colourless reagent is stable for one year when stored at 4° in brown bottles. Beer's law is followed up to 500 mg/100 ml.

Determination of plasma glucose with o-toluidine in dilute acetic acid[182]

Reagent. Dilute 50 ml of glacial acetic acid, 35 ml water, 15 ml o-toluidine and 0·25 g of thiourea to 100 ml with water. Add 5 ml of 10% Cremophor EL to 100 ml of the reagent.

Procedure. To 25 μl of plasma add 3·5 ml of reagent. Mix, heat at 100° for 15 min, cool for 5 min under the tap, and read the absorbance at 630 nm.

o-Toluidine can also be used to determine the glucose liberated from trehalose and sucrose by trehalase and sucrase and can also be used to determine trehalase and sucrase by an automated procedure.[186]

o-Anisidine could also be used to determine glucose.[187] A band is obtained near 600 nm. Pentoses give a band at 465 nm.

REFERENCES

1. R. J. Henry. "Clinical Chemistry. Principles and Techniques", Harper and Row, New York, 1964, pp. 625–659.

2. A. St. G. Huggett and D. A. Nixon. *Lancet* **2**, 368 (1957).
3. J. E. Middleton and W. J. Griffiths. *Brit. Med. J.* **2**, 1525 (1957).
4. G. Discombe, *J. Clin. Pathol.,* **16**, 170 (1963).
5. J. B. Hill and G. Kessler. *J. Lab. Clin. Med.* **57**, 970 (1961).
6. J. P. Comer. *Anal. Chem.* **28**, 1748 (1956).
7. H. U. Bergmeyer and E. Bernt in "Methods of Enzymatic Analysis", H. U. Bergmeyer, Ed., Academic Press, New York, 1963, p. 123.
8. E. F. Beach and J. J. Turner. *Clin. Chem.* **4**, 462 (1958).
9. V. Marks. *Clin. Chim. Acta* **4**, 395 (1959).
10. L. L. Salomon and J. E. Johnson. *Anal. Chem.* **31**, 453 (1959).
11. G. R. Kingsley and G. Getchell. *Clin. Chem.* **6**, 467 (1960).
12. C. Wincey and V. Marks. *J. Clin. Pathol.* **14**, 558 (1961).
13. G. Getchell, F. R. Kingsley and R. R. Schaffert. *Clin. Chem.* **10**, 540 (1964).
14. J. E. Logan and D. E. Haight. *Clin. Chem.* **11**, 367 (1965).
15. R. L. Whistler, L. Hough and J. W. Hylin. *Anal. Chem.* **25**, 1215 (1953).
16. H. H. Schlubach and K. Repenning. *Angew. Chem.* **71**, 193 (1959).
17. M. Damodaran and K. Singh. *J. Sci. Ind. Res. (India)* **13B**, 419 (1954)
18. R. Bentley and A. Neuberger. *Biochem. J.* **45**, 584 (1949).
19. A. St. G. Hugget and D. A. Nixon. *Biochem. J.* **66**, 12P (1957).
20. L. A. Dobrick. *J. Biol. Chem.* **231**, 403 (1958).
21. C. R. Baillod and W. C. Boyl. *Env. Sci. Technol.* **3**, 1205 (1969).
22. J. P. Comer and H. F. Brickley. *Anal. Chem.* **31**, 109 (1959).
23. A. Saifer and S. Gerstenfeld. *J. Lab. Clin. Med.* **51**, 448 (1958).
24. R. B. McComb and W. D. Yushok. *J. Franklin Inst.* **265**, 417 (1958).
25. G. G. Guilbault, M. H. Sadar and K. Peres. *Anal. Biochem.* **31**, 91 (1969).
26. E. J. Wenzel. *Am. J. Med. Technol.* **28**, 117 (1962).
27. M. E. Washko and E. W. Rice. *Clin. Chem.* **7**, 542 (1961).
28. M. E. Washko. *Federation Proc.* **19**, 81 (1960).
29. A. Sola and G. De La Fuente. *Rev. Espan. Fisiol.* **13**, 231 (1957).
30. A. Saifer, S. Gerstenfeld and M. C. Zymaris. *Clin. Chem.* **4**, 127 (1958).
31. E. Raabo and T. C. Terkildsen. *Scand. J. Clin. Lab. Invest.* **12**, 402 (1960).
32. L. K. Jakobsen. *Scand. J. Clin. Lab. Invest.* **12**, 76 (1960).
33. G. Guidotti, J. P. Colombo and P. O. Foa, *Anal. Chem.* **33**, 151 (1960).
34. B. M. Feinsmith. *Clin. Chim. Acta* **7**, 58 (1962).
35. J. Putter and R. Strufe. *Clin. Chim. Acta* **15**, 159 (1967).
36. K. Lorentz and C. Leudemann. *Deut. Med. J.* **18**, 420 (1967).
37. V. Hinterberger. *Arzneimettel. Forsch.* **7**, 1242 (1966).
38. L. G. Levee. *J. Am. Med. Technol.* **31**, 44 (1969).
39. G. Asrow. *Anal. Biochem.* **28**, 130 (1969).
40. J. B. Lloyd and W. J. Whelan. *Anal. Biochem.* **20**, 467 (1969).
41. G. Johnson, C. Lambert, D. K. Johnson and S. G. Sunderwirth. *J. Agric. Food Chem.* **12**, 216 (1964).
42. V. H. Müller. *Starke* **19**, 55 (1967).
43. E. Kawerau. *Z. Klin. Chem.* **4**, 224 (1966).
44. D. E. Faulkner. *Analyst* **90**, 736 (1965).
45. J. E. Middleton. *Clin. Chim. Acta* **22**, 433 (1968).
46. G. G. Guilbault, P. J. Brignac, Jr. and M. Juneau. *Anal. Chem.* **40**, 1256 (1968).
47. R. E. Phillips and F. R. Elevitch. *Am. J. Clin. Pathol.* **49**, 622 (1968).
48. G. G. Guilbault, P. Brignac, Jr., and M. Zimmer. *Anal. Chem.* **40**, 190 (1968).
49. S. J. Miskiewicz, B. B. Arnett and G. E. Simon. *Clin. Chem.* **19**, 253 (1973).

50. J. Schreiber and R. Lachenicht. *Z. Klin Chem. Klin. Biochem.* **11**, 31 (1973).
51. K. H. Deuser and F. C. Sitzmann. *Medsche Klin.* **67**, 1406 (1972).
52. N. Gochman and J. M. Schmitz. *Clin. Chem.* **18**, 943 (1972).
53. P. Sharp. *Clin. Chim. Acta* **40**, 115 (1972).
54. S. Meites and K. Saniel-Banrey. *Clin. Chem.* **19**, 308 (1973).
55. R. Brandt, K. E. Guyer and W. L. Banks, Jr. *Clin. Chim. Acta* **51**, 103 (1974).
56. L. G. Morin and J. Prox. *Clin. Chem.* **19**, 959 (1973).
57. A. T. Romano. *Clin. Chem.* **19**, 1152 (1973).
58. D. Pankow, B. Pankow and W. Ponsold. *Z. Pharm. Pharmakother. Lab-Diagn.* **111**, 165 (1972).
59. M. Hjelm and C. H. De Verdier. *Scand. J. Clin. Lab. Invest.* **15**, 415 (1963).
60. B. Fingerhut. *Am. J. Clin. Pathol.* **51**, 157 (1969).
61. S. Meites and K. Saniel-Banrey. *Clin. Chem.* **19**, 308 (1973).
62. F. E. Sobotka and D. A. Stelzig. *Anal. Biochem.* **54**, 612 (1973).
63. G. A. Cheyne and E. A. Gilmore. *Med. Lab. Technol.* **30**, 191 (1973).
64. S. E. Aw. *Clin. Chim. Acta* **26**, 235 (1969).
65. R. H. Thompson. *Clin. Chim. Acta* **13**, 133 (1966).
66. H. V. Malmstadt and S. I. Hadjiioannou. *Anal. Chem.* **34**, 452 (1962).
67. A. G. Ware and E. P. Marbach. *Clin. Chem.* **11**, 792 (1965).
68. A. Härtel, K. F. Schulte, H. Lang and W. Rick. *Z. Klin Chem.* **6**, 34 (1968).
69. M. W. Slein in "Methods of Enzymatic Analysis", H. U. Bergmeyer, Ed., Academic Press, New York, 1963, p. 117.
70. W. Barthelmai and R. Czok. *Klin. Wochschr.* **40**, 585 (1962).
71. F. H. Schmidt. *Klin. Wochschr.* **39**, 1244 (1961).
72. M. Mager and G. Farese. *Tech. Bull. Reg. Med. Tech.* **35**, 104 (1965).
73. D. M. Keller. *Clin. Chem.* **11**, 471 (1965).
74. M. Y. Kamel, R. R. Hart and R. L. Anderson. *Anal. Biochem.* **18**, 270 (1967).
75. J. I. Peterson and D. S. Young. *Anal. Biochem.* **23**, 301 (1968).
76. R. Zwiebel, B. Hohmann, P. Prohnert and K. Baumann. *Arch. Ges Physiol.* **307**, 127 (1969).
77. J. Tschersich and W. Mauch. *Z. Zuckerind.* **93**, 107 (1968).
78. P. R. Finch, R. Yuen, H. Schachter and M. A. Moscarello. *Anal. Biochem.* **31**, 296 (1969).
79. V. Harding and G. Heinzel. *Z. Klin. Biochem.* **7**, 640 (1969).
80. W. E. Neeley. *Clin. Chem.* **18**, 509 (1972).
81. F. da Fonseca-Wolheim. *Z. Klin. Chem. Klin. Biochem.* **11**, 24 (1973).
82. H. J. Coburn and J. J. Carroll. *Clin. Chem.* **19**, 127 (1970).
83. Warner-Lambert Co. British Patent 1, 322, 951; date appl. 19.10.70. USA. date appl. 29.10.69.
84. A. J. Tomisek and S. Natelson. *Microchem. J.* **19**, 54 (1974).
85. R. Richterich, H. Kuffer, E. Lorenz and J. P. Colombo. *Z. Klin. Chem. Klin. Biochem.* **12**, 5 (1974).
86. A. Tsuji, T. Kinoshita and A. Sakai. *Chem. Pharm. Bull.* **17**, 1304 (1969).
87. F. W. Sunderman, Jr. and F. W. Sunderman. *Am. J. Clin. Path.* **36**, 75 (1961).
88. S. Ikawa and T. Obara. *Japan J. Clin. Path.* **13**, 197 (1965).
89. H. U. Bergmeyer and H. Moellering. *Clin. Chim. Acta* **14**, 74 (1966).
90. R. L. Anderson and M. Y. Kamel. *Methods in Enzymology* **9**, 392 (1966).
91. C. F. Boehringer and G. Soehne. *Neth. Patent Appl.* **6**, 611, 550 (Feb. 1967).
92. D. T. Forman, S. H. Grayson and A. Slonicki. *Lab. Med.* 26 (July, 1972).

93. G. G. Guilbault. "Practical Fluorescence", Marcel Dekker, Inc., New York, 1973, Ch. 14.
94. W. Franke and M. Deffner. *Ann.* **541**, 117 (1939).
95. D. Keilin and E. F. Hartree. *Biochem. J.* **39**, 293 (1945).
96. D. Keilin and E. F. Hartree. *Biochem. J.* **42**, 221, 230 (1948).
97. D. Keilin and E. F. Hartree. *Biochem. J.* **50**, 331, 341 (1952).
98. A. S. Keston. *J. Biol. Chem.* 239, 3241 (1964).
99. R. Bentley and D. S. Bhate. *J. Biol. Chem.* **235**, 1219, 1225 (1960).
100. E. R. Froesch and A. E. Renold. *Diabetes* **5**, 1 (1956).
101. E. Forti. *Diagnosi, Napoli* **21**, 105 (1970).
102. T. Sakaguchi, T. Takahashi, H. Noguchi, K. Takeuchi and Y. Tanabe. *Japan Analyst* **19**, 386 (1970).
103. P. Trinder. *Ann. Clin. Biochem.* **6**, 24 (1969).
104. D. Barham and P. Trinder. *Analyst* **97**, 142 (1972).
105. W. Werner, H. G. Rey and H. Wielinger. *Z. Anal. Chem.* **252**, 224 (1970).
106. R. B. McComb, W. D. Yushok and D. B. Batt. *J. Franklin Inst.* **263**, 161 (1957).
107. M. Dixon and E. C. Webb. "Enzymes", Longmans, Green and Co. Ltd., 1964, p. 210.
108. A. Sols and G. de la Fuente. *Biochem. Biophys. Acta* **24**, 206 (1957).
109. M. Kunitz and M. R. McDonald. *J. Gen. Physiol.* **29**, 393 (1946).
110. S. P. Colowick and N. O. Kaplan. "Methods in Enzymology", Vol. I., Academic Press, New York, 1955, p. 269.
111. T. T. Hlaing, J. P. Hummel and R. Montgomery. *Arch. Biochem. Biophys.* **93**, 321 (1961).
112. R. Richterich. "Clinical Chemistry", Academic Press, New York, 1969, p. 227.
113. K. Lorentz and W. Berndt. *Anal. Biochem.* 18, 58 (1967).
114. M. Blecher and A. B. Glassman. *Anal. Biochem.* **3**, 343 (1962).
115. E. Sawicki, T. W. Stanley, J. Pfaff and H. Johnson. *Anal. Chem.* **35**, 2183 (1963).
116. A. Dahlqvist. *Biochem. J.* **80**, 547 (1961).
117. R. J. Henry. "Clinical Chemistry", Harper and Row, New York, 1964, p. 645.
118. R. Richterich. "Clinical Chemistry", Academic Press, New York, 1969, p. 226.
119. W. Werner, H. G. Rey and H. Wielinger. *Z. Anal. Chem.* **252**, 222 (1970).
120. K. Gawehn, H. Wielinger and W. Werner. *Z. Anal. Chem.* **252**, 224 (1970).
121. K. Kahle, L. Weiss and O. Wieland. *Z. Anal. Chem.* **252**, 228 (1970).
122. M. E. Brown. *Diabetes* **10**, 60 (1961).
123. D. Biltner and M. McClearly. *Am. J. Clin. Pathol.* **11**, 423 (1963).
124. L. P. Cawley, F. E. Spear and R. Kendall. *Am. J. Clin Pathol.* **32**, 195 (1959).
125. D. Kutter. *Das. Arztliche Lab.* **7**, 175 (1961).
126. F. W. Fales, J. A. Russell and J. N. Fain. *Clin. Chem.* **7**, 289 (1961).
127. G. R. Kingsley and G. Getchell. *Clin. Chem.* **6**, 466 (1960).
128. D. M. Pharr and D. B. Dickinson. *Anal. Biochem.* **51**, 315 (1973).
129. G. Halliwell. *Biochem. J.* **95**, 270 (1965).
130. H. V. Malmstadt and G. P. Hicks. *Anal. Chem.* **32**, 394 (1960).
131. R. N. Carey, D. Feldbruegge and J. O. Westgard. *Clin. Chem.* **20**, 595 (1974).
132. D. L. Bittner and J. Manning in N. B. Scova *et al*, Eds. Automation in Analytical Chemistry, Technicon Symposia 1966, I, Mediad, White Plains, N.Y., 1967, p. 33.
133. N. C. Sudduth, J. R. Widish and J. L. Moore. *Am. J. Clin. Pathol.* **58**, 181 (1970).

134. E. Sawicki, T. W. Stanley, T. R. Hauser, W. C. Elbert and J. L. Noe. *Anal. Chem.* **33**, 722 (1961).
135. M. Pays, R. Bourdon and M. Beljean. *Anal. Chim. Acta* **47**, 101 (1969).
136. E. Sawicki, T. W. Stanley and W. C. Elbert. *Microchem. J.* **5**, 225 (1961).
137. E. Sawicki, T. R. Hauser and S. McPherson. *Chemist-Analyst* **50**, 68 (1961).
138. E. Sawicki, D. F. Bender, T. R. Hauser, R. M. Wilson and J. Meeker. *Anal. Chem.* **35**, 1479 (1963).
139. M. W. Slein, G. T. Cori and C. F. Cori. *J. Biol. Chem.* **186**, 763 (1950).
140. Boehringer Mannheim Corp. *Enzymes in Medicine* **7**, No. 6, 1 (1974).
141. M. Y. Kamel, D. P. Allison and R. L. Anderson. *J. Biol. Chem.* **241**, 690 (1966).
142. K. Taufel, V. Behnke and H. Wersuhn. *Nahrung* **9**, 287 (1965).
143. G. Pfleiderer and L. Grein. *Biochem. Z.* **328**, 499 (1957).
144. F. Huijing. *Clin. Chim. Acta* **30**, 567 (1970).
145. C. Rerup and I. Lundquist. *Acta Pharmacol. Toxicol.* **25**, 41 (1967).
146. F. Rosa and F. B. Johnson. *J. Histochem. Cytochem.* **15**, 14 (1967).
147. J. V. Passonneau, P. D. Gatfield, D. W. Schultz and O. H. Lowry. *Anal. Biochem.* **19**, 315 (1967).
148. K. L. Roehrig and J. B. Allred. *Anal. Biochem.* **58**, 414 (1974).
149. C. Bernard. *Compt. Rend. Acad. Sci. (Paris)* **44**, 578 (1857).
150. E. Pflüger. *Arch. Gesamte Physiol.* **103**, 169 (1904).
151. C. A. Good, H. Kramer and M. Somogyi. *J. Biol. Chem.* **100**, 485 (1933).
152. S. R. Nahorski and K. J. Rogers. *Anal. Biochem.* **49**, 492 (1972).
153. W. L. Chick and A. A. Like. *Anal. Biochem.* **32**, 340 (1969).
154. J. A. Johnson, J. D. Nash and R. M. Fusaro. *Anal. Biochem.* **5**, 379 (1963).
155. H. A. Krebs, D. A. H. Bennett, P. De Gasquet, T. Gascoyne and T. Yoshida. *Biochem. J.* **86**, 22 (1963).
156. W. J. Whelan in H. U. Bergmeyer, Ed. "Methods of Enzymatic Analysis", Academic Press, 1963, p. 63.
157. N. O. DeSouza and A. Panek. *J. Chromatog.* **15**, 103 (1964).
158. G. Halliwell, in H. U. Bergmeyer, Ed. "Methods of Enzymatic Analysis", Academic Press, 1963, p. 64.
159. D. L. Liu and C. C. Walden. *Anal. Biochem.* **31**, 211 (1969).
160. F. J. Reithel in H. U. Bergmeyer, Ed. "Methods of Enzymatic Analysis", Academic Press, 1963, p. 103.
161. L. Hankin and A. F. Wickroshi. *J. Assoc. Offic. Agr. Chemists* **47**, 695 (1964).
162. A. Dahlqvist. *Anal. Biochem.* **7**, 18 (1964).
163. D. H. Williamson, P. Lund and H. A. Krebs. *Biochem. J.* **103**, 514 (1967).
164. E. Sawicki, R. Schumacher and C. R. Engel. *Microchem. J.* **12**, 377 (1967).
165. J. Bartos. *Ann. Pharm. Franc.* **20**, 650 (1962).
166. W. E. Neeley and C. A. Cupas. *Clin. Biochem.* **6**, 246 (1973).
167. G. R. Cooper and V. McDaniel. *Clin. Chem.* **6**, 159 (1970).
168. B. Fingerhut. *Clin. Chem.* **19**, 1022 (1973).
169. M. Lever. *Anal. Biochem.* **47**, 273 (1972).
170. M. Lever. *Biochem. Med.* **7**, 274 (1973).
171. H. Y. Yee and J. F. Goodwin. *Anal. Chem.* **45**, 2162 (1973).
172. M. Yamashita and F. Watanabe. *Clin. Chim. Acta* **47**, 211 (1973).
173. E. H. Hultman. *Nature* **183**, 108 (1959).
174. K. M. Dubowski. *Clin. Chem.* **8**, 215 (1962).
175. W. R. Moorehead and E. A. Sasse. *Clin. Chem.* **16**, 285 (1970).
176. H. Y. Yee, E. S. Jenest and F. R. Bowles. *Clin. Chem.* **17**, 103 (1971).

177. P. G. Reitnauer. *Z. Med. Labortechnik* **8**, 208 (1967).
178. J. Bierens de Haan and M. Roth. *Z. Klin. Chem. Klin. Biochem.* **7**, 624 (1969).
179. A. Härtel, R. Helger and H. Lang. *Z. Klin. Chem. Klin. Biochem.* **7**, 14 (1969).
180. C. F. Fasce, Jr., R. Rej and A. J. Pignataro. *Clin. Chim. Acta* **43**, 105 (1973).
181. N. J. Pasquare and A. M. Sotorres. *Clin. Chim. Acta* **49**, 325 (1973).
182. G. Ceriotti. *Chim. Chem.* **17**, 440 (1971).
183. P. L. M. Winckers and P. Jacobs. *Clin. Chim. Acta* **34**, 401 (1971).
184. W. W. Webster, S. F. Stinson and W. H. Wong. *Clin. Chem.* **17**, 1050 (1971).
185. F. Polacco. *Cronache Chim.* 8 (1972).
186. G. Ferard, T. Klumpp and I. Sall. *Clin. Chim. Acta* **50**, 207 (1974).
187. J. F. Goodwin and H. Y. Yee. *Clin. Chem.* **19**, 597 (1973).

10. ALDOHEXOSAMINES, PRECURSORS

I. INTRODUCTION

Just as simple sugars form aldoses or open-chain aldehydes on hydrolysis, the hexosamines can form chain aldehydes. These amines can be acylated, ring-opened, and then determined with MBTH. Alternatively a Schiff base can be formed, the compound can be ring-opened, ionized and analysed as the anion. This has been done with p-nitrobenzaldehyde as the reagent as shown in Fig. 43.[1] The chromogen absorbs at 504 nm in alkaline alcohol and is blue in alkaline pyridine. This red shift with increasing solvent basicity is a property of anionic resonance structures.[2, 3] Many hexosamines and hexosamine derivatives gave positive results. The procedure for the determination of an hexosamine is fairly simple.

A. Determination of hexosamines with p-nitrobenzaldehyde [1]

To 1 ml of aq test solution add 0·5 ml of 1 % p-nitrobenzaldehyde in pyridine.

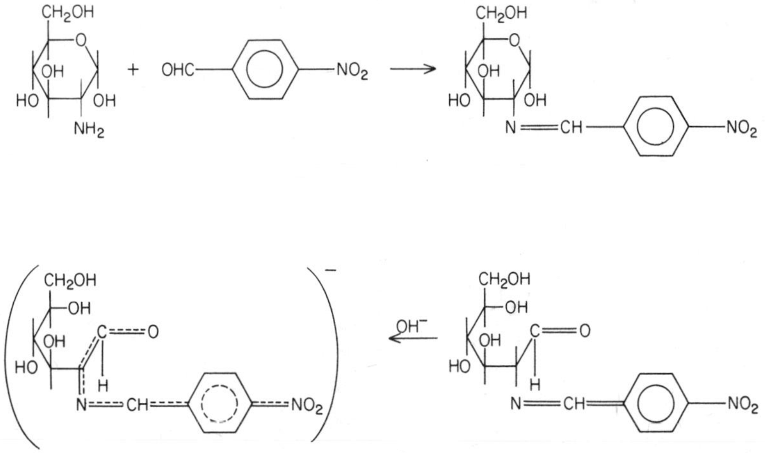

FIG. 43. Determination of an aldohexosamine with p-nitrobenzaldehyde.

179

Mix and warm the mixture for 20 min at 27–28°. Cool for 5 min and then dilute to 10 ml with the alkaline reagent (dilute 3 ml of 10% aq tetraethyl-ammonium hydroxide to 100 ml with alcohol). Read at 504 nm.

The o-toluidine method has been applied to the determination of heparin and glucosamine.[4] Heparin is a polysaccharide composed of glucosamine N-sulphate and the sulphate esters of glucuronic acid. In the analysis the heparin is subjected to acid hydrolysis by heating at 100° with Dowex 50W–X4 resin (H^+ form) in HCl at pH 0·8 or pH 0·3 for 6 or 4h respectively. The colour is then developed by heating the hydrolysate at 100° for 10 min with 8% o-toluidine in acetic acid. After cooling, the absorbance is read at 630 nm. Beer's law is followed from 0·2–1·8 mg of heparin per ml.

D-Glucosamine is determined by direct colorimetry at 630 nm after reaction with o-toluidine. Beer's law is followed from 60–375 µg of D-glucosamine hydrochloride per ml.

REFERENCES

1. A. Nakamura, M. Maeda, K. Ikeguchi, T. Kinoshita and A. Tsuji. *Chem. Pharm. Bull.* **16**, 184 (1968).
2. E. Sawicki, T. W. Winfield and C. R. Sawicki. *Microchem. J.* **15**, 294 (1970).
3. E. Sawicki. "Photometric Organic Analysis", Wiley-Interscience, New York, 1970, p. 590.
4. A. Rahman, A. M. Sotorres and N. J. Pasquare. *An. Assoc. Quim. Argent.* **60**, 111 (1972).

11. ALDOHEXOSES, PRECURSORS

I. o-TOLUIDINE

A. Introduction

Some of the o-toluidine procedures which have been used for the determination of glucose and other aldohexose precursors are listed in Table 39. Strangely enough while p-bromoaniline is highly selective for the determination of aldopentose precursors, e.g. D-xylose,[53–56] o-toluidine (as well as o-anisidine and probably o-bromoaniline) is highly selective for aldohexose precursors. Aldopentose precursors react with o-toluidine but give a chromogen absorbing at much shorter wavelengths. This latter reaction will be discussed in the 2-hydroxyglutaconaldehyde precursors section.

One method of obtaining aldohexoses is through treatment of the pyranose and/or furanose forms of aldo- and ketohexoses with alkali. In this way the aldehyde forms of mannose and glucose are obtained. These aldehydes can then be determined by the appropriate reagents described in the aliphatic aldehyde section.

Many more reactions of aldohexose precursors will be discussed in the aldose precursors section.

This section is concerned mainly with the o-toluidine reaction. With aldohexose precursors, such as glucose, galactose and fructose, maxima (with decreasing intensity) are obtained at 365, 632 and 489 nm; with aldopentose precursors, bands are obtained near 365 and 490 nm, the relative intensity of these being dependent on the composition of the reagent and the experimental conditions, Fig. 44.

B. Acetic acid methods

Since the o-toluidine reagent has glacial acetic acid as a solvent, attempts have been made to substitute a less corrosive solvent. Other drawbacks reported have included poor stability of the final colour, the variability of results with different batches of reagents, the limited life of the chromogenic reagent, irritant vapours, and corrosive effect on pump tubing in the automated method. The use of o-toluidine does not appear to be a hazard in terms of acute toxicity.[23, 24]

Table 39. Determination of aldohexoses with o-toluidine

Mixture[a]	Remarks	Ref.
Body fluids	Method introduced. 2,6- and 2,5-xylidine give similar spectra	1
Physiol. fluids	Modification of original method	2–10
Physiol. fluids	Borates favourably influence colour stability and sensitivity	5, 6, 11, 12
Physiol. fluids	Automated procedure	13, 14
Blood	Automated, Citric and acetic acid used	15
Blood	Less concentrated (1:1) acetic acid used	16
Blood	Citric, glycolic, lactic or malic acid can be substituted for acetic acid	17
Serum	Without protein precipitation	9, 18, 19
Blood	Thiourea to stabilize reagent. Xylose also determined	2, 20
Blood or plasma	In absence of galactose specific for glucose in blood or plasma	21
Blood	Glycolic acid and methyl cellosolve substituted for acetic acid	22
Blood	o-Toluidine not hazardous	23, 24
Plasma	Automated. Replace acetic acid by glycolic acid, hexamethylphosphoric triamide and benzyl alcohol	25
Plasma	Automated. Protein precipitation not necessary	26
Plasma or serum	Automated. Without protein precipitation. Thiourea added to improve sensitivity	18[b], 27, 28
Serum	Automated micro method	29–31
Serum	Citric and boric acid and thiourea added to increase sensitivity	32
Blood	Automated and manual direct method	33
Serum	o-Ethylaniline can also be used	34
Serum and plasma	Effect of lipemia	35
Blood	Reagent is o-toluidine in anhydrous acetic acid	36, 37
Biological fluids	Reagent contains o-toluidine and thiourea in anhydrous acetic acid	38–45
Blood[c]	Preliminary enzymic treatment to destroy glucose	46, 47
Milk	Lactose hydrolysed to glucose and galactose and assayed	48, 49
Urine	Lactose hydrolysed with galactosidase	50
	Maltose and glucose can be assayed	51
Tissue	Glycogen hydrolysed with dil H_2SO_4 and assayed	52

[a]Unless otherwise stated in blood, serum or plasma glucose is determined, in milk or urine lactose.
[b]Manual.
[c]Galactose determined.

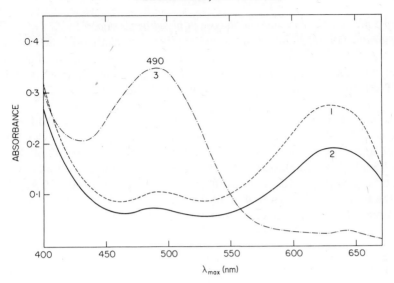

FIG. 44. Visible absorption spectra of (1) 0·2 % glucose solution; (2) 0·1 % galactose solution; (3) 0·1 % xylose solution obtained with *o*-toluidine.[2, 19]

However, it must be admitted that the glacial acetic acid methods do have some advantages, and some of the drawbacks can be obviated. In the following method[18] serum glucose can be determined without protein precipitation or interference by lipemia.[35] Application of this method to whole serum gives results corresponding closely to those of the Nelson–Somogyi method.

Determination of serum glucose without protein precipitation[18]
Reagents: Dissolve 1·5 g of thiourea in 940 ml of glacial acetic acid. Add 60 ml of *o*-toluidine, mix well and store in a brown bottle; this solution is stable for 2 months. Standards: Stock standard contains 10 mg of glucose per 1 ml of solution. Working standards are prepared by diluting the stock standard with 0·2 % benzoic acid.

Procedure. To 5 ml of *o*-toluidine reagent add 0·1 ml serum and mix. Stopper with a glass marble, and heat at 100° for exactly 10 minutes. Cool for 3–5 min in tap water. Read the absorbance at 635–640 nm within 15–30 minutes.

Beer's law is followed up to 150 mg/100 ml.

Glucose in body fluids can also be determined following deproteinization.[2, 20, 37, 45, 57–60] Trace amounts of glucose in urine are determined with the *o*-toluidine reagent following treatment with a mixture of Amberlite IR-45 (OH⁻ form) and IR-120 (H⁺ form).[45]

Rapid method for determining glucose in blood or plasma.[21]
Reagents. Dilute 30 ml of saturated thiourea in methanol and 60 ml of
o-toluidine to 1 l with glacial acetic acid. Prepare the solution 24 h before
use; it is stable for at least 2 weeks at room temperature. Glucose standards.
0·05, 0·1 and 0·25 % in saturated benzoic acid solution.

Procedure. Plasma. If grossly haemolysed, treat as whole blood. Add 0·05 ml
of plasma or standard to 4 ml of colour reagent, mix, heat at 100° for 5 min,
cool, and read the absorbance at 640 nm within 30 minutes. Whole blood.
To 1.5 ml of 3 % trichloroacetic acid in a centrifuge tube add 0·1 ml of whole
blood or standard. Mix and centrifuge for 5 min at about 1500 rcf. Add 1 ml
of the supernatant liquid to 4 ml of the reagent, mix, heat at 100° for 5 min,
and read the absorbance at 640 nm within 30 minutes.

C. Aqueous acetic acid

To avoid the drawbacks in the reagent, dilute acetic acid has been substituted as solvent.[5, 9] It was found the ferrous and ferric compounds inhibit
the reaction strongly, while borates favourably influence colour stability,
and an emulsifier obviates the need for deproteinization. In the following
procedure the colour is stable for at least 24 h at room temperature.

Determination of blood glucose with aqueous acetic acid solution of o-tolu-
idine.[5]
Reagent. To 50 ml of acetic acid add 35 ml of saturated aq boric acid, 15 ml
of o-toluidine, 0·25 g of thiourea and 5 ml of a 10 % Cremophor EL (a derivative of castor oil and ethylene oxide obtained from Badische Anilin and Soda
Fabrik, Ludwigshafen am Mein, West Germany). This is stable for 1 year
when stored at 4° in brown bottles.

Procedure. To 25 μl of plasma add 3·5 ml of reagent. Mix, heat at 100° for
15 min, cool for 5 min under running tap water, and read at 630 nm.
   The effect of water in the acetic acid–o-toluidine reagent has been examined.[33] At water concentrations less than 10 % (v/v), marked enhance-
ment of colour due to borate ion was observed; in glacial acetic acid, borate
more than doubles the colour produced. The addition of trichloroacetic acid
inhibits the reaction. At concentrations of water greater than 15 %, significant serum blanks were obtained. The blank is due in part to protein turbidity
and is dependent upon the presence of both glucose and β-lipoprotein. It is
claimed that the reagent utilizing glacial acetic acid yields consistently better
recoveries with good chromogen stability while the reagent with aq acetic
acid cannot be used satisfactorily in the direct manual method.[33] However,

in an automated direct assay the inclusion of borate in the reagent to increase sensitivity is possible, since automation with its highly reproducible timing obviates fade-rate influence.

D. Other acids

o-Toluidine reagents have been developed in which acetic acid has been substituted by a less caustic acid mixture, e.g. glycolic acid and β-methoxy-ethanol,[22] glycolic acid in a mixture of benzyl alcohol and hexamethyl-phosphoric triamine,[25] and β-hydroxytricarballylic acid in ethylene glycol.[33] An example of this type of procedure is the following wherein the new reagent is non-volatile, odourless, colourless, of low viscosity, stable for weeks at room temp, and does not precipitate serum proteins. The absorbance loss after cooling is less than 0·25% per minute. Beer's law is obeyed up to 6 g/l plasma glucose. Haemoglobin or bilirubin do not interfere.

Direct microdetermination of blood glucose with acidic o-toluidine[25]
Reagent. Mix after each addition in the order indicated: thiourea 5 g, distilled water 200 ml, glycolic acid 200 g, hexamethylphosphoric triamide-200 ml, benzyl alcohol 380 ml, and *o*-toluidine 100 ml.

Procedure. To 10 µl plasma add 2 ml reagent, mix, heat at 100° for 10 min, cool in running tap water, and read the absorbance at 650 ± 10 nm.

The reactions of aniline and its alkyl derivatives with pentoses, hexoses, furfural and 5-hydroxymethylfurfural have been studied.[34] Shifting of the methyl group on aniline from the ortho to the meta or para position alters the absorption spectra obtained with the hexoses. In all cases spectra of the furfural reaction products are dissimilar to corresponding ones for hexoses or pentoses with a given aniline derivative. The absorption spectrum of the reaction products of 5-hydroxymethylfurfural with *o*-toluidine is entirely different from that obtained with glucose and *o*-toluidine. In the former case bands are obtained near 340 and 480 nm while in the latter case bands are obtained near 370, 480 and 630 nm. Using the following procedure *o*-ethyl-aniline reacts with hexoses and pentoses to yield products with spectra identical to its methyl analogue (*o*-toluidine), Fig. 45.

o-*Ethylaniline determination of aldohexose precursors*[34]
To 0·1 ml of the test solution add 5 ml of the reagent (Add 5 ml of *o*-toluidine to 95 ml of 0·15% thiourea and 0·35% boric acid in glacial acetic acid). Heat at 100° for 10 min, cool and read absorbance at 630 nm.

To increase the sensitivity of the reagent containing aq acetic acid as solvent various additives have been used. An increase in sensitivity of approx. 1·6-fold has been reported when boric acid is used.[6, 12, 32] Thiourea not only acts as an antioxidant, but causes a sharp absorbance peak to be formed at 385 nm for the condensation product.[32] Citric acid enhances the absorbance of the condensation product at 385 and 630 nm; this is probably through its effect in increasing the dissociation of acetic acid.

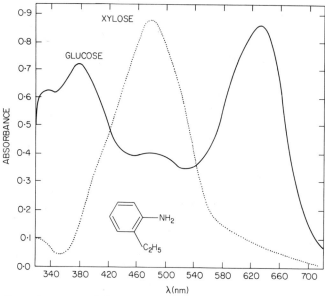

Fig. 45. Absorption spectra of glucose (150 μg) and xylose (100 μg) reaction products with o-ethylaniline.[34]

In the manual method[32] the additives collectively enhance absorption (as compared to the aq acetic acid reagent) approx. 2·8-fold. Analysis at 385 nm is about twice as sensitive as analysis at 630 nm. Beer's law is obeyed from 50–500 mg/100 ml. The manual procedure was developed for use with either 0·2 ml (for reading at 385 nm) or 0·5 ml (630 nm) of a 1:10 protein-free filtrate (10 g trichloroacetic acid per l) with 4 ml of the reagent (300 ml acetic acid, 120 ml o-toluidine, 100 g citric acid, 1·5 g thiourea, and 10 g boric acid per litre of reagent).

E. Automated methods

The manifold diagram for automated analysis using this system of analysis is shown in Fig. 46. The correlation between the results obtained with a manual hexokinase method[61] and the above method was 0·997, and the regression equation was Y (hexokinase) = −0·8 + 1·03X, $S_{y,x}$ = ±6·7,

$n = 30$. Recoveries of 10–500 mg of glucose to 100 ml of serum ranged from 97–130%, averaging 107%.

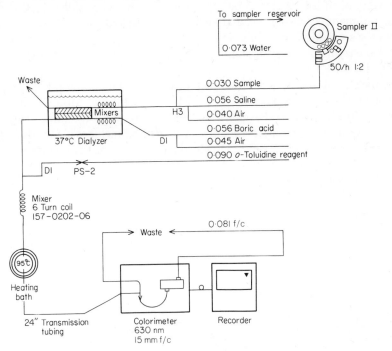

Fig. 46. Manifold diagram for automated analysis.[32]

Other automated methods for glucose have been described.[10, 13–15, 26–33] In some of the methods, deproteinization with perchloric acid[30] or with trichloroacetic acid[10, 31] was found to be useful before assay for capillary blood sugar. Where the reagent solvent was glacial acetic acid, silicone rubber tubing was recommended for the apparatus.[31] When the reagent solvent was dilute acetic acid, Tygon pump tubing could be used.[10]

In the direct automated methods reagents utilizing glacial acetic acid as the solvent with[27, 28] and without thiourea[26] have been described.

In one of the thiourea methods[28] the reagent used contains 6% of o-toluidine in anhydrous acetic acid, with 0·15% of thiourea as stabiliser. With use of an Auto Analyser system, the sample of blood or serum is diluted with approximately 23 times its volume of reagent and the mixture is heated at 95° for 9 min, then cooled. The extinction is then measured at 620 nm. Up to 50 samples per h can be analysed. Because of the high dilution factor, protein does not interfere; dialysis is therefore unnecessary, and blank tests are not normally required. The method is applicable over the range 0–250 mg of glucose per 100 ml, with a standard deviation of ± 1.2 mg per 100 ml. Recovery of added glucose (50–100 mg per 100 ml) averaged 96·6%. Galactose and mannose also react, and lactose reacts less strongly. For 42 specimens the o-toluidine method gave an average result 3% lower than that of a specific enzymic method; in contrast the average result by the ferricyanide method was 7% higher.

In the automated aq acetic acid methods standard manifold tubing made of polyvinyl chloride can be used.[10, 29] In the method of Moorehead and Sasse[29] the reagent is 1·3 times as sensitive as the o-toluidine reagent commonly used in manual procedures. The method includes a dialysis step, obeys Beer's law from 25 to 350 mg glucose per 100 ml, is very reproducible with a coefficient of variation of approx 1·5%, requires 75 µl of sample, recovers about 100% of added glucose, is compatible with currently available automated equipment, and is economically feasible to leave "on stream" continuously for automated analysis of both emergency (including paediatric) and routine samples.

In the second method of this type dextran products do not interfere, as they do with other o-toluidine reagents. Beer's law is obeyed up to a concentration of at least 30 mmol 1^{-1}. The method gives a standard deviation of 0·16 mmol 1^{-1} and a coefficient of variation of 2·8%. The high order of selectivity of the reagent is shown in Table 40. Urea and creatinine do not interfere. A mean recovery of 98·5% has been obtained for 5 and 10 mmol glucose per litre of serum.

Automated determination of glucose in body fluids with an aq acetic acid reagent[10]

Sample preparation. Blow 0·2 ml of freshly drawn capillary blood from a pipette into 2 ml of 3% trichloroacetic acid solution. After 10 min, centrifuge for 5 minutes.

Reagent. Dissolve 12 g borax in 800 ml water. Dissolve 3 g thiourea in 950 ml glacial acetic acid and add 250 ml of pure o-toluidine. Slowly add the aq solution to the acetic acid solution and mix. Store in an amber-coloured bottle. After 1 d the reagent is ready for use and is stable for at least 1 month at room temperature. Before use add Brij-35 to 1 litre of the reagent.

Automated method. Pour the supernatant into the cups of the sampler. The flow diagram for the procedure is shown in Fig. 47. Aspirate the sample, mix with the o-toluidine reagent, heat for about 6 min at 95° by passing through two standard heating coils, each of 28 ml capacity, and measure the absorbance immediately at 620 nm. The sample passes through the whole

Table 40. Selectivity of the *o*-toluidine
reaction for glucose[10]

Sugar, 1 mmol 1^{-1}	Glucose equivalent, in mmol 1^{-1}
Galactose	1·60
Mannose	0·98
Lactose	0·15
Xylose	0·12
Fructose	0·03
Uric acid	
1·0 mmol 1^{-1}	0·0
5·0 mmol 1^{-1}	0·1
8·0 mmol 1^{-1}	0·2

system in about 7·5 minutes At the beginning of each series of analyses, determine the standard curve with the working glucose standards. A straight line is obtained when plotting concentration against absorbance up to a glucose concentration of at least 30 mmol 1^{-1}. At regular intervals, according to usual practice, determine one or more working standards as running controls. After the analysis, rinse the flow system with acetic acid (500 ml 1^{-1}) for 5 min, then with distilled water for 10 minutes.

Manual method. Measure 0·25 ml supernatant, 0·25 ml trichloroacetic acid (30 g/l) for the blank, and 0·25 ml of one or more glucose working standards

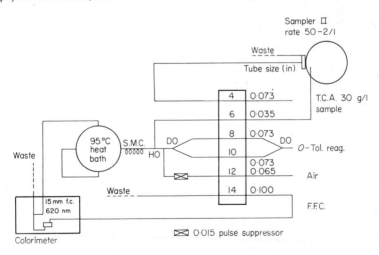

Fig. 47. Flow-diagram of the automated glucose determination.[10]

into test tubes, and add 2·25 ml modified reagent to each tube. After heating in a boiling waterbath for exactly 9 min, cool the test tubes in cold water, and measure the absorbance of standard(s) and samples within 30 min at 620 nm against the blank.

F. Other carbohydrates

Several methods are available for the determination of blood galactose with the o-toluidine reagent.[46, 47] In one method[46] 0·4 ml of blood is haemolysed by freezing, mixed with 0·6 ml of 40% yeast suspension, and allowed to stand for 5 min to remove glucose. After centrifuging, 0·5 ml of the supernatant fluid is mixed with 0·5 ml of 10% trichloroacetic acid and centrifuged. The galactose in the supernatant fluid is determined by one of the described o-toluidine methods.

In the other method[47] 0·2 ml of heparinized blood is incubated at 56° with 1·7 ml of Fermcozyme and 5 ml of 1 M acetate buffer (pH 5·6), and set aside for 20 minutes. Then 0·3 ml of 0·34 M zinc sulphate is added, followed by 0·2 ml of 0·3 N NaOH. The mixture is mixed, and centrifuged. One millilitre of the supernatant fluid is mixed with 7 ml of the reagent (6% of o-toluidine and 0·15% of thiourea dissolved in acetic acid) and heated for 8 min at 100°. The absorbance is then measured at 630 nm.

Maltose, fructose, glutathione, glucuronic acid, sulphonamides, salicylates, and chloramphenicol did not interfere at the concentrations tested. The concentration of galactose in the blood of 40 infants (aged from 1–5 d) varied between 20 and 100 µg per ml.

Lactose in urine[50] and in milk[48, 49] can also be determined with o-toluidine after hydrolysis to glucose and galactose.

Glycogen in tissue can be determined by the following procedure.

Determination of glycogen with o-toluidine[52]

Homogenize 50–200 mg of tissue samples in 10% trichloroacetic acid. Adjust the solution to a concentration of 100 mg of tissue per 10 ml and centrifuge. Treat one volume of supernatant fluid, containing 25–800 µg of glycogen with 2 volumes of 96% ethanol, allow to stand for 30 min, and then centrifuge for 20 min at 3500 rev min^{-1}. Decant and drain the tube. Dissolve the precipitate in 0·2 to 1 ml of 2 N H_2SO_4 and heat at 100° for 1 h and cool. Add 8 ml of a solution containing 6% of o-toluidine and 0·15% of thiourea in anhydrous acetic acid and boil the mixture for 8 minutes. Measure the absorbance at 635 nm against a blank of 0·2 ml of 2 N H_2SO_4 and 8 ml of o-toluidine reagent.

II. o-ANISIDINE

This reagent reacts like o-toluidine with hexoses and pentoses.[62] Thus, with o-toluidine, glucose gives bands at 380, 480 and 630 nm; with o-anisidine, bands are obtained at 340, 430 and 670 nm. Xylose and other pentoses react with o-toluidine to yield spectra having a maximum near 460 nm, with o-anisidine a band is obtained at 465 nm. Automated and manual methods have been developed for pentoses and hexoses. Blood and urinary carbohydrates can be measured. o-Anisidine should not be used to measure pentoses in serum or other samples in which the hexose concentration is more than 8 times the concentration of pentose. Bilirubin, in concentrations up to 19 mg dl^{-1}, does not interfere while haemoglobin concentrations greater than 40 mg dl^{-1} do.

A. Determination of hexoses with o-anisidine[62]

To 0·1 ml of the test solution add 6 ml of o-anisidine reagent (dissolve 1 volume of o-anisidine in 9 volumes of a solution of 1·5 g thiourea and 10 g of boric acid diluted to 950 ml with glacial acetic acid). Heat for exactly 5 min at 90°. Cool and measure the absorbance at 670 nm.

For pentoses measure the absorbance at 465 nm and subtract the absorbance due to hexose (as determined with standard hexose solutions).

REFERENCES

1. E. Hultman. *Nature* **183**, 108 (1959).
2. A. Hyvarinen and E. A. Nikkila. *Clin. Chim. Acta* **7**, 140 (1962).
3. K. M. Dubowski. *Clin. Chem.* **8**, 215 (1962).
4. R. Zender. *Clin. Chim. Acta* **11**, 88 (1965).
5. G. Ceriotti and A. D. Frank. *Clin. Chim. Acta* **24**, 311 (1969).
6. J. F. Goodwin. *Clin. Chem.* **16**, 85 (1970).
7. G. R. Cooper and V. McDaniel. *Standard Methods Clin. Chem.* **6**, 159 (1970).
8. W. W. Webster, S. F. Stinson and W. H. Wong. *Clin. Chem.* **17**, 1050 (1971).
9. G. Ceriotti. *Clin. Chem.* **17**, 440 (1971).
10. P. L. M. Wickers and P. Jacobs. *Clin. Chim. Acta* **34**, 401 (1971).
11. T. Sasaki, K. Tanemura, M. Sasaki and S. Shibata. "Atti VI Congresso Intern. Patol. Clin., Roma", 118 (1966).
12. S. Shibata. *Bull. Yamaguchi Med. School* **9**, 13 (1962).
13. R. Zender. *Clin. Chem. Acta* **8**, 351 (1963).
14. K. Lorentz. *Z. Klin. Chem.* **1**, 127 (1963).
15. H. Y. Yee and E. S. Jenest in E. C. Barton, *et al.* Eds, "Advances in Automated Analysis", Technicon 1969 International Congress, Volume 1, Mediad, White Plains, New York, 1970, p. 69.
16. H. Braun. *Arztl. Lab.* **13**, 177 (1967).
17. A. Härtel and H. Lang. *Arztl. Lab.* **15**, 60 (1969).

18. W. A. Feteris. *Am. J. Med. Tech.* **31**, 17 (1965).
19. J. Michod and J. Frei. *Med. Laborat.* **18**, 25 (1965).
20. C. J. R. Mink and L. Habets. *Clin. Chim. Acta* **14**, 704 (1966).
21. J. D. Pryce. *Analyst* **92**, 198 (1967).
22. A. Härtel, R. Helger and H. Lang. *Z. Klin. Chem. Klin. Biochem.* **7**, 14 (1969).
23. A. Härtel, R. Helger and H. Lang. *Z. Klin. Chem. Klin. Biochem.* **7**, 183 (1969).
24. W. D. Thomitzek and H. Bemm. *Z. Klin. Chem. Klin. Biochem.* **7**, 361 (1969).
25. J. Bierens de Haan and M. Roth. *Z. Klin. Chem. Klin. Biochem.* **7**, 624 (1969).
26. R. E. Wenk, R. J. Creno, V. Loock and J. B. Henry. *Clin. Chem.* **15**, 1162 (1969).
27. C. S. Frings, C. R. Ratliff and R. T. Dunn. *Clin. Chem.* **16**, 282 (1970).
28. N. C. Sudduth, J. R. Widish and J. L. Moore. *Am. J. Clin. Path.* **53**, 181 (1970).
29. W. R. Moorehead and E. A. Sasse. *Clin. Chem.* **16**, 285 (1970).
30. E. Henkel and A. Delbrueck. *Aerztl. Lab.* **14**, 458 (1968).
31. W. Schuetz. *Aerztl. Lab.* **14**, 500 (1968).
32. H. Y. Yee, E. S. Jenest and F. R. Bowles. *Clin. Chem.* **17**, 103 (1971).
33. C. F. Fasce, Jr., R. Rej and A. J. Pignataro. *Clin. Chim. Acta* **37**, 105 (1972).
34. J. F. Goodwin. *Anal. Biochem.* **48**, 120 (1972).
35. C. S. Frings and C. Queen. *Clin. Chem.* **18**, 488 (1972).
36. J. Ek and E. Huetman. *Nature* **181**, 780 (1958).
37. G. Ahlert, E. Hofer, W. Hoffmann and G. Bestvater. *Deut. Gesundheits W.* **19**, 2256 (1964).
38. E. Hofer and G. Ahlert. *Z. Med. Labortech.* **7**, 26 (1966).
39. A. B. Raitsis and A. O. Ustinova. *Lab. Delo.* **11**, 33 (1965).
40. G. Muller. *Deut. Z. Ver. Stoffwechselkrankh.* **25**, 77 (1965).
41. J. C. Torlotin. *Ann. Biol. Clin.* **24**, 173 (1966).
42. G. Ahlert, E. Hofer and G. Bestvater. *Deut. Gesundheitsw.* **20**, 349 (1965).
43. G. Bakos. *Orv. Hetilap* **108**, 1033 (1967).
44. L. A. Salomon and J. E. Johnson. *Anal. Chem.* **31**, 453 (1959).
45. N. G. Soler and R. Adams. *Clin. Chim. Acta* **30**, 289 (1970).
46. A. Relander. *Scand. J. Clin. Lab. Invest.* **15**, 218 (1963).
47. D. Watson. *Anal. Biochem.* **5**, 260 (1963).
48. M. Steiger and J. Schulz. *Arch. Tierernaehr.* **20**, 297 (1970).
49. A. M. Desmaison, J. C. Breton, M. Tixier and M. J. Chatelut. *Bull. Soc. Pharm. Bordeaux.* **109**, 118 (1970).
50. R. Humbel and S. Ludwig. *Z. Klin. Chem. Klin. Biochem.* **8**, 318 (1970).
51. C. Franzini. *Biochim. Appl.* **12**, 217 (1965).
52. K. Tarnoky and S. Nagy. *Clin. Chim. Acta* **8**, 627 (1963).
53. R. Richterich. "Clinical Chemistry: Theory and Practice", Academic Press, New York, 1969, p. 227.
54. J. Kerstell. *Scand. J. Clin. Lab. Invest.* **13**, 637 (1961).
55. J. H. Roe and E. W. Rice. *J. Biol. Chem.* **173**, 507 (1948).
56. D. B. Towers, E. L. Peters and M. A. Pogorelskin. *Neurology* **6**, 37, 125 (1956).
57. A. Hyvarinen and E. A. Nikkila. *Clin. Chim. Acta* **9**, 234 (1963).
58. J. Bergstrom and E. Hultmann. *Nature* **198**, 97 (1963).
59. G. Muller. *Deut. Z. Verdaungs Stoffwechselkrankh.* **25**, 76 (1965).
60. H. Krause. *Deut. Gesundheitsw.* **20**, 2045 (1965).
61. H. U. Bergmeyer, Ed., "Methods of Enzymatic Analysis", 2nd printing, revised, Academic Press, New York, N.Y., 1965, p. 117.
62. J. F. Goodwin and Y. Yee. *Clin. Chem.* **19**, 597 (1973).

12. ALDOHEXURONATES, PRECURSORS

I. NAPHTHORESORCINOL

A. Mechanism of reaction

In this section we will discuss the determination of hexuronic acids with naphthoresorcinol. In 1908, Tollens and Rorive found that glucuronic acid gives a violet colour when heated with naphthoresorcinol in approximately 6 N HCl.[1] A dye was isolated from this reaction mixture and on the basis of the analytical data of its derivatives was postulated to be **I**.[2, 3]

I

However, it has been pointed out that **I** cannot explain the fact that furfural and pentoses give a different colour with naphthoresorcinol while penturonic acid, which forms no furfural on treatment with HCl, gives a violet colour with this reagent.[4] The violet dye is also formed by fusion of naphthoresorcinol with glucuronic acid and is believed to be a xanthene or dinaphthylmethane derivative.[5] In line with this last mechanism, further work has indicated that 2 mol of naphthoresorcinol were necessary for every mole of glucuronic acid. This analytical reaction was further studied and it was found that a dye, **II**, was formed which could then be changed to **I** by carrying out the reaction for a longer time or at a higher temperature.[6, 7] The mechanism of the reaction, can be postulated as shown in Fig. 48. These derivatives were methylated, isolated, analysed, and examined spectrally. The methylated derivatives of **I**, e.g. **III**, and of **II**, e.g. **IV**, are shown.

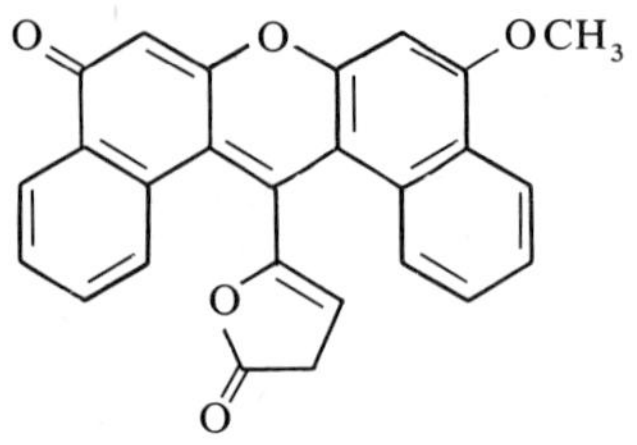

III

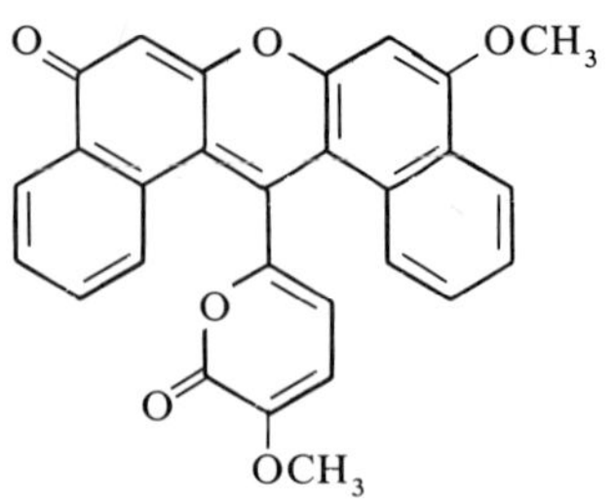

Solvent	Benzene	n-BuOH	Benzene	n-BuOH
λ_{max}	564	565	572	578
$m\varepsilon$	42·7	37·2	41·7	30·9

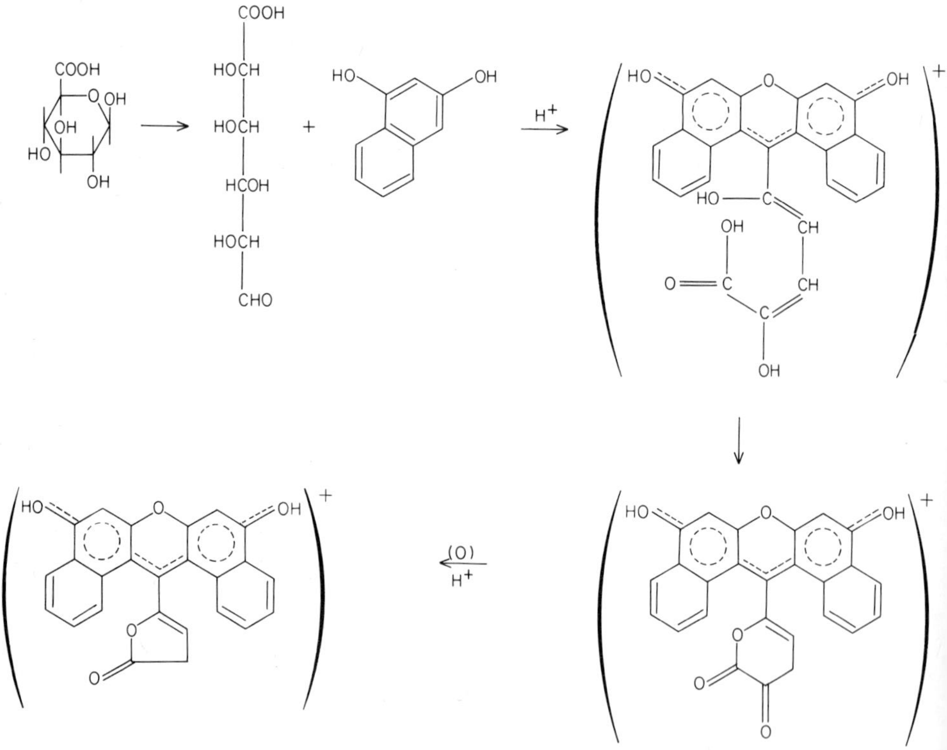

IV

(I)

(II)

FIG. 48. Reaction of glucuronic acid with naphthoresorcinol.

In strong acid solution, **III** and **IV** would form cationic resonance structures absorbing in the 600 nm region and resembling the spectrum obtained in the procedure for the determination of the hexuronic acids with naphthoresorcinol wherein the chromogen cation absorbed at 600 nm in butanol.[6]

B. Extractive procedures

An example of a procedure for the determination of glucuronic acid with naphthoresorcinol followed by extraction of the chromogen is the following. Beer's law is obeyed from about 15–150 µg. Glucose interferes since it gives a chromogen absorbing at 740 nm.

Determination of glucuronic acid with naphthoresorcinol[8]

To 2 ml of aq test solution add 2 ml of 0·2 % aq naphthoresorcinol followed by 2 ml of 6 N HCl. Heat at 100° for 1 h and cool in an ice bath for 10 minutes. Add 5 ml of a saturated solution of sodium chloride followed by 6 ml of benzyl alcohol and shake vigorously for 10 seconds After 30 min, filter the upper layer and measure the absorbance at 615 nm.

In other somewhat similar procedures, the solvent extractants used are as follows: toluene, λ 565 to 580,[9–12] ether, λ 570,[13] 2,2'-dichloroethyl ether, λ 580,[14] ethyl acetate, λ 565[15] or 580,[16] n-butyl acetate, λ 570,[17, 18] and 1-pentanol, λ 607.[19]

A reagent that is stable for several months at 5° in the cold can be made, e.g. dissolve 200 mg of naphthoresorcinol (recrystallized from aq acidified sodium chloride solution and washed with water) in 80 ml of water, adjust the pH to 8–8·5 by the slow addition of approx 1 ml of 0·5 N NaOH: after 15 min bring the pH to 2–2·5 by the addition of 10 % H_3PO_4 ($\sim$ 2 ml), then add 100 mg of $NaHSO_3$, dilute to 100 ml with water, and filter.

In the following determination with this reagent the colour is stable at least 1 h and Beer's law is obeyed up to 100 µg of D-glucuronic acid.

Determination of glucuronate with naphthoresorcinol[16]

To 2 ml of test solution, add 2 ml of reagent and 2 ml of conc HCl. Heat at 100° for 30 min, cool in ice-water for 10 min, shake vigorously for 30 s with 10 ml of ethyl acetate and measure the absorbance of the ethyl acetate phase at 580 nm.

Dialysis can also be used for deproteinization so as to avoid adsorption of glucuronic acid on to protein removed by conventional methods.

Determination of glucuronic acid in blood plasma by dialysis[9]

Add 0·1 volume of 10 % sodium citrate solution to the sample, centrifuge, dilute the supernatant liquid two-fold with Ringer solution, and dialyse a

0·18 ml portion against 0·18 ml water for 5·5 h at 0°. Dilute 0·09 ml of the aq phase with 0·91 ml water, add 0·5 ml of 18 N H_2SO_4 and 0·5 ml of 0·4% naphthoresorcinol, and heat at 100° for 1·5 hours. Cool, shake with 2·5 ml of 95% ethanol and 2 ml of toluene, and measure the absorbance of the toluene phase at 580 nm.

Interferences that have to be overcome in these methods include the effect of light on the reagent,[12] glucose and other sugars,[10, 11, 14] ascorbic acid,[11] and the effect of strong acid in forming interfering chromogens.[10]

In one procedure,[10] glucuronic or galacturonic acid can be determined in the presence of an excess of carbohydrates such as glucose and fructose. The uronosides commonly found in urine do not interfere, but certain easily hydrolysable compounds, such as menthol glucuronoside and borneol glucuronoside, are determined as the free acid.

In another method glucose interference is eliminated by its oxidation to gluconic acid with glucose oxidase (EC 1.1.3.4), ascorbic acid interference by the destruction of this acid with hot mild alkali treatment, and oxidative effects of H_2SO_4 by its replacement with HCl and a shorter heating treatment.[11]

Determination of unconjugated glucuronic acid in deproteinized human blood[11]

To 5 ml of the tungstic acid filtrate add 1 ml (15 units) of glucose oxidase and 3 ml of 0·1 N acetate buffer (pH 5·6). Incubate for 3 h at 37°. Make the digest alkaline with 1 ml of 1 M carbonate buffer (pH 10·1) and heat at 100° for 2 minutes. Acidify with 0·3 ml of 6 N HCl, shake and adjust to 10 ml with distilled water. Pipette duplicate 4 ml aliquots into boiling tubes followed by 2 ml of 0·4% aq naphthoresorcinol and 2 ml of conc HCl. Shake the tubes, stopper, and heat at 100° for 1 hour. Cool, add 10 ml ethanol and extract the chromogen with 8 ml of toluene. Separate the toluene layer, warm it for 5 min at 37°, and read the absorbance at 565 nm.

Since the procedure for the determination of glucuronic acid with naphthoresorcinol is fairly simple,[20, 21] the method has been applied to plasma, blood and serum[9, 11, 22] and urine.[13, 20] In the analysis of urine for this acid[13] the urine is diluted, hydrolysed for 30 min in 2 N HCl at 100° and determined by heating with the naphthoresorcinol reagent at 100° for 1 hour. The chromogen is extracted with ethyl ether and the absorbance is read at 570 nm.

In the case of severe burns and malignant growths, the excretion of this acid in urine can be increased ten-fold.

C. Thin-layer chromatography

The uronic acids and their lactones can be separated by thin layer chromatography and then assayed with naphthoresorcinol. Neutral monosaccharides (up to 100 μg) and low concentrations of inorganic compounds do not interfere. The following method is believed to be applicable to sea-bed samples.

TLC separation and estimation of uronic acids and their lactones[15]

Separate the test mixture containing 1–50 μg of each uronate or lactone at room temp on 0·25 mm layers of Kieselguhr G impregnated with 0·1 M NaH_2PO_4 buffer with acetone–butanol–0·1 M NaH_2PO_4 (8:5:7) as solvent. Galacturonic, guluronic, glucuronic and mannuronic acids have R_F values in the range of 0·4–0·6, while the corresponding lactones have R_F values in the range of 0·76–0·94.

Spray with a naphthoresorcinol–H_3PO_4–ethanol reagent. Extract the separated acids into 3 ml of ethyl acetate. Add 0·2 ml of 2 N H_2SO_4 and measure the absorbance at 565 nm.

D. Conjugated uronic acids

Conjugated uronic acids can also be determined following their hydrolysis[23, 24] and following separation from[25, 26] or destruction of[24, 26–29] the free acids. O-Glucuronides can be hydrolysed by incubation with β-glucuronidase (EC 3.2.1.31) for 3 h at 37°.[24] Separations and clean-up have been accomplished with paper chromatography on Whatman ET20 paper,[25] or by conventional column chromatography on DE-50 floc cellulose[25] or alumina followed by Amberlite CG-4B resin.[26] Free uronic acids can be eliminated by treatment with sodium borohydride,[26, 27] sodium hydroxide[24, 29] or alkaline hypoiodite.[28]

II. ENZYMATIC METHODS

A highly selective enzymatic method for galacturonic acid has been reported.[30] It can be used in the presence of large quantities of di-, tri-, or tetra-galacturonic acid. The presence of a NADH-linked enzyme system for the reduction of galacturonic acid has been demonstrated in bacterial cells. Both the isomerase and the dehydrogenase have been partially purified, separated from interfering NADH oxidase, and isolated from *Erwinia carotovora* and *Escherichia coli*. The following reaction takes place, Fig. 49. The rate of oxidation of NADH was measured at 340 nm, estimation of the galacturonic acid being based on an mε of 13·6 for NADH.

The high selectivity of the reaction is shown by the data in Table 41. In addition, negative results were obtained with unsaturated galacturonic acid (4-deoxy-L-threo-5-hexoseuloseuronic acid) and saturated and unsaturated di-, tri-, and tetra-galacturonic acids.

Table 41. Substrate specificity[30]

Substrate	Activity, ΔOD, at 340 nm min^{-1}
Arabinose	$2 \cdot 5 \times 10^{-4}$
Fucose	$4 \cdot 3 \times 10^{-4}$
Fructose	$4 \cdot 0 \times 10^{-4}$
Glucose	$4 \cdot 3 \times 10^{-4}$
Glucuronic acid	$4 \cdot 3 \times 10^{-4}$
Galactose	$4 \cdot 3 \times 10^{-4}$
Galacturonic acid	$199 \cdot 0 \times 10^{-4}$
Mannose	$2 \cdot 5 \times 10^{-4}$
Rhamnose	$3 \cdot 5 \times 10^{-4}$
Sorbose	$2 \cdot 0 \times 10^{-4}$
Xylose	$4 \cdot 0 \sim 10^{-4}$
Control (none)	$3 \cdot 1 \times 10^{-4}$

Reaction mixture: 5×10^{-3} M substrate, 0·1 M potassium phosphate buffer, pH 7·0, $1 \cdot 67 \times 10^{-4}$ M NADH, and 0·01 unit of the enzyme in 3·0 ml. Assay method is described in the text.

Table 42. Possible interferences in benzidine method[31]

Compound	Amount applied (μmol)	A at 410 nm[a]
Glucurolactone	0·1	0·089 ($\pm$0·008)[b]
	0·25	0·223 ($\pm$0·007)
	0·5	0·425 ($\pm$0·010)
	1·0	0·845 ($\pm$0·009)
Galacturonic acid	0·1	0·075 ($\pm$0·005)
	0·25	0·201 ($\pm$0·011)
	0·5	0·438 ($\pm$0·010)
	1·0	0·862 ($\pm$0·020)
Ribose	1·0	0·307 ($\pm$0·013)
Arabinose	1·0	0·100 ($\pm$0·004)
Galactose	1·0	0·059 ($\pm$0·006)
Glucose	1·0	0·048 ($\pm$0·005)
α-Oxoglutaric acid	1·0	0·026 ($\pm$0·006)
D-Glucosamine hydrochloride	1·0	0·007
Muramic acid	1·0	0·005
Saccharic acid	1·0	0·005

[a] Each value represents the mean $\pm$ S.D. of four separate experiments.
[b] Standard deviations of the mean.

III. OTHER METHODS

Direct spectrophotometric assay of glucuronic acid in the presence of labile glucosiduronic acid has been shown to be possible. The Fishman–Green naphthoresorcinol method[32] measures total glucuronic acid in a mixture and then that remaining after hypoiodite oxidation at pH 10·1; the value for free glucuronic acid is then obtained by the difference in uronic acid content before

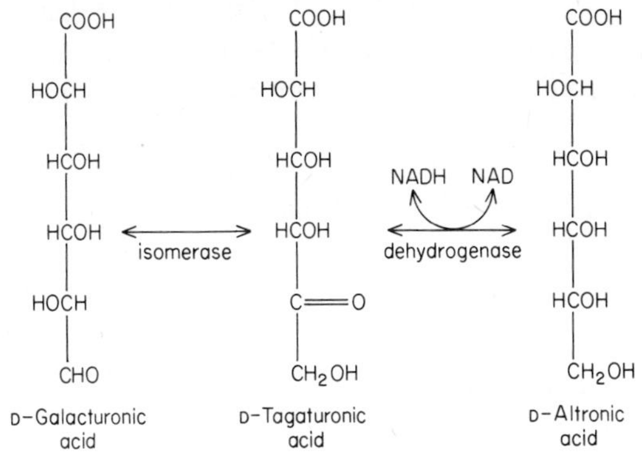

FIG. 49. Determination of galacturonic acid through the oxidation of NADH.

and after oxidation. The same oxidation procedure has been used in a carbazole method[33, 34] for the differential analysis of free and conjugated glucuronic acid mixtures.[35] The carbazole reactions have been more extensively covered in the 5-carboxyfurfural precursors section. Other reagents could also be substituted for naphthoresorcinol in the use of this reagent for the direct determination of glucuronic acid in the presence of difficulty hydrolysable phenolic conjugates; the procedure involves treatment with conc orthophosphoric acid at 70° for more than 1 hour.[10]

Benzidine is another reagent that has been used to determine various carbohydrate aldehyde precursors. Essentially a yellow Schiff base is formed as shown with 5-hydroxymethylfurfural.[36] The absorption maximum is near 420 nm.

Benzidine can be used to measure glucuronic acid in mixtures containing glucuronic acid and labile glucosiduronic acids.[31] The colour is stable for at least five hours. Beer's law was followed from 10–100 µg of glucuronic acid. The reagent blank gave an absorbance of about 0·015 ± 0·003. Three micrograms of glucuronic acid can be detected. The optimum concentration range for analysis was about 3–20 µg ml^{-1}. The standard deviation of the procedure was 2·5% at 50 and 70 µg and 6% at 10 µg. In the investigation of the possible hydrolysis of glucuronic esters under assay conditions it was found that the percentage of 1-O-benzoyl-β-D-glucopyranuronic acid and 1-O-veratroyl-β-D-glucopyranuronic acid hydrolysed under assay conditions ranged from 3·5–5·5%. An mε of 5·7 was obtained at 410 nm. The selectivity of the method is shown in Table 42.

Determination of glucuronic acid in the presence of labile glucosiduronic acids[31]

To the test sample (5–100 μl) add 0·1 ml acetic acid, acetate buffer (pH 5·0) to bring the volume to 2 ml, and 1·5 ml of 0·6% benzidine in glacial acetic acid. Mix, cap the tube tightly, heat at 100° for 15 min, and then cool under the tap for five minutes. Read the absorbance at 410 nm within 3 h after removal from the boiling water bath.

Conjugates could be analysed following incubation with bovine liver β-glucuronidase in acetate buffer at pH 5·0.

REFERENCES

1. B. Tollens and F. Rorive. *Ber.* **41**, 1783 (1908).
2. A. Ogata and Y. Nozaki. *J. Pharm. Soc. Japan* **63**, 416 (1942); **64**, 42 (1943).
3. Y. Nozaki. *J. Pharm. Soc. Japan* **64**, No. 7A, 9 (1944).
4. S. Machida. *J. Japan Chem.* **7**, 634 (1953).
5. A. H. Guerrero and R. T. Williams. *Nature* **161**, 930 (1948).
6. T. Momose, Y. Ueda and M. Iwasaki. *Pharm. Bull. Tokyo* **4**, 49 (1956).
7. T. Momose, Y. Ueda and M. Iwasaki. *Pharm. Bull. Tokyo* **3**, 321 (1955).
8. T. Momose, Y. Ueda, M. Yoshinaga, J. Masui and M. Nagasaki. *Yakugaku Zasshi* **78**, 1064 (1958).
9. Z. Tamura, T. Nakajima, M. Tanaka and T. Miyake. *Japan Analyst* **11**, 1279 (1962).
10. W. Wagner. *Anal. Chim. Acta* **29**, 227 (1963).
11. S. Green, C. Anstiss and W. H. Fishman. *Biochim. Biophys. Acta* **62**, 574 (1962).
12. W. Wagner. *Anal. Chim. Acta* **29**, 182 (1963).
13. P. Cornillot. *Clin. Chim. Acta* **7**, 42 (1962).
14. R. E. Mosher. *Clin. Chem.* **8**, 378 (1962).
15. W. Ernst. *Anal. Chim. Acta* **40**, 161 (1968).
16. I. Nir. *Anal. Biochem.* **8**, 20 (1964).
17. E. Weigert and E. Kaiser. *Sci. Pharm.* **23**, 89 (1955).
18. T. Miettinen, V. Ryhanen and H. Salomaa. *Ann. Med. Exptl. Biol. Fenniae* **35**, 173 (1957).
19. S. W. F. Hanson, G. T. Mills and R. T. Williams. *Biochem. J.* **38**, 274 (1944).
20. I. Kapetanidis. *Pharm. Acta Helv.* **40**, 331 (1965).
21. K. Meyer, H. S. Boch and E. Chaffee. *Fed. Proc* **1**, 125 (1942).
22. M. Akashi. *Fukoaka Igaku Zasshi* **48**, 2112 (1957).
23. J. A. Mandel and C. Neuberg. *Biochem. Z.* **13**, 148 (1908).
24. R. Sadahiro, Y. Hinohara and A. Yamamoto. *J. Biochem.* **57**, 815 (1965).
25. G. W. Oertel and E. Kaiser. *Clin. Chim. Acta* **7**, 700 (1962).
26. I. Nir, J. Sicé and D. Ivery. *Clin. Chim. Acta* **14**, 756 (1966).

27. S. Ogiya and H. Kataoka. *J. Pharm. Soc. Japan* **79**, 949 (1959).
28. W. H. Fishman and S. Green. *J. Biol. Chem.* **215**, 527 (1955).
29. H. Takabayashi. *Nippon Syokakibyokai Zasshi* **55**, 22 (1956).
30. C. W. Nagel and S. Hasegawa. *Anal. Biochem.* **21**, 411 (1967).
31. J. Tomasic and D. Keglevic. *Anal. Biochem.* **45**, 164 (1972).
32. W. H. Fishman in D. Glick, Ed. "Methods of Biochemical Analysis", Vol. 15, Interscience, New York, pp. 77–145.
33. C. A. Marsh in G. J. Dutton, Ed. "Glucuronic Acid, Free and Uncombined," Academic Press, New York, 1966, pp. 3–136.
34. J. D. Gregory. *Arch. Biochem. Biophys.* **89**, 157 (1960).
35. H. Yuki and W. H. Fishman. *Biochim. Biophys. Acta* **69**, 576 (1963).
36. B. Y. Rao and M. G. Taiwade. *Indian J. Technol.* **4**, 221 (1966).

13. ALDOPHOSPHAMIDE, PRECURSORS

Cyclophosphamide, **I**, (Fig 50) is probably one of the most effective drugs against more different types of neoplastic disease than any other known drug and thus is used extensively around the world to fight cancer. Potentially it can cause cross-linkage. It is a much weaker alkylating agent than nor-nitrogen mustard, $HN(CH_2CH_2Cl)_2$. However it does not appear to be the active carcinostatic agent. Its metabolite, aldophosphamide, **II**, appears to be the active agent. **II** can be oxidized readily by aldehyde oxidase to the major urinary metabolite, carboxyphosphamide, **III**, from which the minor metabolite, 4-ketocyclophosphamide, **IV**, is derived. The reaction is shown in Fig. 50.

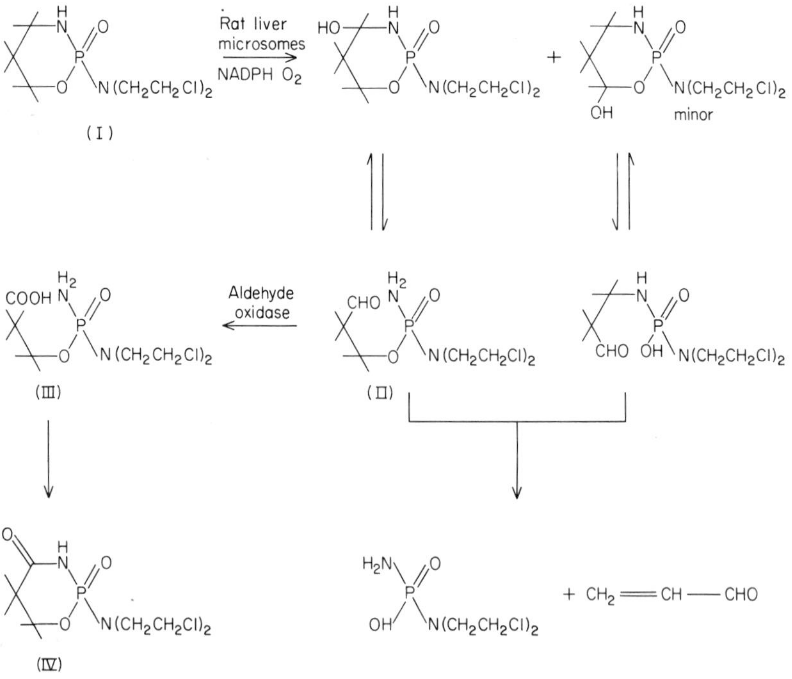

FIG. 50. Metabolism of cyclophosphamide.

Nicotine is probably metabolized through an aldehyde to cotinine in a somewhat similar fashion, Fig. 51.

Cyclophosphamide is used not only to treat cancer, but also to suppress the normal immune response of animals to a foreign protein (antigen) entering the body. It is very effective in suppressing the cell-mediated immune response in human transplant patients.

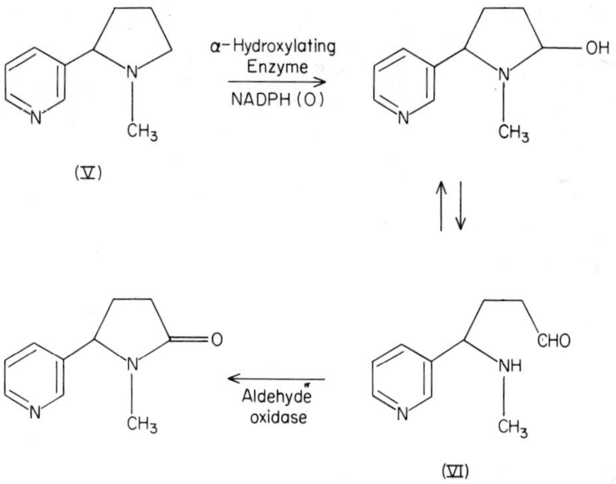

Fig. 51. Metabolism of nicotine.

However, there is a third factor that must be considered here. From its structure one would expect aldophosphamide to be a mutagen and even a carcinogen. It resembles the nitrosamine aldehydes postulated to be the ultimate carcinogens of the nitrosamine family. In this respect, evidence is becoming available which indicates that cyclophosphamide may be an extremely potent human carcinogen. Treatment of individuals with multiple myeloma or ovarian carcinoma with melphalan and/or cyclophosphamide results in remission and then in some cases an onset of acute leukaemia.[1] In line with this is the teratogenicity of cyclophosphamide in the rat,[2] its mutagenicity in Drosophila[3-5] and mice,[6] its induction of in vivo chromosome aberrations in chinese hamster bone marrow[7] and murine and human cells,[8] and in vitro chromosome aberrations in human leukocytes [9]

It is probable that aldophosphamide plays an important role in these genotoxic reactions. It can cross-link with amino or hydroxy groups in important molecules and thus affect cellular memory. Analytical methods could be developed to investigate the role of this aldehyde and acrolein in antitumor activity[10,11] and in the various types of cellular mutations resulting from treatment with cyclophosphamide.

In a report from the Southern Research Institute it was stated that a single viable leukemia cell (of a type of mouse-leukemia called L 1210) can multiply to about 1 billion cells and cause the death of a mouse in about 15 days. However, 200,000 leukemia cells that had been treated with a few micrograms of aldophosphamide and then washed free of the drug caused the death of only a few animals of a large experimental group.

In a somewhat similar fashion if the aldehyde were formed in the malignant tissue, it would regress the tissue. Here again an aldehyde precursor is a powerful carcinostatic agent. But because of the structure of this compound, it would also have tumorigenic activity. Much more needs to be known about these types of reactions.

REFERENCES

1. R. K. Karchmer, M. Amare, W. E. Larsen, A. G. Mallouk and G. G. Caldwell. *Cancer* **33**, 1103 (1974).
2. T. von Kreybig. *Arch. Exptl. Pharmakol.* **252**, 173 (1965).
3. C. Bertram and G. Höhne. *Strahlentherapie* **43**, 388 (1959).
4. S. Frye. *Brit. Empire Cancer Campaign, Ann. Rept.* **38**, 670 (1960).
5. G. Rohrborn. *Mol. Gen. Genet.* **102**, 50 (1968).
6. D. Brittinger. *Humangenetik* **3**, 156 (1966).
7. I. W. Schmid and G. R. Staiger. *Mutation Res.* **7**, 99 (1969).
8. F. E. Arrighi, T. C. Hsu, and D. E. Bergsagel. *Texas Rept. Biol. Med.* **20**, 545 (1962).
9. K. E. Hampel, M. Fritzsche and D. Stopik. *Humangenetik* **7**, 28 (1969).
10. R. A. Alarcon and J. Meienhofer. *Nature New Biol.* **233**, 250 (1971).
11. T. A. Connors, P. J. Cox, P. B. Farmer, A. B. Foster, M. Jarman and J. K. MacLeod. *Biomed. Mass Spectrometry* **1**, 130 (1974).

14. ALDOSES, PRECURSORS

I. INTRODUCTION

In this section the term "aldose" is defined as a chain polyhydroxyaldehyde; an "aldose" precursor is then a compound with a furanose, pyranose, or straight chain structure from which straight chain polyhydroxy aldehydes can be formed. Examples of some "aldose" precursors are aldoses, ketoses, deoxy sugars, amino sugars, and uronic acids. Once formed, the aldehyde or its enol form can be analysed with the help of an oxidizing agent or a reagent for aldehydes.

The monosaccharides are one division of that highly important group of natural substances—the carbohydrates. These compounds are present—free and bound—in living tissue and in the environment. They are either polyhydroxy aldehydes or polyhydroxyketones, usually in the furanose or pyranose form. An example is fructose which in aqueous solution is present in the pyranose (80%) and furanose (20%) forms (Fig. 52). However, in cane sugar, inulin, and in several of its phosphate esters, fructose exists in the furanose form. The failure to react with certain reagents for aldehydes under normal conditions indicates a partial masking of the aldehyde group through formation of the five-membered furanose ring and the six-membered pyranose ring, as shown in Figs 52 and 53.

In most monosaccharides the pyranose form is the dominant and more stable structure. Examples are glucose, galactose and ribose. The free aldehyde content of D-glucose in water has been estimated as only 0·0026% by polarographic means.[1] Examples of the different possible forms are shown in Figure 53 for galactose. Neuraminic acid also exists in the pyranose form. Most common sugars with pyranose hemiacetal structures react only weakly in the MBTH test and thus aldehydes can be determined in the presence of relatively high levels of hexoses and pentoses.[2]

Some monosaccharides exist in the furanose form, e.g. 2-deoxygalactose and 2-deoxyribose, the latter in equilibrium with the aldose form. Ribose-5-phosphate is in the furanose form, as is ribose in the nucleic acids. In oligo- and polysaccharides some sugars are present in the furanose form. Erythrose is probably present in the aldose form in equilibrium with the furanose form to a large extent since it reacts readily in the MBTH reaction.[3] And of course

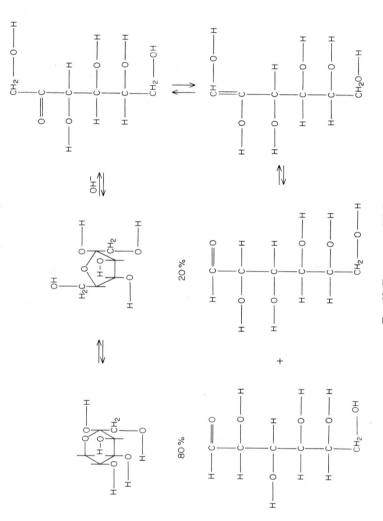

Fig. 52. Fructose equilibrium.

glyceraldehyde is present as the free aldehyde or its hydrated form since it cannot form a furanose ring. The millimolar absorptivities obtained with various sugars in the MBTH test (see section on aliphatic aldehydes) is in line with the above information, Table 43.[3]

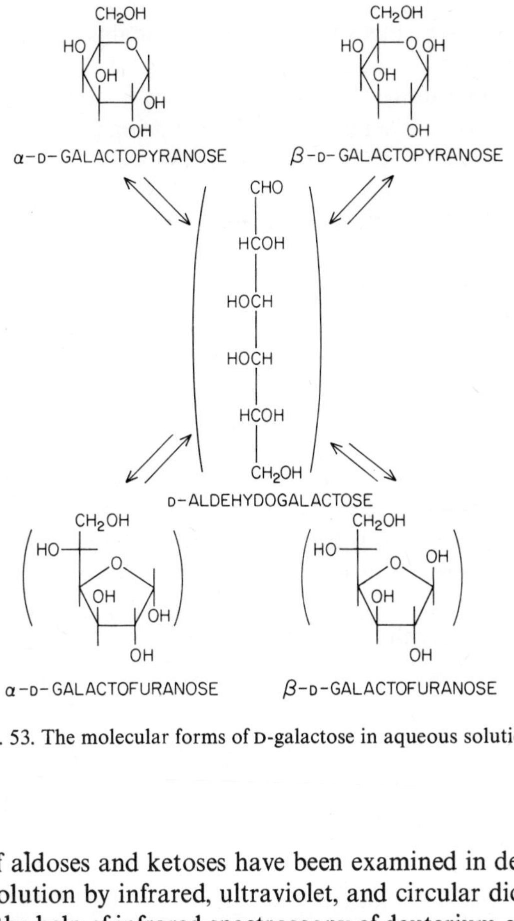

α–D–GALACTOPYRANOSE   β–D–GALACTOPYRANOSE

D–ALDEHYDOGALACTOSE

α–D–GALACTOFURANOSE   β–D–GALACTOFURANOSE

FIG. 53. The molecular forms of D-galactose in aqueous solution.

A number of aldoses and ketoses have been examined in deuterium oxide and aqueous solution by infrared, ultraviolet, and circular dichroic spectroscopy.[4] With the help of infrared spectroscopy of deuterium oxide solutions, the percentages of keto or aldehyde forms in the sugars tested are D-fructose, <0·4; D-fructose-1-phosphate, <1·0; D-fructose-6-phosphate, 2·5; D-glucose-6-phosphate, <0·4; D-glyceraldehyde, 4·4; and D-glyceraldehyde-3-phosphate, 4·4. Proton magnetic resonance spectroscopy has also been used to examine aldoses for the presence of aldehyde forms; e.g., D-glyceraldehyde-3-phosphate[5] and a number of acetylated aldehyde-aldoses.[6]

Ring opening and the rate of enolization of monosaccharides increases with the temperature and the concentration of base.[7] Heating of the haemiacetal form of aldoses in aqueous solution promotes transformation to open-chain aldehydo-sugar, possibly *via* the hydrated intermediate.[8] The increase of absorption at 275–286 nm can be attributed largely to the $n \rightarrow \pi^*$ band of the C=O group in the aldehydo-sugars.[8–11] However, the ultraviolet absorption spectrum of a carbohydrate can be difficult to account for because of the presence of ultraviolet-absorbing contaminants in the sugar.

The bond between the oxygen and hydrogen of the hydroxyl at carbon atom C-1 of hexopyranoses and pentofuranoses is slightly ionic and, consequently, bond strength is weakened with increasing pH.[12] The rate of ring-sugar aldehyde transformation would thus increase with pH as shown by the report that the rate of increase of the carbonyl absorption at 275 nm is maximal at neutral pH or pH 8 for glucose and lactose.[11] On the other hand the rate of conversion of the cyclic hemiacetal to the acyclic aldehyde is accelerated at very low pH.[13] In line with this the rate constant for exhange of glucose with H_2O^{18} decreases by a factor of ten when the pH is raised from 1·5 to 2·5 while the same pH change decreases the rate of glucose mutarotation by a factor of two.[14]

In the presence of alkali, ring-opening and enolization can take place. Thus, D-glucose in an alkaline media undergoes a keto-enol shift between C-1 and C-2, resulting in the formation, in part, of D-mannose and D-fructose in a solution that originally contained only D-glucose.[15–17] In a somewhat similar manner D-fructose could undergo isomerization to D-mannose and D-glucose. This process is called epimerization and is made use of in the analysis of monosaccharides, as will be shown in this section. Epimerization promoted by alkali proceeds *via* a 1,2-enediol intermediate.[18]

Table 43. Millimolar absorptivities at 670 nm obtained with carbohydrates in the MBTH test[3]

Compound	mε
Hydroxyethanal	60
L-Glyceraldehyde	60
DL-Erythrose	33·6
D-Ribose-5-phosphate	6·6
D-2-Deoxyribose	3·3
D-Glucuronic acid	2·3
D-Glucose	<0·6
D-Levulose	<0·6

II. REDOX METHODS

A. Historical

In the reduction methods, the course of the copper reduction reaction can be expressed schematically and simply by the equation

$$2Cu(OH)_2 + \underset{\overset{|}{CHOH}}{\overset{CHO}{|}} \rightleftharpoons \underset{\overset{|}{COH}}{\overset{CHOH}{\parallel}} \rightarrow \underset{\overset{|}{CHOH}}{\overset{COOH}{|}} + Cu_2O + H_2O$$

Since the reaction takes place in alkaline solution, ketoses isomerize to aldoses and thus can react. On the other hand, it has been suggested that the enediol form (fructose and glucose give the same enediol) is highly reactive and is the component oxidized in the reaction.[19]

It appears that more methods have been published for the determination of glucose than for any other chemical. There are few other procedures for which so many modifications have been reported than the reduction methods for sugar in human blood and urine. In 1838 Bouchardat and Peligot proved that the sugar in urine from patients with diabetes was D-glucose. Trommer[20] in 1841 introduced the detection of reducing sugars by metallic oxide reduction. In 1848 Fehling modified and quantitated Trommer's test.[21] Significant improvements were made in 1909 by Benedict.[22, 23] By 1932 there were 90 modifications of Fehling's reagent.[19] Since then the modifications of modifications have proliferated and modifications for the determination of glucose are still pouring out at a rapid rate. Much of this material has been ably and thoroughly reviewed by Henry.[19] The fifteenth most-cited scientific paper in the 1961–1972 literature is a copper reduction method.[24, 34]

B. Copper methods

When conditions are carefully controlled in the copper reduction tests, the cuprous oxide produced is directly proportional to the glucose present in the test solution. The cuprous oxide can then be determined by reduction of phosphomolybdate,[25–31] phosphotungstate[32, 33] or arsenomolybdate[34–40] or by [41] complexation with neocuproine.[41, 42] The latter method has been automated for the estimation of blood sugar at a higher sampling rate of 100–120 per hour.

Ever since its introduction in 1920, the Folin-Wu phosphomolybdate method[25] with its tungstic acid precipitation has probably been the most widely used method for glucose in the United States. The more recently introduced Nelson-Somogyi arsenomolybdate method has a more sensitive and more stable colour than the phosphomolybdate method, while the stable colour formed with neocuproine is thirty times more intense than the colour formed with phosphomolybdate. The complex of cuprous ion with neocuproine or 2,9-dimethyl-1,10-phenanthroline has the structure, **I**:

I

In dilute aqueous sodium carbonate, **I** has $m\varepsilon = 7 \cdot 8$ at 456 nm.[43]

The Cu-2,2'-bicinchoninate system may replace the Cu-neocuproine method.[43] In dilute sodium carbonate solution, in the presence of 2,2'-bicinchoninate, amine complexes of **Cu(II)** are readily reduced to the deep lavender Cu(I) complex of 2,2'-bicinchoninate by urate or hydroxylamine at room temperature or glucose at elevated temperatures. Protein can also reduce Cu(II) to Cu(I), so a dialysate has to be used in the analysis. Cu(I)-2,2'-bicinchoninate has $m\varepsilon = 8 \cdot 1$ at 562 nm. Because of the negative charge, the Cu(I) chelate of 2,2'-bicinchoninate cannot be extracted from aq solution by organic solvents, unlike the corresponding Cu(I)-neocuproine chelate. This is a great advantage in automated assay since, unlike Cu(I)-neocuproine, the Cu(I)-2,2'-bicinchoninate chelate cannot deposit on or otherwise stain the plastic tubing.

The advantages of the non-specificity of the copper methods in rapid screening tests have been discussed.[44] This test will detect the interesting genetic metabolic disorders such as alkaptonuria, pentosuria, fructosuria, galactosuria, and diabetes.

A few of these clinical methods are described in the following procedures.

Determination of blood glucose[25, 45, 46]

Reagents. Protein-precipitating reagent. 10% $ZnSO_4.7H_2O.0 \cdot 5N$ NaOH. Ten millilitres of the zinc reagent requires $10 \cdot 8$–$12 \cdot 2$ ml alkali to produce a permanent pink colour with phenolphthalein. Before titrating slowly with continuous shaking dilute the $10 \cdot 0$ ml zinc sulphate reagent with 50–70 ml water.

Copper reagent. Dissolve 40 g anhydrous Na_2CO_3 and then 7·5 g tartaric acid in about 400 ml water followed by 4·5 g $CuSO_4.5H_2O$. Mix and dilute to 1 litre. This reagent is stable indefinitely at room temperature.

Phosphomolybdic acid reagent. Add 400 ml 10% NaOH and 400 ml water to 70 g molybdic acid and 10 g sodium tungstate. Boil for 20–40 min to drive off NH_3. Cool and add water to about 700 ml. Add 250 ml conc orthophosphoric acid (85% H_3PO_4) and dilute to 1 litre.

Stock glucose standard. 1% in saturated benzoic acid. This is stable indefinitely in a refrigerator. 1 ml ≡ 10 mg.

Dilute glucose standard. Prepare fresh daily by diluting stock standard 1:100. 1 ml ≡ 0·1 mg.

Procedure. Add 1 ml oxalated blood to 7·0 ml water and mix. Add 1 ml 10% zinc sulphate, mix, add 1 ml 0·5 N NaOH, and mix again. Let stand for 5 min and filter or centrifuge. (If necessary, a 1:10 tungstic acid protein-free filtrate can be prepared as shown for spinal fluid. Add 0·5 ml spinal fluid to 4 ml water, 0·25 ml 2/3 N H_2SO_4 and 0·25 ml 10% sodium tungstate and treat as for the protein-free blood filtrate)

Add the following to Folin-Wu sugar tubes: Blank. 2 ml water. Standard. 2 ml dilute standard. Unknown. 2 ml filtrate.

Add 2·0 ml copper reagent to each tube and mix. Heat in boiling water for 6 min and then immediately add 2 ml phosphomolybdic acid reagent and continue heating for 2 min. After cooling in tap water, dilute to 25 ml with water and mix by inversion. Read absorbances of blank, standard and unknown against water at 420 nm.

Calculation:

$$\text{mg glucose/100 ml} = \frac{Ax - Ab}{As - Ab} \times 100.$$

If the calculated concentration exceeds 450 mg/100 ml repeat the analysis using 1 ml of filtrate and 1 ml of water. Multiply the result by 2.

Determination of blood sugar[34, 39, 47, 48]
Reagents. Copper reagent.[39] Dissolve 12 g Rochelle salt and 24 g anhydrous sodium carbonate in about 250 ml of water. Add, with stirring, a solution of 4 g $CuSO_4.5H_2O$ followed by 16 g of $NaHCO_3$. Add this solution to a boiled (to expel air) solution of 180 g anhydrous Na_2SO_4 in 500 ml of water and dilute to 1 l. After 1 week of standing, use the clear supernatant solution.

Arsenomolybdate reagent.[34] Add 21 ml of 96% sulphuric acid to 25 g of ammonium molybdate in 450 ml of water followed by 3 g of $Na_2HAsO_4.7H_2O$

in 25 ml of water. Incubate this solution for 24 h at 37° and store in a glass-stoppered brown bottle.

Procedure. Add an equal volume of copper reagent to 1–5 ml of aq test solution (containing not more than 600 µg of D-glucose or its equivalent). Heat samples, blanks and standards for 10 min at 100° and then cool. Add either 1 or 2 ml of arsenomolybdate reagent to determine either 100 µg or less D-glucose or 100–600 µg of D-glucose, respectively. Mix to dissolve the cuprous oxide and then dilute to either 10 or 25 ml. After standing for at least 15 min but not more than 40 min read the absorbance at 500 nm.

From 5–600 µg of sugar can be determined. Reproducible results are obtained with D-glucose, D-fructose and maltose. Maximum sensitivity is obtained at 660 nm but measurements are more reproducible at 500, 560 or 770 nm.

Detection of glucose and other reducing substances in urine[19, 23, 49–51]

Benedict's Reagent. Dissolve 17·3 g $CuSO_4.5H_2O$ in 100 ml hot water. With the aid of heat dissolve 173 g sodium citrate and 100 g anhydrous Na_2CO_3 in 800 ml water. When cool, pour the second solution into the first while stirring, and dilute to 1 l with water. The solution is stable at room temp.

Procedure. Add 8 drops of urine to 5 ml of Benedict's reagent in a test tube. Boil over a flame for 2 min or heat in a boiling water bath for 3 minutes. Read immediately.

The sensitivity of the test is approx 50–80 mg glucose per 100 ml urine. The results can be reported as follows.

Colour	Qual. result	glucose ($\sim$ mg 100 ml^{-1})
Clear blue or green opacity and no ppt.	0	<100
Green with yellow ppt.	1+	250
Yellow to olive	2+	800
Brown	3+	1400
Orange to red	4+	>2000

Positive results are given by aldose precursors, aldehydes, uric acid, ketones, creatinine, phenols, oxalic acid, hippuric acid, glucuronic acid and glucuronates, salicylic acid, p-aminosalicylic acid, homogentisic acid, isoniazide, caronamide, cincophen, uronates, and salicyluric acid.[19]

C. Other reductive tests

Urinary, blood and other sugars can be characterized through paper chromatography and location tests. Some methods are given here; these and many others have been described elsewhere in more detail.[19, 52] Thin-layer chromatography has also been used for the characterization of the aldose precursors through separation and chemical tests.[53-55]

Other reductive methods by which the aldose precursors can be characterized, located on a chromatogram or determined, include reduction of the aldose with silver salts,[19] ferricyanide,[56-67] molybdate,[71-75] iodine in alkali,[76] tetrazolium salts,[77-86] nitroarenes[87-103] and enzymatic methods, some of which have been discussed in the aldoglucose section.

D. Ferricyanide methods

1. Direct procedures

Yellow ferricyanide ions are reduced in alkaline solution by glucose and other aldose precursors to colourless ferrocyanide ions, e.g.

$$Fe(CN)_6^{3-} \rightarrow Fe(CN)_6^{4-}$$

An advantage of this procedure is the stability to air oxidation of ferrocyanide. The decrease in ferricyanide can be measured photometrically[59, 104] or the ferrocyanide can be determined photometrically as Prussian blue, $Fe_4[Fe(CN)_6]_3$,[57, 60] uranyl ferrocyanide[105] or molybdenum ferrocyanide.[106] Lactose or 4-β-galactosido-glucose, which is the most important carbohydrate in mammalian milk, can be readily hydrolysed to the aldose and then following oxidation with ferricyanide determined as ferric ferrocyanide (Prussian blue).[107]

The stoichiometric properties of the alkaline ferricyanide reagent has been investigated for glucose and the maltodextrins (maltose through maltoheptose).[63] The data show that, on a molar basis, glucose gives a greater amount of reduction than the maltodextrins. However, the maltodextrins are chemically distinct from glucose in that glucose has a free C-4 hydroxyl in the residue carrying the hemiacetal group, while the maltodextrins have this C-4 hydroxyl substituted, as shown in **II**, where $n = 0$ is maltose.

II

Although this study stopped with maltoheptaose, the authors claim that equimolar reducing values should be expected for higher maltodextrin homologs and polysaccharides. The ferricyanide procedure is a reliable way of quantitatively determining the number of hemiacetal groups (reducing or aldose precursor groups) for maltodextrins and α-1,4-polysaccharides when maltose is used as a standard, Fig. 54.[64] With the alkaline ferricyanide method 3 automated reducing value procedures are described: a general procedure for aldose precursors, a carbohydrase assay, and a continuous-sampling system for carbohydrase kinetic studies.[64]

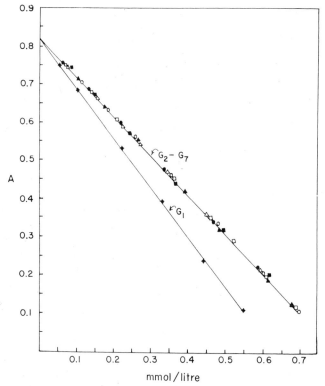

FIG. 54. Loss of absorbance (at 420 m) of ferricyanide as function of increasing concentrations of glucose (G 1) and maltodextrins, maltose through maltoheptaose (G 2 through G 7). Points on upper curve: (●) maltose;(□) maltotriose; (■) maltotetraose; (△) maltopentaose, (▲) maltohexaose, (○) maltoheptaose.[64]

In a somewhat similar fashion glucose oligomers were separated on a Bio-gel P-2 column and assayed automatically with an alkaline ferricyanide reagent, Fig. 55[65] Measurement was at 230 nm. The presence of zinc or borate prevented the reaction.

2. *Glucose*

The ferricyanide test can be used to determine one particular aldose precursor in the absence of other chemicals of this type. Thus, it has been used in the study of infertility. The cervical mucus is a complex mixture of inorganic and organic substances consisting of glycogen, glucose, maltose, hexosamine,

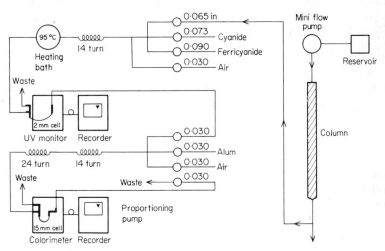

FIG. 55. Flow diagram of the automatic sugar analyser.[65]

fructose, mannose, galactose, cholesterol, lipids, amino acids and proteins. The amount of true glucose in cervical mucus rises to a peak at ovulation in the normal fertile female.[66] Clomiphene treatment in some infertile women causes a marked increase in the quantity of cervical glucose, a possible factor in enhancing conception. Sperm survival appears to depend on optimal concentrations of glucose in cervical mucus. The procedure of Schales and Schales[68] has been used.

3. *Ferrous ion-ligands*

Other ferricyanide procedures utilizing the formation of a ferrous ion–ligand chelate can be utilized for the aldose precursors. An example is the following for glucose utilizing a benzodiazepin-2-one as the ligand.[67] The coupled redox reactions in the analysis are

$$\text{Glucose} + [\text{Fe(CN)}_6]^{3-} \rightarrow \text{Gluconic acid} + [\text{Fe(CN)}_6]^{4-}$$
$$[\text{Fe(CN)}_6]^{4-} + \text{Fe}^{3+} \rightarrow [\text{Fe(CN)}_6]^{3-} + \text{Fe}^{2-}$$
$$\text{Fe}^{2-} + \text{ligand} \rightarrow (\text{Fe}^{2+}/3) - \text{ligand chelate}$$

This reaction has been used in the automated determination of plasma or serum glucose with 7-bromo-1,3-dihydro-1-(3-dimethylaminopropyl)-5-(2-pyridyl)-2H-1,4-benzodiazepin-2-one dihydrochloride as the ligand.[67] Beer's law is obeyed from about 50–400 mg of glucose per 100 ml. Mean coefficients of variation averaged around 3–4%. Recovery of added glucose averaged 100·4% (range, 96·7–104·8%).

Further studies are necessary on the various glucose methods when used with azotemic sera since significant differences are obtained between the automated reductimetric (ferricyanide)[68] and enzymic (glucose oxidase)[69] or automated o-toluidine methods.[70]

E. Halogens

Aldoses, in contrast to ketoses, are oxidized to aldonic acids by halogen in alkaline solution. Iodine[76, 108–111] and bromine[112] have been used. Only relatively pure sugar solutions can be assayed in this way since many other organic substances are also oxidized in this fashion.

F. Molybdate

Aldose precursors can be determined with molybdate following thin-layer chromatography.[72, 73]

Molybdate determination of aldose precursors. Spray the chromatogram with 10% aq ammonium molybdate to detect the carbohydrate spots. Elute appropriate spots with acid molybdate reagent (17 g ammonium molybdate in 700 ml water followed by 17 ml conc sulphuric acid followed by dilution with water to 1 l after cooling). Heat at 100° for 15 min and cool to room temperature. After 5 min read at 700 nm.

G. Tetrazolium salts

1. *Introduction*

Aldose precursors heated with a solution of a water-soluble tetrazolium salt in alkaline media form highly coloured water-insoluble formazans, Fig. 56. Formazans can form neutral, cationic or anionic chromogens, each showing a different visible spectrum, as shown for 1,3-diphenyl-5-4′-nitrophenylformazan, Fig. 57.[113] The neutral chromogen absorbs at the shortest wavelength because of the violet-shift effect of the separation of charge in the excited state of the molecule. The anion would absorb at increasingly longer wavelength with increasing basicity of the solvent.

Many of the formazans have a favourable redox potential, for example,

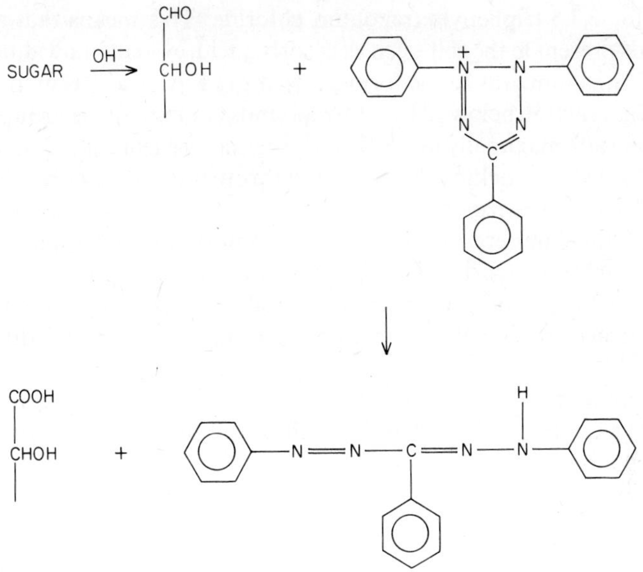
SUGAR
OH⁻
CHO
CHOH
COOH
CHOH
+
N
N
N
N
C
H

FIG. 56. Reaction of aldose precursors with a tetrazolium salt.

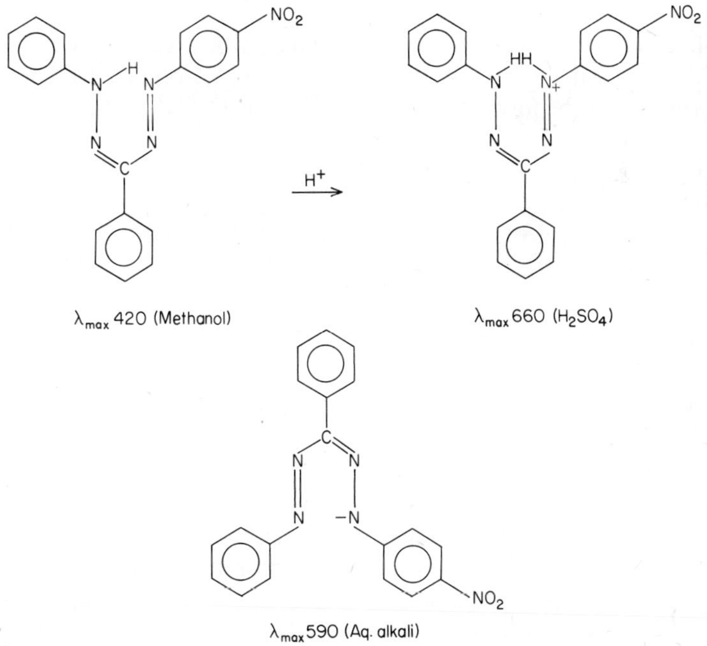
NO2
H+
λmax 420 (Methanol)
λmax 660 (H2SO4)
λmax 590 (Aq. alkali)

FIG. 57. Effect of pH on long wavelength maximum of 1,3-diphenyl-5-4′-nitrophenylformazan.

−0·08 V for 2,3,5-triphenyltetrazolium chloride. This means that reducing compounds present in the cell, such as ascorbic acid, cysteine, and glutathione, convert tetrazolium salts to the formazans at pH 9. Aldose precursors do not undergo this reaction below pH 11. Compounds containing SH groups reduce tetrazolium salts maximally at pH 9. The interference from these compounds can be cancelled by blocking the SH group through reaction with iodoacetate or p-chloromercuribenzoate.[114]

Some of the interferences in the tetrazolium determination of aldose precursors are polyhydric phenols, benzoquinones, napthoquinones and thiols,[115] epinephrine, apomorphine and analogous compounds,[116] adrenocortical steroids with their α-ketolic group,[117–122] and 1,3-dihydroxyacetone.[123]

The α-ketolic steroids, like the aldoses and ketoses, form reductones (which can in most cases be considered as the enolic forms of the aldehyde) in alkaline solution, which readily reduce tetrazolium salts to highly coloured formazans. An example of the formation of a reductone is shown for 1,3-dihydroxyacetone and glyceraldehyde, e.g.

$$\underset{CH_2}{\overset{\overset{\displaystyle OH}{|}}{}}-\underset{C}{\overset{\overset{\displaystyle O}{\|}}{}}-\underset{CH_2}{\overset{\overset{\displaystyle OH}{|}}{}}\;\overset{OH^-}{\rightleftharpoons}\;\underset{CH}{\overset{\overset{\displaystyle OH}{|}}{}}=\underset{C}{\overset{\overset{\displaystyle OH}{|}}{}}-\underset{CH_2}{\overset{\overset{\displaystyle OH}{|}}{}}\;\overset{OH^-}{\rightleftharpoons}\;\underset{CH}{\overset{\overset{\displaystyle O}{\|}}{}}-\underset{CH}{\overset{\overset{\displaystyle OH}{|}}{}}-\underset{CH_2}{\overset{\overset{\displaystyle OH}{|}}{}}$$

Thus, 1,3-dihydroxyacetone on reaction with alkaline blue tetrazolium, e.g. 3,3′-(3,3′-dimethoxy-4,4′-biphenylene) bis [2,5-diphenyl-2H-tetrazolium chloride] gave the formazan, **III**, λ_{max} 530, mε 47·5.[123]

III

Various aldose precursors can be determined with tetrazolium salts[77, 124–126] This has also been done densitometrically on paper following paper chromatography.[127] Although the reaction is non-stoichiometric,[78] the quantity of formazan formed is directly proportional to the concentration of the sugars.[126] The reaction rate is different for different sugars, Fig. 58. Thus, fructose has a seven-fold faster rate of reaction than glucose.[77, 126]

The following procedure has been used.

Determination of aldose precursors with p-*anisyl tetrazolium blue.*[83] To 0·1 ml of a 1% solution of *p*-anisyl tetrazolium blue, add 0·3 ml of 1·2% sodium hydroxide solution followed by 1 ml aq test solution containing 1–200 µg of glucose. Boil, cool, add dioxane to 10 ml, and read at the wavelength maximum.

p-Anisyl tetrazolium blue could also be used to determine glucose in blood.[86] The error is within ±0·08 µg for 2·9–13 µg of glucose.

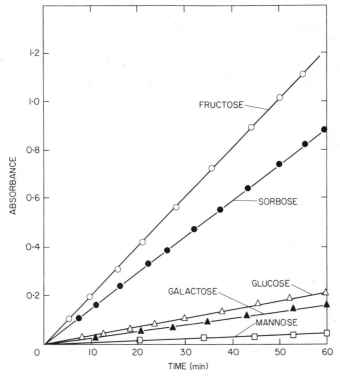

Fig. 58. Reaction rate curves of 5 hexoses. Concentration of hexose = 1 × 10⁻³ M; concentration of triphenyltetrazolium chloride = 0·94 × 10⁻³ M; temperature = 25° ± 0·05°.[126]

Determination of glucose with p-*anisyl tetrazolium blue.*[86] To 0·3 ml of test solution add 0·3 ml of reagent (0·95 ml of 0·3 N NaOH, 1 ml of 1% tetrazolium blue in 50% methanol in 2·05 ml water), set aside in the dark for 20 min, heat to the boiling point in a glycerol bath at 135°, immerse for 70 s in a glycerol bath at 120°, cool in water for 5 min and read the absorbance at 640 nm.

2. *Thin-layer chromatography*

A technique for obtaining a satisfactory separation of nine or ten sugars through separation by cellulose thin-layer chromatography utilizes a mixture of distilled water with freshly distilled ethyl acetate and pyridine (25:100:35, V/V/V) for development, Table 44.[128] To achieve effective separation, the chromatographic run is preferably made 3 times, the second and third treatment being carried out after the solvent front in the preceding run had reached

Table 44. Average R_G values for various types of sugar.[128] Conditions: layer thickness, 0·3 mm; material, cellulose powder MN 300 (Macherey, Nagel & Co); developing mixture, water–ethyl acetate–pyridine (25:100:35). Three consecutive runs.

Type of sugar	R_G value (glucose = 100)
Lactose	36
Maltose	53
Sucrose	66
Galactose	83
Glucose	100
Mannose/fructose	115
Arabinose	131
Xylose	155
Rhamnose	210

the top of the cellulose layer and the plate had been dried. For quantitative sugar determinations a reference mixture is applied to the base line at the left and right-hand side of the plate. The right-hand side reference separation is sprayed with the visualization reagent (1·3 ml of 85 % orthophosphoric acid and 0·93 ml of freshly distilled aniline in 100 ml of 70 % ethanol; this solution keeps for several weeks in the dark at 5°) and dried for 15 min at 100°.

A tetrazolium procedure[83, 128, 129, 137] can be used to assay the separated sugars by the following procedure. Beer's law is obeyed from about 25–100 μg of sugar.

Thin-layer chromatographic analysis of sugars[128]
Reagents. Stock solution: Dissolve 1 g of tetrazolium blue (3,3′-dianisole-4,4′-bis-2,5-diphenyltetrazolium chloride) in 50 ml of lukewarm methanol or ethanol and dilute to 100 ml with water. This is stable in a refrigerator for over 1 year. Reagent, Mix 1 part of stock solution with 3 parts of 0·3 M NaOH solution. Solvent mixture: chloroform and 96 % ethanol, freshly distilled (5:4, V/V).

After the separation, scrape each spot carefully into a small centrifuge tube. Add 1 ml water and centrifuge for 10 min at 3000 rev min^{-1}.

Procedure. To 0·5 ml of the sugar solution add 0·5 ml of the reagent. Boil for 45 s and then cool immediately under the tap. Dissolve the insoluble formazan in a small volume of solvent mixture, transfer to a 50 ml volumetric flask and dilute to the mark with solvent mixture. Measure the absorbance at 615 nm.

3. *Glycoproteins*

Glycoproteins are composed of carbohydrate and protein. Much of the work on glycoproteins has been summarized.[130] Some of the aeroallergens prevalent in the human environment and believed to trigger many hayfever attacks are thought to be glycoproteins[131] according to Berrens (discussed later).

In the characterization of glycoproteins the determination of the sugar components has always been a problem.[130] Glycoproteins contain uronic acids, neutral sugars and amino sugars, all of which can be separated by paper chromatography in a single run without the formation of derivatives.[132,133]

Since 2,3,5-triphenyltetrazolium chloride can detect 1 μg amounts of glycoprotein sugars on paper chromatograms,[134] the reagent has been adapted to the colorimetric estimation of carbohydrate components in polysaccharides and glycoproteins.[135-139] The conditions of colour development have to be strictly adhered to for reproducible results, since the rate and extent of the reduction of triphenyltetrazolium chloride varies with humidity, reaction time, temperature and, to a lesser extent, alkalinity.[77,79]

Following hydrolysis of the glycopeptide, sugars have been separated by thin-layer chromatography, stained with triphenyltetrazolium chloride, and analysed directly on the plate[137] or after elution.[136]

Gas chromatography is as sensitive, but the apparatus is more complicated and expensive and each sugar component gives at least two peaks, through the separation of α- and β-anomers, complicating the quantitative evaluation of complex mixtures.[137]

Conditions for the release of sugars from glycoproteins have been discussed by Neuberger and Marshall.[140] For the liberation of non-nitrogenous sugars other than deoxy sugars, treatment with 0·5–2 N HCl or H_2SO_4 at 100° for periods varying between 3 and 8 h have generally been employed. Procedures of hydrolysis involving treatment of the glycopeptide with 2 N H_2SO_4, 25% trichloroacetic acid or an ion exchange resin in H^+-form for 4 h at 100° have been described.[136]

The key substances in the structural study of the sugar moiety of the glycoproteins are the glycopeptides obtained by the enzymatic digestion of the glycoproteins.[141] The first step of the structural investigation of glycopeptides usually consists of the characterization and determination of the sugar components and the estimation of their molecular ratio. The following method has been applied to the study of the structure and composition of glycoproteins isolated from connective tissue.[142]

Microdetermination of neutral sugars and aminosugars in glycopeptides by thin-layer chromatography.[137] For the determination of hexoses hydrolyse 30–100 µg of a glycopeptide with 10–40% hexose content in a sealed tube with 200 µl 2 N HCl at 100° for 1·5 to 3 h depending on the nature of the glycopeptide. Evaporate the acid in a desiccator *in vacuo* in the presence of KOH and dissolve the residue in 20 µl of water. (For hexosamines hydrolyse with 4 N HCl at 100° for 4–8 hours).[143]

For thin-layer chromatography use Eastman Kodak 511 V sheets impregnated with 0·2 M phosphate buffer (pH 6·8). Propanol-ethyl acetate-water (5:1:1) mixture served as the mobile phase in the development by the ascending method. (For hexosamines use ethanol–25% aq ammonia–water (85:0·5:14·5, v/v)).

After drying, dip the developed sheets in a freshly prepared 1:1 mixture of a 1% ethanolic triphenyltetrazolium chloride solution and a fresh 1% methanolic sodium hydroxide solution. Develop the red colour of the spots by heating the sheets at 90° in a water-saturated atmosphere for 15 minutes. After cutting the strips, measure the colour intensity of the spots on a recording densitometer and estimate the area of the peak by planimetry or triangulation.

Galactose, glucose, and mannose give almost equal intensities in the 0·2–2 µg range, while fucose is less intense. A linear relationship is found between the peak area and the concentration. Standard sugar mixtures are run on the same sheet. The method is standardized through the determination of the ratio of the hexoses in the fibrinoglycopeptide mixture[144] and in ovomucoid.[145] The standard error of repeated determinations was about ±2%.

In the following procedure three types of sugars can be estimated following paper chromatography.[135] The use of steam for the visualization of the sugars on the chromatograms diminished the reaction time from the usual 15 min to 2 min with equal sensitivity and better reproducibility. The pure formazan obtained from triphenyltetrazolium chloride absorbed at 482 nm with $m\varepsilon = 15·6$. However, 1 mol of reducing sugar gave 1·5 mol of formazan. This increased the sensitivity. The precision of the method was well within 10% and the recovery of standard sugar was close to 100%.

Paper chromatographic determination of sugars present in glycoproteins.[135] Spot 0·2 mM of the appropriate sugars and mixtures on Whatman No. 1 paper and develop by descending chromatography with ethyl acetate–pyridine–

water (12:5:4) for 16 h at 10°. Air-dry the paper for 4 hours. After dipping the paper in 0·5% 2,3,5-triphenyltetrazolium chloride solution in 0·25 N methanolic NaOH, place it in a steam chamber for two minutes. Each complete spot was cut out with the same rectangular area. The formazan was extracted into 10 ml of methanol-acetic acid (8:1, v/v) for 24 h with vortex agitation at the beginning and end of this period. Absorbances were read at 482 nm and corrected for background colour. Separation of D-glucuronic acid, hexosamines, galactose, mannose, and ribose was effected with a precision within ±9%.

H. Polynitroarenes

1. Dinitrobenzoic acids

Many polynitroarenes have been used for the determination of aldose precursors, e.g. 3,5-dinitrosalicylic acid,[87, 93–100] 3,4-dinitrobenzoic acid,[88, 101] picric acid,[89–91, 103] 2,4-dinitrophenol,[92, 146] and 3,6-dinitrophthalic acid.[102, 147–151] Reductone anions derived from the sugars probably play a role in the analyses. Probably one of the chromogens formed is a nitroamine,

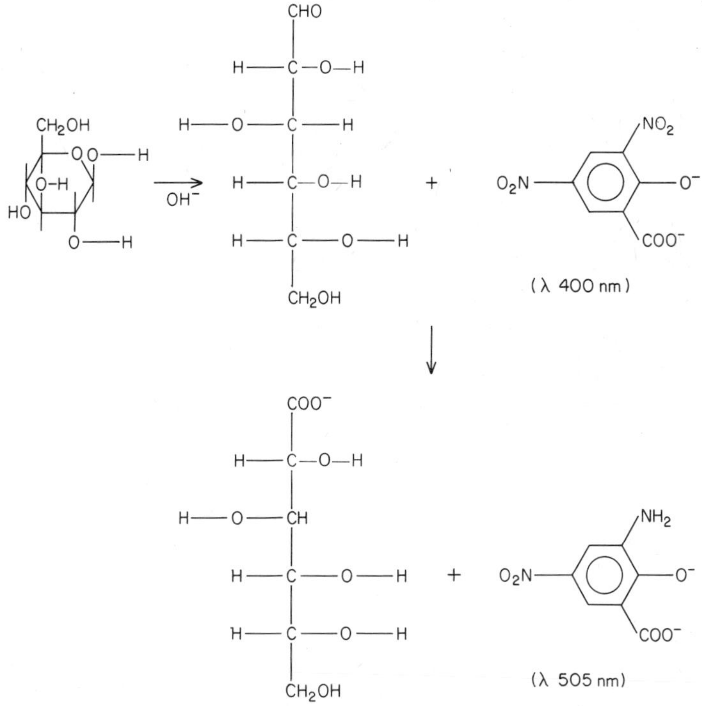

FIG. 59. Reaction of aldose precursors with 3,5-dinitrosalicylic acid.

as shown in Fig 59. In the case of 3,6-dinitrosalicylic acid as the reagent, the long wavelength absorption of the chromogen is due to the ortho effect of the newly formed amino group on the oxygen resonance terminal of the *p*-nitrophenol anion.[152]

Procedures for the determination of reducing sugars with 3,5-dinitrosalicylic acid and with 3,4-dinitrobenzoic acid are examples of the use of these reagents. With the latter reagent an *o*-nitroaniline chromogen is formed.

Determination of aldose precursors with 3,5-dinitrosalicylic acid.[87] To 3 ml aq test solution containing up to 600 µg of glucose add 3 ml reagent (aq solution containing 1% dinitrosalicylic acid, 0·2% phenol, 0·05% sodium sulphite and 1% sodium hydroxide). Heat for 15 min at 100° and add 1 ml

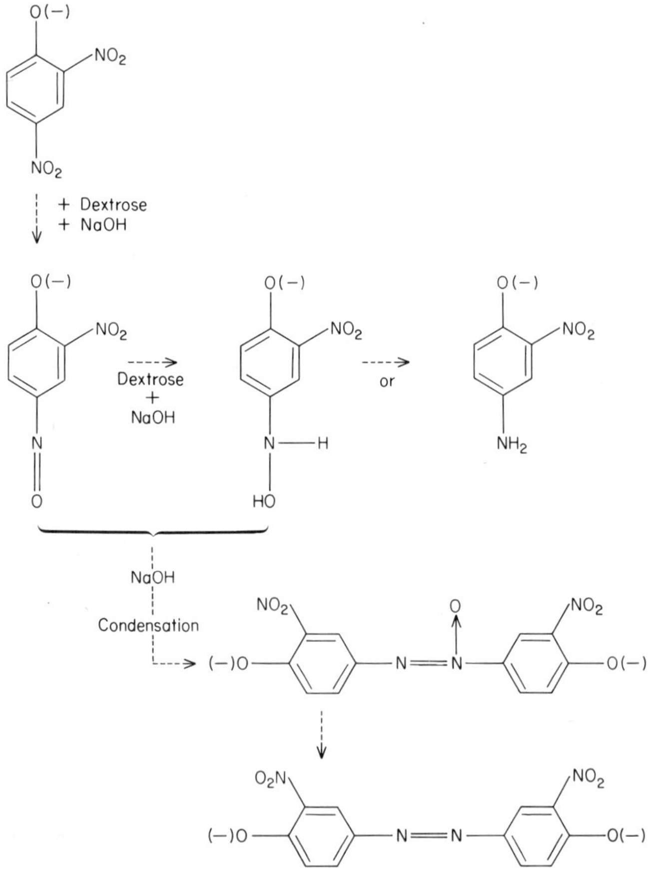

FIG. 60. Proposed reaction between dextrose and 2,4-dinitrophenol.[146]

of 40 % Rochelle salt solution. Cool to room temp and read at 505 nm.

Determination of aldose precursors with 3,4-dinitrobenzoic acid.[88] Heat 1 ml aq test solution with 1 ml of reagent (2 g of 3,4-dinitrobenzoic acid and 31·8 g of sodium carbonate in 1 l of water) for 10 min at 100°. Cool and add 0·2 ml of conc sulphuric acid and 6 ml of isoamyl alcohol. Shake and collect the isoamyl alcohol layer. Dehydrate with 50 mg of anhydrous sodium sulphate. Read at 395 nm.

2. *2,4-Dinitrophenol*

2,4-Dinitrophenol has been used in the automated determination of reducing sugars and sucrose in food products such as peanut butter, mayonnaise, salad dressing, danish pastries, egg and potato products, etc.[146] The postulated reactions for this determination are given in Fig. 60. The wavelength maximum obtained is at 425 nm, but the baseline of the automated system at this wavelength is erratic. Measuring the absorbance at 550 nm reduces the sensitivity but improves the selectivity and creates a very stable automated system. The absorbance at 550 nm is directly proportional to the reducing sugar concentration. Sucrose is analysed by the same method after automated hydrolysis. Samples are clarified and filtered manually before the analysis.

Some serious interferences are given by acetone, 2-butanone, acetaldehyde, and benzaldehyde.

Table 45. Response of common sugars relative to dextrose in the DNP reaction[146]

Sugar	mε of sugar/mε of dextrose	
	Reducing sugar method	Sucrose method
Dextrose	1·00	1·00
Sucrose	0·00	2·00
Galactose	1·25	1·20
Fructose	1·02	1·00
Maltose	1·48	1·44
Lactose	1·68	1·65

The response of various sugars in the two procedures are given in Table 45. The 2·0 ratio shown by sucrose indicates that it is completely hydrolysed in 6 min at 95° in 0·1 N HCl. Since a disaccharide containing a 1 → 4 glycosidic linkage exhibits about 1·4 times the molecular reducing power of glucose under specific conditions, the maltose: glucose ratio of 1·48 is reasonable. Lactose and maltose give the same response in both procedures so it is evident that these sugars are not converted to their monosaccharide components.

3. Picric acid

Picric acid in hot alkaline solution is reduced by aldose precursors to the picramic acid anion, e.g.

λ_{max} 375 nm λ_{max} 460 nm

The red shift is due to the ortho effect of the amino group. The method was introduced in 1913[153, 154] but has fallen into disuse in analysis of body fluids because even creatinine, acetone and diacetic acid give positive results. Interferences in whole blood are found to the extent of 30–50 mg glucose/ml whole blood.[155]

The method has been recommended for the determination of mixtures of lactose, sucrose, invert sugar, glucose and fructose, and for lactose after fermentation with yeast.[156]

4. 3,6-Dinitrophthalic acid

This acid has been used in the determination of blood and urine sugar.[102] It has also been used in the determination of other reducing sugars,[147] invert sugar in sucrose,[148] lactose in milk,[150, 151] and lactose and sucrose in condensed milk.[150]

Sodium thiosulphate was found to stabilize the colour in the procedure. The reagent solution is stable for one month even at summer temperatures. The colour was stable for 3 days at room temperature. Sucrose could be determined after hydrolysis with 0·1 N HCl.[151] For determinations in milk or milk products basic zinc carbonate is used for deproteinization.[150] Glucuronic and ascorbic acids interfere in the procedure as do 2,4-pentanedione and pyruvic acid to a lesser extent.[149] Fairly large amounts of albumin, creatine, creatinine, acetone and ethyl acetoacetate do not interfere in the dinitrophthalic acid procedure.[102, 149] Acetone in large amounts and isothiocyanates in small amounts reduced the reagent in potassium carbonate solution to 3-amino-6-nitrophthalic acid, λ_{max} = 400 nm.[149, 157]

Procedures for blood and urine sugar are available.

3,6-Dinitrophthalic acid determination of blood sugar[102]

Reagents. 3,6-Dinitrophthalic acid solution containing 0·2% of the acid and 0·1% of anhydrous sodium carbonate.

Sodium carbonate solution containing 20% anhydrous sodium carbonate and 5% sodium thiosulphate pentahydrate is filtered after 3 d standing through a washed filter paper and stored in a light-resistant bottle. Protect from carbon dioxide.

Deproteinizing agents.[36] 5% zinc sulphate heptahydrate. 5% barium hydroxide octahydrate protected from carbon dioxide. To adjust the concentration dilute 2 ml of the zinc sulphate solution with 20 ml water and titrate with barium hydroxide solution using phenolphthalein as indicator.

Procedure. Hemolyse 0·1 ml blood with 3·5 ml water in a test tube and add 0·2 ml of barium hydroxide solution. When the mixture turns brown add 0·2 ml of zinc sulphate solution and shake the tube vigorously. Transfer the mixture to a centrifuge tube and centrifuge. Pipette 2 ml of the clear supernatant into a test tube and add successively 1 ml of the 3,6-dinitrophthalic acid solution and the sodium carbonate solution. At the same time, mix 2 ml water with the developing solutions in another test tube as a blank. Heat both tubes in a boiling water bath for exactly 10 min, cool in running water for 3 min, and dilute with water to the 20 ml mark. Read the absorbance at 450 nm.

Beer's law was obeyed from 10–100 µg ml^{-1}. Replicate values were within ±5%.

3,6-Dinitrophthalic acid determination of urinary sugar.[102] Dilute 0·1 ml of urine to 20 ml with water. Treat 2 ml of this solution with 1 ml of 3,6-dinitrophthalic acid and 1 ml of sodium carbonate solution in the same way as in the determination of blood sugar.

Table 46. Relative mobilities* of carbohydrates on silica gel G.[158] Solvent: Pyridine–ethyl acetate–water (26:66:8). Detection: Aniline (0·95 ml)–phthalic acid (1·66 g)–ethyl ether (48 ml)–isobutanol (48 ml)–water (4 ml).

Carbohydrate	Approximate R_F
Xylulose	0·70
Ribose	0·64
Arabinose	0·44
Fructose	0·39
Glucose	0·34
Galactose	0·27
Lactose	0·15

* Double-pass chromatography.

III. NON-REDUCTIVE METHODS

A. Carbohydrate dyscrasias

Techniques for the preparation of blood, plasma or urine and a TLC system of separation have been devised for the routine screening of carbo-hydrate dyscrasias, such as diabetes mellitus, essential and alimentary pentosuria, ribosuria, lactose intolerance, and galactosemia.[158] Table 46 lists the R_F values of the saccharides important to a clinician screening for carbohydrate disorders. The sugars could be eluted from the plate and esti-mated quantitatively by one of the many methods described in this section.

B. Allergenic glycoproteins

Amines and aldose precursors have been shown to react to give products absorbing near 310 nm[159, 160] and fluorescing at about F315 to 365/430 to 490.[161–164] Some analytical use has been made of these reactions in studying the chemistry of the allergens involved in the syndrome of atopia in man.[161] Berrens has postulated that Maillard reactions between aldoses and the lysine portion of proteins creates allergens containing the following struc-ture:

$$-HN-\overset{\overset{\displaystyle O}{\|}}{C}-CH-NH-\overset{\overset{\displaystyle O}{\|}}{C}-$$
$$\underset{\underset{\displaystyle HN-CH=C-CHOH-}{|}}{\underset{\displaystyle (CH_2)_4}{|}}$$
$$\underset{\displaystyle OH}{|}$$

The lysine–sugar conjugation is proposed as the universal structural deter-minant of atopic allergens. It is difficult to visualize this small chain of con-jugation fluorescing at or near F315–365/430–490. Berrens has suggested that, in atopic allergy, low molecular weight 1-amino-1-deoxy-2-ketose-(lysine) peptide conjugates, and in contact allergy, hapten-oligopeptide conjugates, act as intermediate immunogenic substances, binding to s-RNA to form the template molecules directing the synthesis of specific antibody. If the lysine sugar structure were of importance, compounds containing this structure could be analysed through a derived "aldose".

C. p-Hydroxybenzoylhydrazide

Alkaline solutions of acid hydrazides react with aldose precursors and other reducing sugars to give yellow solutions.[165, 166] β-Diketones react similarly. In the determination of the reducing sugars p-hydroxybenzoic acid hydrazide gave the most intense absorbance with a relatively low reagent blank. A chromogen is obtained that absorbs at 395 nm maximally with shoulders at 415 and 440 nm.[165] The colour is stable for at least 5 minutes. In the 2 procedures Beer's law is obeyed from 0·5–5 mg glucose/ml and 1–10 μg glucose/ml. No significant reaction occurs with pyruvate or α-oxoglutarate. Very high protein concentrations can cause a small error. Calcium causes an increase in the response of glucose standards so calcium is added to the reagent to take advantage of this reaction. Other substances giving negative results include glutathione, creatinine, uric acid, urea and bilirubin.

For the higher concentrations of carbohydrates the following procedure is used.

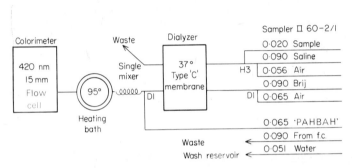

FIG. 61. Flow diagram of the automated glucose procedure utilizing p-hydroxybenzoic acid hydrazide.[166]

p-Hydroxybenzoic acid hydrazide determination of carbohydrates.[165] Mix 10 μl of test solution with 3 ml of 0·5% hydrazide in 0·4 M NaOH (Dissolve hydrazide in 0·5 M HCl to 5% solution and then dilute to 0·5% hydrazide with 0·5M NaOH. Prepare daily). Heat at 100° for 5 minutes. Cool and read absorbance at 410 nm.

For lower concentrations mix 0·5 ml of test solution with 1·5 ml of 1% hydrazide in 0·5 M NaOH, heat at 100° for 5 min, and read absorbance at 410 nm.

The yellow solution also fluoresces at $F410/520$; the carbohydrates could be determined fluorimetrically with this reagent.

The colorimetric procedure has been automated, Fig. 61.[166] The response of various carbohydrates with the hydrazide reagent and with an automated ferricyanide procedure and a semi-automated o-toluidine method[167] are compared in Table 47. The effects of some non-carbohydrate interfering substances on these three methods are compared in Table 48.

Table 47. Comparative specificity of the PAHBAH, ferricyanide and o-toluidine procedures for carbohydrates[a(166)]

Carbohydrates	Relative response glucose = 100		
	PAHBAH	Ferricyanide	o-Toluidine
Glucose	100	100	100
Mannose	102	88	101
Galactose	66	83	154
Fructose	105	105	15
Ribose	84	109	13
Xylose	70	101	14
Deoxyribose	12	41	1
Glucuronic acid	53	85	2
Glucosamine	63	104	59
Maltose	72	101	11
Lactose	48	83	61
Sucrose	0	0	16
Ascorbic acid	10	57	3

[a] Automated PAHBAH, automated ferricyanide and semiautomated o-toluidine procedures carried out on 10 mM solutions of carbohydrates.

D. Cyanide reagent

Aldose precursors, and even polysaccharides in which aldehyde groups can be uncovered, can react with cyanide to form cyanohydrins. Excess cyanide can be driven off and the cyanohydrin can then be hydrolysed and the resultant ammonia can be steam-distilled and determined fluorimetrically with reagents such as 2,4-pentanedione[168] or reduced nicotinamide adenine dinucleotide (NADH)[169] or colorimetrically with phenol,[170–173] bispyrazolone,[174,175] or 2,5-dimethoxytetrahydrofuran plus p-dimethylaminobenzaldehyde or p-dimethylaminocinnamaldehyde.[176] With the pentane-

Table 48. Comparative study of noncarbohydrate interfering substances[a(166)]

Interfering substance	Apparent glucose (mg/100 ml)		
	PAHBAH	Ferricyanide	o-Toluidine
Glutathione	7	28	0
Uric acid	2	56	0
Creatinine	2	115	0
Bilirubin	0	0	102

[a] Automated PAHBAH, ferricyanide and semiautomated o-toluidine procedures carried out on 100 mg/100 ml solutions of glutathionine, uric acid, creatinine in water and bilirubin, 10 mg/ml in dimethyl sulphoxide, diluted 1:10 with phosphate buffer (pH 7·4).

dione reagent 2,6-dimethyl-3,5-diacetyl-1,4-dihydropyridine, **IV**, is the fluorogen formed in the reaction.

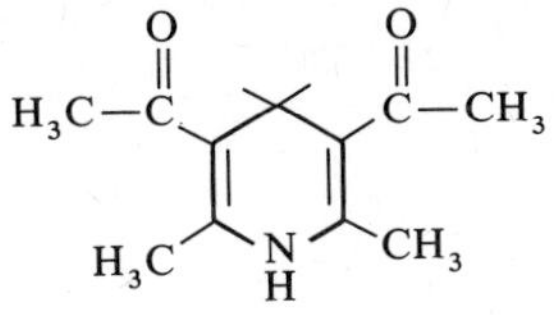

IV

1,3-Cyclohexanedione,[177] dimedone,[177] or acetoacetaldehyde acetal[178] could probably be also used in the fluorimetric determination of ammonia.

With the phenol reagent the indophenol anion is formed. This anion obtained in the determination of ammonia absorbs at 625, $m\varepsilon = 42$ in aqueous alkali and at 655, $m\varepsilon = 41\cdot3$ in alkaline isobutanol.[173] The isobutanol method is five times as sensitive as the aq alkali method; the colour in the isobutanol method is stable for more than a week, while the other method has a colour stability of about two hours. The much longer wavelength maximum of the anion in isobutanol is due to the fact that anionic resonance structures absorb at increasingly longer wavelengths with increasing solvent basicity.[179, 180]

This type of anion is formed when the reducing end-group of polysaccharides is determined colorimetrically with phenol[170] as shown in Fig. 62 for a monosaccharide-derived aldehyde.

In the determination of ammonia (formed from an aldose precursor) with bispyrazolone, e.g. 3·3′-dimethyl-5,5′-dioxo-1,1′-diphenyl-(4,4′-bi-2-pyrazoline), rubazoic acid, **V**, is formed.[174]

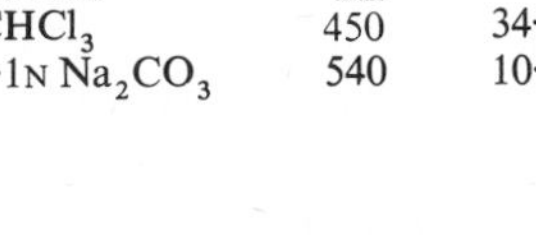

V

Solvent	λ_{max}	$m\varepsilon$
CHCl$_3$	450	34·7
0·1N Na$_2$CO$_3$	540	10·0

E. Ethylenediamine

Ethylenediamine can also be used to determine aldose precursors and analogous compounds.[182] Essentially, the fluorogen ($F394/470$) was formed

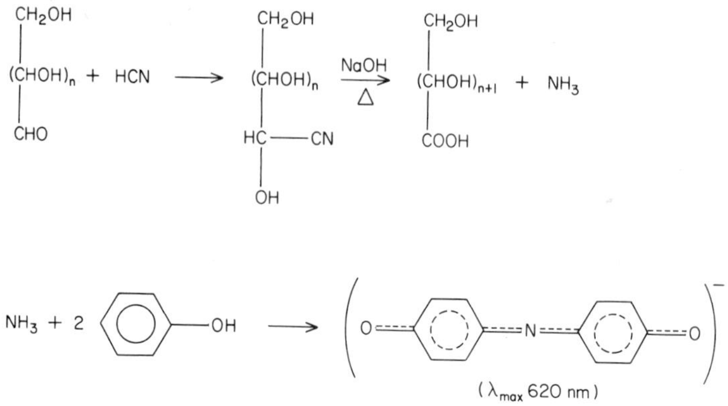

FIG. 62. Determination of an aldose precursor with cyanide and phenol.

by spraying an aq 10% solution of ethylenediamine sulphate onto a paper chromatogram containing carbohydrate spots followed by heating. Approx $0.05\ \mu g$ of D-mannose or $0.1\ \mu g$ of arabinose, ribose, xylose, galactose, glucose, fructose, rhamnose, or lactose can be detected. Deoxy sugars are as sensitive as aldoses and ketoses to this reagent, whereas uronic acids and amino sugars appear to be less sensitive $(1–5\ \mu g)$. Reducing oligosaccharides could also be detected. Ethylenediamine HCl could not be used as the reagent due to the quenching effect exerted by the chloride ion. The method has been quantitated.

Since the reaction conditions in the determination were neutral or weakly alkaline, reducing sugars could react in the aldehyde or enol form and could be determined accurately without interference from cleavage of glycosidic linkages in concomitant glycosides.[181] The mechanism of the reaction between the aldose precursor and ethylenediamine is not known. A Schiff base is probably first formed from which the fluorogen is derived. All the reducing sugars, e.g. aldoses, ketoses, deoxy sugars, amino sugars and uronic acids, form a fluorogen, $F400/465$. The data are given in Table 49. Some of the high results are probably due to contamination. Erythrose gave a value of 4.16 as compared to a value of 1 for D-glucose. Non-reducing oligosaccharides gave no fluorescence, while reducing oligosaccharides gave fluorescence at $F375,400s/463$. A rectilinear relation between the concentration of D-glucose and the fluorescence intensity was found for sample concentrations of 2×10^{-6} to 2×10^{-4} M. This corresponded to sample amounts of 4×10^{-3}–$4 \times 10^{-1}\ \mu mol$. Linear calibration curves were also obtained for D-galactose, D-mannose, D-fructose, D-arabinose, D-ribose and D-xylose. The recoveries and the reproducibility were excellent. The buffered reagent solution used in the procedure was stable for at least one month. D-Glucose could be determined in the presence of 100-fold amounts of methyl α-D-glucopyranoside or amylose.

Table 49. Fluorescence intensities obtained in the determination of aldose precursors with ethylenediamine[a][181]

Carbohydrate	λ_{max} (Ex) (nm)	λ_{max} (Em) (nm)	Relative intensity[b] at λ_{max}	No fluorescence obtained for
DL-Glyceraldehyde	400	465	1·53	Glycerol
D-Arabinose	400	465	1·25	Erythritol
D-Ribose	400	465	2·09	D-Dulcitol
D-Xylose	400	465	1·25	D-Mannitol
D-Galactose	400	465	0·98	D-Sorbitol
D-Glucose	400	465	1	D-Arabonic acid
D-Mannose	400	465	1·01	D-Gluconic acid
D-Fructose	400	465	1·12	Methyl α-D-gluco-pyranoside
L-Sorbose	400	465	1·16	Methyl β-D-gluco-pyranoside
2-Deoxy-D-ribose	400	490	0·36	Phenyl α-D-gluco-pyranoside
2-Deoxy-D-glucose	400	460	0·12	Phenyl β-D-gluco-pyranoside
L-Rhamnose	400	465	1·47	Adenosine
D-Galactosamine HCl	400	465	1·61	2′-Deoxyadenosine
D-Glucosamine HCl	400	465	1·66	Sucrose
N-Acetyl-D-galactosamine	390	465	1·55	Raffinose
N-Acetyl-D-glucosamine	375	465	2·04	Amylose
D-Galacturonic acid	400	465	1·67	Glycogen
D-Glucuronic acid	400	465	1·83	Dextran
Maltose	375	463	1·37	
Cellobiose	375	463	1·30	
Lactose	375	463	1·30	

[a] A sample amount of $4·00 \times 10^{-1}$ μmol was used for each carbohydrate.
[b] Average values of five measurements.

Determination of an aldose precursor with ethylenediamine.[181] To a buffered reagent solution (3·00 ml), prepared by mixing $2·10^{-2}$ M ethylenediamine sulphate (1 volume) and 0·6 M phosphate buffer (pH 8·00, 2 volumes), add the sample solution (2·00 ml) containing 4×10^{-3}–4×10^{-1} μmol of a reducing sugar. Heat the mixture for 3 h on a boiling water bath. Read the fluorescence intensity at 400 nm (excitation) and 465 nm (emission) within 24 hours. A standard, a reagent blank and an unknown should be run in triplicate. Calculation is made on the basis that the fluorescence intensity is directly proportional to the amounts of reducing sugars.

F. Ethyl Malonate

Ethyl malonate can also be used to determine aldose precursors.[183, 184] Glucose can be determined in the presence of cellobiose or maltose. Beer's law is obeyed from 40–200 µg of xylose per ml and 200–2000 µg of glucose per ml. The method is obviously not sensitive.

Ethyl malonate determination of sugars.[183] To 1 ml of test solution add 2 ml of 0·325 M Na_2CO_3 and 2 ml of 5% ethyl malonate in propanol. Heat at 90° for 12 min, cool, and read the absorbance at 558 nm.

G. Quinaldinium and lepidinium salts

Other groups of reagents which could be used for the determination of the aldose precursors are the quinaldinium and lepidinium salts. Trimethine cationic resonance structures would be formed from these two reagents absorbing near 600 nm and 700 nm, respectively. The reaction between 2-deoxy-D-glucose and 1-ethylquinaldinium iodide is shown in Fig. 63. The procedure used in the determination involves this type of reaction. Negative results are obtained with deoxyinosine, deoxyguanosine, deoxy-

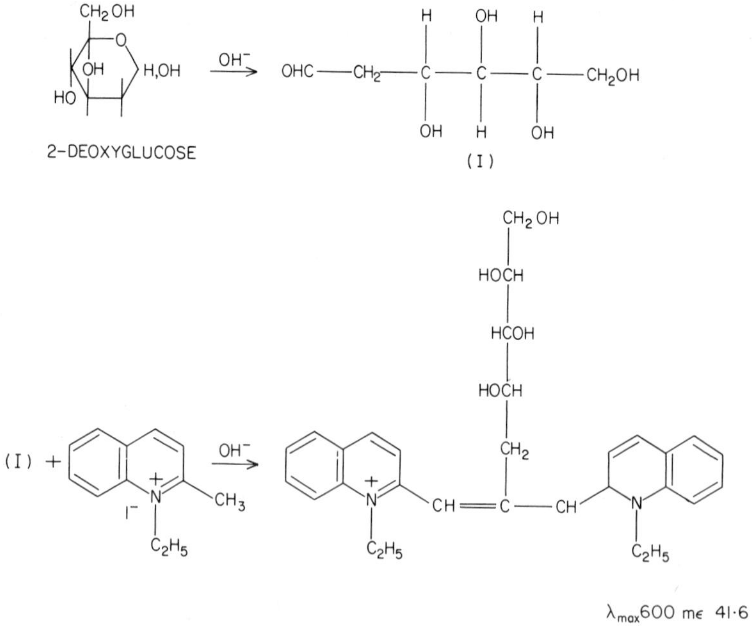

Fig. 63. Reaction between 2-deoxy-D-glucose and 1-ethylquinaldinium iodide.

adenosine, 1,1,3,3-tetramethoxypropane, 1,3,3-trimethoxypropene, deoxy-cytidine, raffinose, melezitose, trehalose, maltose, dulcitol, mannitol, and benzaldehyde.

1-Ethylquinaldinium iodide determination of aldose precursors. To 1 ml of aq test solution add 1 ml of 0·17% 1-ethylquinaldinium iodide (prepared fresh daily). Mix thoroughly and then add 1 ml 3% aq tetraethylammonium hydroxide (diluted daily from 40%). Mix well. Heat at 100° for 35 minutes. Cool in an icebath. Add 1 ml acetone. Stopper and shake. Read at λ_{max} 600 nm. Beer's law is obeyed from 1·6–16 µg of 2-deoxy-D-glucose. Results for various compounds are shown in Table 50.

Table 50. Spectral results obtained in determination of aldoses with 1-ethylquinaldinium iodide at λ_{max} 600

Compound	mε
2-Deoxy-D-glucose	41·5
2-Deoxy-D-galactose	21·0
Glucose	20·0
Fructose	18·0
Galactose	15·5
Arabinose	15·0
Tagatose	14·5
6-Deoxy-L-mannose	12·8
Ribose	11·5
6-Deoxy-D-galactose	9·8
2-Deoxy-D-ribose	9·0
Formaldehyde	17·0
5-Hydroxymethylfurfural	11·5
Furfural	5·8
5-Methylfurfural	4·4
Acrolein	2·2

The molar absorptivities obtained with the different aldose precursors could be considerably improved, since pure pinocyanol, a dye which can be formed from formaldehyde and 1-ethylquinaldinium iodide in a reaction similar to that in Figure 63, has a millimolar absorptivity of around 200 in alcoholic solvents and around 100 in aq solvents.[185, 186]

H. Hydrazines

Hydrazines can also be used as reagents in the analysis of aldose precursors. Highly coloured formazans are obtained through the reaction of a hydrazine and aldose to form a hydrazone which is subsequently reacted with a dia-zonium salt, as shown for mannose, Fig. 64. In acetic acid the mannose formazan absorbs at 455 nm, mε 18·0 and in perchloric acid the cation of this compound absorbs at 550 nm, mε 27·5.[187] Formazans of other aldoses[188, 189] and of hexuronic acids[190] have been described. The formazan chromogen could be determined as the neutral compound, the cation or the anion.

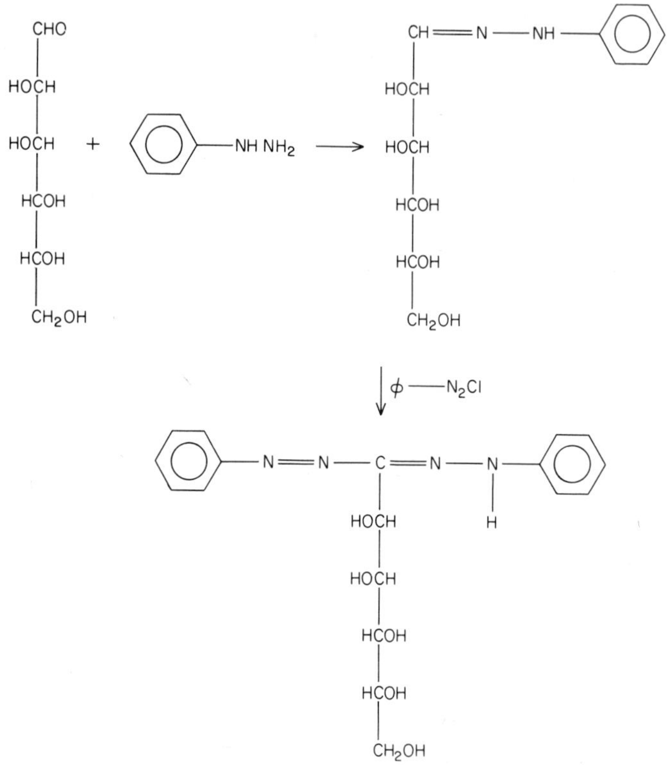

FIG. 64. Reaction of an aldose precursor with phenylhydrazine and phenyldiazonium chloride.

1. HBT

With 2-hydrazinobenzothiazole[191] as the reagent aldose precursors can be determined by the following procedure.

HBT determination of aldose precursors[191] To 1 ml aq test solution add 0·5 ml HBT (dissolve 40 mg of 2-hydrazinobenzothiazole in 2·5 ml of 0·1 N HCl and dilute to 10 ml with water) followed by 0·5 ml of 0·1 N NaOH. Heat for 10 min on the boiling water bath and then allow to cool in a water bath at 15°. Add 2 ml of 2·5% H_2O_2. After 10 min add 2 ml ethanol. After 5 min read at 580 nm.

In this procedure the best results were obtained with ribose, which gave $m\varepsilon = 28$.[192] This method could be improved. The final chromogen has the structure **VI**.

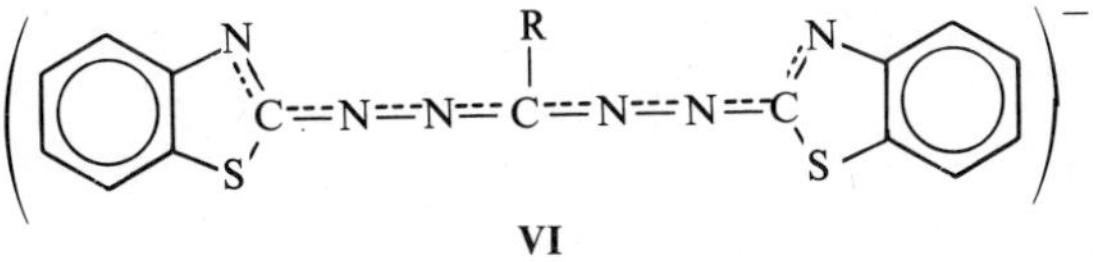

VI

These precursors could also be determined by reaction with 2-hydrazino-benzothiazole to form the hydrazone and this reacted with a *p*-nitrobenzene-diazonium salt to form a formazan anion, **VII**, as has been done with aldehydes.[193]

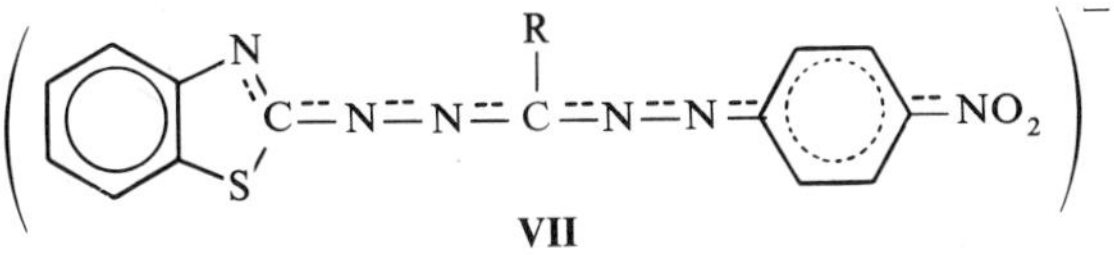

VII

2. MBTH

Since MBTH is one of the better reagents for the determination of aliphatic aldehydes, it can be used for the analysis of the aldose precursors. Thus, ribose can be hydrolysed to its free aldehyde and this determined with MBTH, Fig. 65.

A variety of sugars have been determined with MBTH.[192, 194] The results for the following procedure are summarized in Table 51.[194] Higher absorbances can be obtained with any of the sugars by appropriate modification of the procedure.

MBTH determination of atmospheric aldose precursors.[194] Extract 1–10 mg of urban airborne particles, pollen, fungi, or dust with 5 ml of water on a test tube vortex mixer for 15–20 minutes. Centrifuge, and pipette the supernatant into a 10-ml volumetric flask. Repeat with an additional 5 ml of water. Combine the extracts and dilute to 10 ml with water.

To 2 ml of aq test solution add 1 ml of 0·5% aq MBTH·HCl followed by 1 ml of 0·1 N aq sodium hydroxide solution. Heat the mixture for 8 min on a boiling water bath. Cool, and add 1 ml of the oxidizing reagent (2 g of ferric perchlorate and 8·3 ml of conc hydrochloric acid diluted to 100 ml).

Read the absorbance in 10–12 min at 620 nm against a blank containing 1 ml of distilled water instead of 0·1 N aq sodium hydroxide. This blank essentially represents adsorbed aliphatic aldehydes.

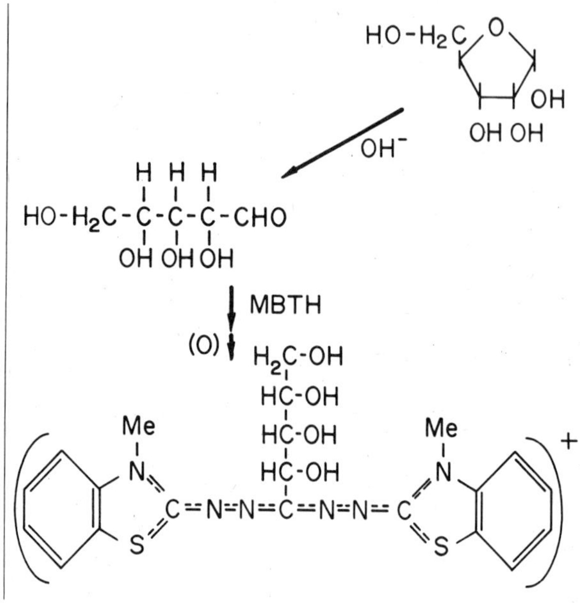

FIG. 65. Reaction of Ribose with MBTH.

The concentration of these precursors is then calculated with the following formulae

$$\mu g \text{ aldose precursors (in terms of ribose)/g particles} = \frac{21 \cdot 9A}{V_{ts}} \cdot \frac{V_t}{V_{ts}} \times \frac{1000}{Wmg}$$

$$\text{Therefore: } \mu g \text{ aldose precursors/g particles} = \frac{109500A}{Wmg}$$

$$\text{Percent aldose precursors in particles} = \frac{21 \cdot 9A \cdot V_t}{V_{ts}} \times \frac{1000}{Wmg} \times \frac{100}{106}$$

$$\text{Therefore: Percent aldose precursors in particles} = \frac{10 \cdot 95A}{Wmg}$$

where 21·9 is the number of micrograms of ribose giving an absorbance of 1 in the procedure, A is the absorbance obtained in the method at λ 650, V_t is the total volume in ml of the aq extract (essentially 10 ml) of Wmg of airborne particles. The millimolar absorptivity of ribose is 35·5 at 620 nm, and 34·3 at 656 nm.

Table 51. MBTH determination of aldoses and ketones[194]

Compound[a]	λ_{max} 620	λ_{max} 655
Maltose	54	50
Cellobiose	50	48
Dextrose	47	45
Galactose	44	42
Arabinose	44	42
Xylose	43	41
Fructose	43	41
Ribose	42	40
Sorbose	41	38
Sodium galacturonate	40	38
Dihydroxyacetone	38	36
Mannuronic acid lactone	37	36
Glucuronic acid	34	32
Fucose	33	32
Rhamnose	25	24
2-Deoxyglucose	23	23
Glucosamine HCl	18	18
2-Deoxyribose	15	15
Ascorbic acid	3	3
Hydroxyacetone	2	2

[a] Essentially negative results were obtained with adenosine, adenosine 5'-monophosphate, alcohol, deoxyadenosine, ducitol, gluconolactone, melizitose, raffinose, sedoheptulose anhydride, sucrose, uridine, and trehalose at a final concentration of 4×10^{-4} M. For the compounds in the table the concentration was 4×10^{-5} M.

Ribose was used as a standard in checking the variables of the method. Since ferric perchlorate is hygroscopic, the oxidizing solution was standardized spectrally by diluting the reagent 1:10 with water, obtaining the absorbance, and then adjusting the reagent solution so that the diluted solution gave an absorbance of 0·78 at 333 nm. After the oxidizing agent was added, the colour intensity gradually increased, reached a maximum at 10–18 min, and then gradually decreased. The precentage deviation for the method was ±4·5 for 16 determinations. Beer's law was obeyed from 1·5 ($A = 0·1$) to 25 µg of ribose.

The analysis of polysaccharides was also investigated. The two glucose disaccharides, maltose and cellobiose, gave positive results since they were easily hydrolysed to aldoses. Glycogen gave weak results; other poly-saccharides gave negative results, e.g. melizitose, raffinose, sucrose, and trehalose. By standard hydrolysis techniques these polysaccharides could be analysed by the MBTH method.

When the alkaline MBTH method was used for ribose with the only difference being the oxidizing reagent containing 70% perchloric acid instead of conc HCl, an additional band was found at 775 nm.

I. Final comments

Reagents, such as dimedone and 1,3-cyclohexanedione could probably also be used in the fluorimetric determination of some of the aldose precursors.

Other α,β-dihydroxyaldehyde precursors, such as the corticosteroids, will be discussed in a later section.

REFERENCES

1. J. M. Los, L. B. Simpson and K. Wiesner. *J. Am. Chem. Soc.* **78**, 1564 (1956).
2. O. O. Blumenfeld, M. A. Paz, P. N. Gallop and S. Seifter. *J. Biol. Chem.* **238**, 3835 (1963).
3. M. A. Paz, O. O. Blumenfeld, M. Rojkind, E. Henson, C. Furfine and P. M. Gallop *Arch. Biochem. Biophys.* **109**, 548 (1965).
4. C. A. Swenson and R. Barker. *Biochemistry* **10**, 3151 (1971).
5. D. R. Trentham, C. H. McMurray and C. I. Pogson. *Biochem. J.* **114**, 19 (1969).
6. D. Horton and J. D. Wander. *Carbohydrate Res.* **16**, 477 (1971).
7. H. S. Isbell, H. L. Frush and C. W. R. Wade. NBS Technical Note 405, National Bureau of Standards, Washington, D.C.
8. F. Petuely and N. Meixner. *Chem. Ber.* **86**, 1255 (1953).
9. E. Pascu and L. A. Hiller. *J. Am. Chem. Soc.* **70**, 523 (1948).
10. B. Singh, G. R. Dean and S. M. Cantor. *J. Am. Chem. Soc.* **70**, 517 (1948).
11. L. Berrens. *Rec. Trav. Chem. Des Pays-Bas* **84**, 1555 (1965).
12. J. Delahay and J. E. Stranner. *J. Am. Chem. Soc.* **74**, 893 (1952).
13. E. B. Sanders and J. Schubert. *Anal. Chem.* **43**, 59 (1971).
14. D. Rittenberg and C. Groff. *J. Am. Chem. Soc.* **80**, 3370 (1958).
15. C. A. L. deBruyn and W. A. vanEkenstein. *Rec. Trav. Chim.* **16**, 262 (1897).
16. H. O. L. Fischer, C. Faube and E. Baer. *Ber.* **60**, 479 (1927).
17. S. N. Danilow, E. D. Venus-Danilowa and P. Shantarowitsch. *Ber.* **63**, 2269 (1930).
18. E. F. L. J. Anet. *Adv. Carbohydrate Chem.* **19**, 181 (1964).
19. R. J. Henry. "Clinical Chemistry: Principles and Techniques", Hoeber of Parker and Row, New York, 1964, pp. 620–689.
20. C. A. Trommer, see E. Mitscherlich. *Ann. Chem. Pharm.* **39**, 360 (1841).
21. H. V. Fehling. *Arch. Physiol. Heilk* **7**, 64 (1848).
22. S. R. Benedict. *J. Biol. Chem.* **5**, 485 (1909).
23. S. R. Benedict. *J. Am. Med. Assoc.* **57**, 1194 (1911).
24. E. Garfield. Current Contents No. 2, January 9, 1974, p. 5.
25. O. Folin and H. Wu. *J. Biol. Chem.* **41**, 367 (1920).
26. O. Folin. *J. Biol. Chem.* **67**, 357 (1926).

27. O. Folin and A. Svedberg. *J. Biol. Chem.* **70**, 405 (1926).
28. S. R. Benedict. *J. Biol. Chem.* **76**, 457 (1928).
29. O. Folin. *J. Biol. Chem.* **82**, 83 (1929).
30. S. R. Benedict. *J. Biol. Chem.* **92**, 141 (1931).
31. H. J. Fister. Manual of Standardized Procedures for Spectrophotometric Chemistry, Standard Scientific Supply Corp., New York, 1950, p. 1.
32. S. R. Benedict. *J. Biol. Chem.* **64**, 207 (1925).
33. D. Melnick, H. Field, Jr. and W. D. Robinson. *J. Nutrition* **18**, 593 (1939).
34. N. Nelson. *J. Biol. Chem.* **153**, 375 (1944).
35. M. Somogyi. *J. Biol. Chem.* **160**, 61 (1945).
36. M. Somogyi. *J. Biol. Chem.* **160**, 69 (1945).
37. J. L. Pope. *Am. J. Clin. Pathol.* **20**, 801 (1950).
38. H. Frank and E. Kirkberger. *Biochem. Z.* **320**, 359 (1950).
39. M. Somogyi. *J. Biol. Chem.* **195**, 19 (1952).
40. A. M. Asatoor and E. J. King, *Biochem. J.* **56**, xliv (1954).
41. G. R. Moore, I. C. Barnes, and C. A. Pennock. *Clin. Chim. Acta* **41**, 439 (1972).
42. M. E. Brown. *Diabetes* **10**, 60 (1961).
43. E. M. Gindler. Presented at American Medical Technologists National Meeting, Denver, Colorado, July 1970; *Clin. Chem.* **16**, 519, 536 (1970).
44. I. Schoen. *Tech. Bull. Reg. Med. Technologists* **30**, 188 (1960).
45. D. B. Tonks. *Am. J. Clin. Pathol.* **22**, 1009 (1952).
46. F. V. Lauber and M. R. Mattice. *J. Lab. Clin. Med.* **29**, 113 (1944).
47. H. G. Wager. *Analyst* **79**, 34 (1954).
48. J. E. Hodge and B. T. Hofreiter. *Methods in Carbohydrate Chem.* **1**, 38 (1962).
49. M. Samson. *Am. J. Clin. Pathol.* **22**, 1106 (1952).
50. J. P. Comer. *Anal. Chem.* **28**, 1748 (1956).
51. H. Bickel. *J. Pediat.* **59**, 641 (1961).
52. I. S. Menzies and J. W. T. Seakins, in I Smith, Ed. "Chromatographic and Electrophoretic Techniques", Vol. I, 3rd. ed., Wiley, New York, 1969, pp. 310–329.
53. J. G. Kirchner, "Thin-Layer Chromatography", Interscience, New York, 1967, pp. 353–371.
54. B. A. Lewis and F. Smith, in E. Stahl, Ed. "Thin-Layer Chromatography", 2nd ed., Springer-Verlag, New York, 1969 pp. 807–837.
55. R. M. Scott. "Clinical Analysis by Thin-Layer Chromatography Techniques", Humphrey Science Publishers, Ann Arbor, 1969, pp. 47–78.
56. O. Folin. *J. Biol. Chem.* **81**, 231 (1929).
57. F. W. Landgrebe and K. A. Munday. *Quart. J. Exp. Physiol.* **39**, 17 (1954).
58. D. L. Rucknagel, E. B. Page and W. N. Jensen. *Blood* **10**, 999 (1955).
59. J. Johnson. *Am. J. Med. Technol.* **24**, 271 (1958).
60. R. I. Mateles. *Nature* **187**, 241 (1960).
61. M. Herbain. *Bull. Soc. Chim. Biol.* **31**, 1104 (1949).
62. S. Nussenbaum and W. Z. Hassid. *Anal. Chem.* **24**, 501 (1952).
63. W. S. Hoffman. *J. Biol. Chem.* **120**, 51 (1927).
64. J. F. Robyt, R. J. Ackerman and J. G. Keng. *Anal. Biochem.* **45**, 517 (1972).
65. S. Watanabe, S. Rokushika, F. Murakami, H. Aoshima and H. Hatano. *Anal. Letters* **6**, 363 (1973).
66. J. C. Weed and A. E. Carrera. *Fertil. Steril.* **21**, 866 (1970)..
67. B. Klein and L. B. Lucas. *Clin. Chem.* **17**, 97 (1971).
68. O. Schales and S. S. Schales. *Arch. Biochem.* **8**, 285 (1945).

69. B. Fingerhut. *Tech. Bull. Reg. Med. Technol.* **38**, 315 (1968).
70. W. R. Moorehead and E. A. Sasse. *Clin. Chem.* **16**, 285 (1970).
71. M. Z. Barakat and M. E. A. El-Wahab. *J. Pharm. Pharmacol.* **3**, 511 (1951).
72. H. El Khaden and G. Wissam. *Anal. Chem.* **33**, 645 (1961).
73. H. El Khaden and S. Hanessian. *Anal. Chem.* **30**, 1965 (1958).
74. A. J. Lombard. *J. Chromatog.* **26**, 283 (1967).
75. S. Aronoff and L. Vernon. *Arch. Biochem. Biophys.* **28**, 424 (1950).
76. G. L. Miller and A. L. Burton. *Anal. Chem.* **31**, 1790 (1959).
77. A. M. Mattson and C. O. Jensen. *Anal. Chem.* **22**, 182 (1950).
78. R. A. Fairbridge, K. I. Willis and R. G. Booth. *Biochem. J.* **49**, 423 (1951).
79. A. Wallenfels, E. Bernt and G. Limberg. *Angew. Chem.* **23**, 581 (1953).
80. A. Carruthers and A. E. Wootton. *Intern. Sugar J.* **62**, 193 (1955).
81. K. Amako. *Proc. Res. Soc. Japan Sugar Refineries Technologists* **7**, 65 (1958); through *Anal. Abstr.* **6**, No. 3183 (1959).
82. E. M. Livingston. *Microchem. J.* **1**, 265 (1957).
83. N. D. Cheronis and M. C. Zymaris. *Mikrochim. Acta* 769 (1957).
84. W. E. Trevelyn, D. P. Procter and J. S. Harrison. *Nature*, **166**, 444 (1950).
85. K. Wallenfels. *Naturwissenschaften* **37**, 491 (1950).
86. D. Karba and A. Stalc. *Farmaceutski Vest.* **20**, 277 (1969).
87. G. L. Miller. *Anal. Chem.* **31**, 426 (1959).
88. T. Takemoto, K. Daigo and T. Takoi. *J. Pharm. Soc. Japan* **75**, 1024 (1955); through *Anal. Abstr.* **4**, No. 162 (1957).
89. H. J. Wissfeld. *Die Medizinische* 712 (1955).
90. G. Giannettasio. *Laboratorie* **7**, 515 (1952).
91. W. Thomas and R. A. Dutcher. *J. Am. Chem. Soc.* **46**, 1662 (1924).
92. C. F. Poe and F. G. Edson. *Ind. Eng. Chem. Anal. Ed.* **4**, 300 (1932).
93. J. B. Sumner. *J. Biol. Chem.* **62**, 287 (1924).
94. E. Borel, F. Hostettler and H. Deuel. *Helv. Chim. Acta* **35**, 115 (1952).
95. D. J. Bell, D. J. Manners and A. Palmer. *J. Chem. Soc.* **3760** (1952).
96. J. Lee. *Brit. Med. J.* 1087 (1954).
97. R. T. Bottler and G. A. Gilbert. *Chem. Ind. London* 575 (1956).
98. R. T. Bottler and G. A. Gilbert. *Analyst*, **83**, 403 (1958).
99. V. V. Kozlov and V. N. Khrustaleva. *Sbornik Nauch. Rabot. Mosk. Inst. Nar. Khoz.* 353 (1957); through *Anal. Abstr.*, **6**, No. 960 (1959).
100. J. B. Sumner. *J. Biol. Chem.* **65**, 383 (1925).
101. E. Borel and H. Deuel. *Helv. Chim. Acta* **36**, 801 (1953).
102. T. Momose, A. Inaba, Y. Mukai and M. Watanabe. *Talanta* **4**, 33 (1960).
103. W. M. Dehn and F. A. Hartman. *J. Am. Chem. Soc.* **36**, 403 (1914).
104. J. Sanduzzi. *Am. J. Med. Technol.* **26**, 264 (1960).
105. R. F. Milton. *Analyst* **87**, 183 (1942).
106. I. St. Lorant. *J. Clin. Pathol.* **10**, 136 (1957).
107. J. C. Godfrain, P. Bertrand and L. Liandier. *Lait* **39**, 32 (1959).
108. E. L. Hirst, L. Hough and J. K. N. Jones. *J. Chem. Soc.* 928 (1949).
109. J. R. Hawthorne. *Nature* **160**, 714 (1947).
110. U. Lippold. *Biochem. Z.* **323**, 115 (1952).
111. R. Jeanloz. *Helv. Chim. Acta* **29**, 57 (1946).
112. C. Yoshimura and M. Kiboku. *J. Chem. Soc. Japan* **77**, 1546 (1957); through *Chem. Abstr.* **52**, 3377 (1958).
113. H. Ziegler. *Ind. Chim. Belge* **22**, 533 (1957).
114. A. G. E. Pearse and H. Zimmermann. *J. Histochem. Cytochem.* **7**, 298 (1959).

115. J. E. Sinsheimer and E. F. Salim. *Anal. Chem.* **37**, 566 (1965).
116. E. F. Salim, P. E. Manni and J. E. Sinsheimer. *J. Pharm. Soc.* **53**, 391 (1964).
117. D. Barnes. *J. Am. Pharm. Assoc., Sci. Ed.* **42**, 669 (1953).
118. C. Chen, J. Wheeler and H. E. Tewell. *J. Lab. Clin. Med.* **42**, 749 (1953).
119. A. Henly. *Nature* **169**, 877 (1952).
120. H. Hofmann and H. Staudinger. *Naturwissenschaften* **38**, 213 (1951).
121. H. Hofmann and H. Staudinger. *Biochem. Z.* **322**, 230 (1951).
122. W. J. Mader and R. R. Buck, *Anal. Chem.* **24**, 666 (1952).
123. P. E. Manni and J. E. Sinsheimer. *Anal. Chem.* **33**, 1900 (1961).
124. K. Lorentz and H. Hoffmeister. *Mikrochim. Acta* 1062 (1966).
125. A. M. Mattson, C. O. Jenson and R. A. Dutcher. *Science* **106**, 294 (1947).
126. H. B. Mark, Jr., L. M. Backes and D. Pinkel. *Talanta* **12**, 27 (1965).
127. R. Tinelli. *Bull. Soc. Biol.* **48**, 182 (1966).
128. C. W. Raadsveld and H. Klomp. *J. Chromatog.* **57**, 99 (1971).
129. J. Koops. *Neth. Milk Dairy J.* **15**, 248 (1961).
130. A. Gottschalk. "Glycoproteins", Elsevier, Amsterdam. 1966.
131. E. Sawicki. *Critical Reviews in Anal. Chem.* **1**, 300 (1970).
132. I. Smith. "Chromatographic Techniques", Heinemann, London, 1958, Ch. 9.
133. E. N. McIntosh. *J. Food Sci.* **30**, 986 (1965).
134. J. Mes and L. Kamm. *J. Chromatog.* **38**, 120 (1968).
135. J. Mes and L. Kamm. *J. Chromatog.* **43**, 480 (1969).
136. D. Grässlin and H. Weicker. *Clin. Chem. Acta* **21**, 15 (1968).
137. E. Moczar, M. Moczar, G. Schillinger and L. Robert. *J. Chromatog.* **31**, 561. (1967).
138. F. G. Fischer and H. J. Nebil. *Z. Physiol. Chem.* **302**, 10 (1955).
139. F. G. Fischer and H. Dörfel. *Z. Physiol. Chem.* **301**, 225 (1955).
140. See ref. 109, p. 197.
141. G. S. Marks, R. D. Marshall, A. Neuberger and G. Papkoff. *Biochem. Biophys. Acta* **63**, 340 (1962).
142. L. Roberts, J. Parlebas, P. Oudea, A. Zweibaum and B. Robert, in G. R. Tristram, Ed. "Biochemistry of Connective and Skeletal Tissues", Butterworths, London, 1965, p. 406.
143. Ref. 109, p. 190.
144. L. Mester, E. Moczar, G. Wass and L. Szabados. *Compt. Rend.* **269**, 2342 (1965).
145. J. Montreuil, A. Adam-Chausson and G. Spik. *Bull. Soc. Chim. Biol.* **47**, 1867 (1965).
146. R. E. Oborn, R. A. Libby, J. M. Ernst and J. C. Henderson. *Cereal Chem.* **48**, 270 (1971).
147. T. Momose, Y. Mukai and M. Watanabe. *Talanta* **5**, 275 (1960).
148. T. Momose, J. Tomita and Y. Yano. *Japan Analyst* **13**, 877 (1964).
149. T. Momose, Y. Mukai, S. Kawabe, J. Suzuki and K. Yamamoto. *Japan Analyst* **11**, 956 (1962).
150. T. Momose and Y. Mukai. *Yakugaku Zasshi* **81**, 227 (1961).
151. T. Momose, Y. Yano and Y. Itakura. *Japan Analyst* **14**, 240 (1965).
152. E. Sawicki. "Photometric Organic Analysis", Wiley-Interscience, New York, 1970, p. 608.
153. R. C. Lewis and S. R. Benedict. *J. Biol. Chem.* **20**, 61 (1915).
154. R. C. Lewis and S. R. Benedict. *Proc. Soc. Exp. Biol. Med.* **11**, 57 (1913–1914).
155. W. Thalhimer and H. Updegraff. *J. Am. Med. Assoc.* **78**, 1383 (1922).
156. F. Tateo. *Industrie aliment. Pinerolo* **8**, 71 (1969).

157. I. Nishioka, R. Matsuo and Y. Ohkura. *Yakugaku Zasshi* **88**, 1281 (1968).
158. C. Szustkiewicz and J. Demetriou. *Clin. Chim. Acta* **32**, 355 (1971).
159. L. Berrens and E. Bleumink. *Rec. Trav. Chim.* **85**, 59 (1966).
160. L. Berrens and E. Bleumink. *Intern. Arch. Allergy* **28**, 150 (1965).
161. L. Berrens. *Rec. Trav. Chim.* **85**, 1117 (1966); Progress in Allergy, Vol 14, Karger, Basel, 1970, pp. 259–339. Monographs in Allergy, Vol 7, Karger, Basel, 1971, pp. 1–298.
162. H. S. Burton, D. J. McWeeny, P. N. Pandhi and D. O. Biltcliffe. *Nature* **196**, 948 (1962).
163. H. S. Burton, D. J. McWeeny and D. O. Biltcliffe. *Chem. Ind. London* 219 (1962).
164. H. S. Burton, D. J. McWeeny and D. O. Biltcliffe. '*Chem. Ind. London* 1682 (1962).
165. M. Lever. *Anal. Biochem.* **47**, 273 (1972).
166. J. C. Powell and M. Lever. *Biochem. Med.* **6**, 543 (1972).
167. K. M. Dubowsky. *Clin. Chem.* **8**, 215 (1962).
168. V. M. Sardesai and H. S. Provido. *Microchem. J.* **14**, 550 (1969).
169. M. Rubin and L. Knott. *Clin. Chim. Acta* **18**, 409 (1967).
170. F. Smith and R. Montgomery, in D. Glick, Ed., "Methods of Biochemical Analysis", Vol. III, Interscience, New York, 1956, p. 153.
171. J. K. Fawcett and J. E. Scott. *J. Clin. Pathol.* **13**, 156 (1960).
172. A. L. Chaney and E. P. Marbach. *Clin. Chem.* **8**, 130 (1962).
173. P. J. Rommers and J. Visser. *Analyst* **94**, 653 (1969).
174. L. Prochazkova. *Anal. Chem.* **36**, 865 (1964).
175. H. Kala. *Die Pharmazie* **18**, 29 (1963).
176. E. Sawicki and H. Johnson. *Chemist-Analyst* **55**, 101 (1966).
177. E. Sawicki and R. A. Carnes. *Mikrochim. Acta* **148** (1968).
178. E. Sawicki, C. R. Sawicki, C. C. Golden and T. Kober. *Microchem. J.* **15**, 25 (1970).
179. E. Sawicki, "Photometric Organic Analysis", Wiley-Interscience, New York, 1970, ch. 10.
180. E. Sawicki, T. Winfield and C. R. Sawicki. *Microchem. J.* **15**, 294 (1970).
181. S. Honda, K. Kakimoto, K. Sudo, K. Kakehi and K. Takiura. *Anal. Chim. Acta* **70**, 133 (1974).
182. S. Honda, K. Kakimoto, K. Kakehi and K. Takiura. *Anal. Chim. Acta* **64**, 310 (1973).
183. T. Harada, Y. Kin-Nou, K. Kamakura, K. Toda and R. Nakai *J. Agric. Chem. Soc. Japan* **37**, 80 (1963).
184. T. Harada. *Biochem. Biophys. Acta* **63**, 334 (1962).
185. E. Sawicki, T. W. Stanley and J. Pfaff. *Anal. Chim. Acta* **28**, 156 (1963).
186. E. Sawicki, T. W. Stanley, J. Pfaff and J. Ferguson. "Analytical Chemistry 1962", Elseview, Amsterdam, 62.
187. H. S. Isbell and A. J. Fatiadi. *Carbohydrate Research* **11**, 303 (1969).
188. L. Mester and A. Major. *J. Am. Chem. Soc.* **78**, 1403 (1956).
189. L. Mester. *Advances in Carbohydrate Chemistry* **13**, 105 (1958).
190. L. Mester and E. Moczar. *J. Chem. Soc.* **1699** (1958).
191. E. Sawicki and T. R. Hauser. *Anal. Chem* **32**, 1434 (1960).
192. J. Bartos. *Ann. pharm. fr.* **20**, 650 (1962).
193. E. Sawicki and T. W. Stanley. *Mikrochim. Acta* **510** (1960).
194. E. Sawicki, R. Schumacher and C. R. Engel. *Microchem. J.* **12**, 377 (1967).

15. ALDOSTERONE, PRECURSORS

Mixed function oxidation of corticosterone and 18-hydroxycorticosterone is involved in the biosynthesis of aldosterone, Fig. 66.[1] Cytochrome P-450 is involved in the biosynthesis of aldosterone from corticosterone by adrenal mitochondria[2] and is also involved in the conversion of 18-hydroxycorticosterone to aldosterone. Oxygen and NADPH are required in the reaction.

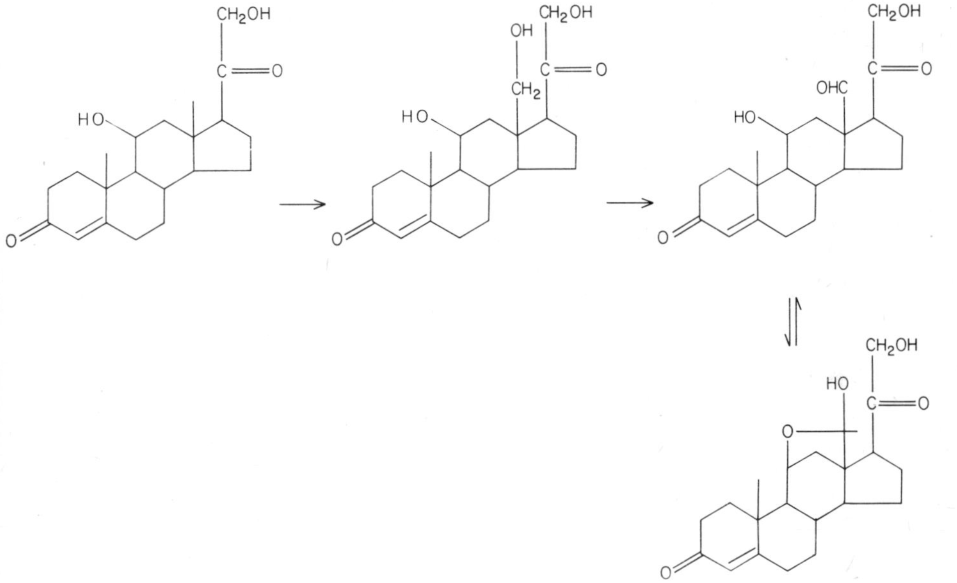

FIG. 66. Formation of aldosterone from corticosterone.

This type of reaction is a fairly general phenomenon which fits in with the presence of aerobic alcohol-oxidizing enzyme systems in the liver.[3] In the biosyntheses of the gibberelins there is an analogous conversion of an alcohol group to an aldehyde apparently catalysed by a mixed function oxidase system.[4, 5] Other reactions involving a mixed function oxidation of a methyl group to an alcohol and to an aldehyde have been reported in mammals and plant systems.[3, 4, 6]

245

REFERENCES

1. E. T. Marusic, A. White and A. R. Aedo. *Arch Biochem.* **157**, 320 (1973).
2. P. Greengard, S. Psychoyos, H. H. Tallan, D. Y. Cooper, O. Rosenthal and R. W. Estabrook. *Arch. Biochem. Biophys.* **121**, 298 (1967).
3. W. H. Orme-Johnson and D. M. Siegler. *Biochem. Biophys. Res. Commun.* **21**, 78 (1965).
4. D. T. Dennis and C. A. West. *J. Biol. Chem.* **242**, 3293 (1967).
5. P. J. Murphy and C. West. *Arch. Biochem. Biophys.* **133**, 395 (1969).
6. W. L. Miller, D. R. Brady and J. L. Gaylor. *J. Biol. Chem.* **246**, 5147 (1971).

16. ALKOXY AND ARYLOXY ACETALDEHYDES, PRECURSORS

The existence of acylated alk-1-enyl and alkyl α-glycerol ethers as naturally occurring lipids is well established[1-4] but very little work has been done on the analysis of the latter ethers. Since these compounds can be oxidized by periodate to alkoxyacetaldehyde,[5, 6] many of the methods described in the formaldehyde, acetaldehyde and aliphatic aldehyde sections could be readily modified to the determination of the alkyl (or aryl) α-glycerol ethers. The methods of periodate oxidation described in the formaldehyde and aliphatic aldehyde precursor sections could also be used.

Glycide ethers can be converted by catalytic hydration to alkyl or aryl α-glycerol ethers,[7] which can then be oxidized to alkoxy or aryloxy acetaldehydes. Many 2,4-dinitrophenylhydrazones of these latter acetaldehydes have been prepared.[5] Using paper chromatography with Whatman No. 4 paper impregnated with dimethylformamide or paraffin and the solvent systems petroleum ether–hexane (3:1), saturated with dimethylformamide or acetone–water–dimethylformamide (5:2:3), these various dinitrophenyl-hydrazones were separated.

In the analysis of an alkyl or aryl α-glycerol ether, the following reaction takes place:

$$RO—CHOH—CH_2OH \xrightarrow{IO_4^-} ROCH_2CHO + CH_2O$$

Any of the methods we have described for formaldehyde, for CH_2CHO compounds or for aliphatic aldehydes could be used. In the literature a p-nitrophenylhydrazone and a chromotropic acid procedure were used.[6, 8]

Alkyl α-glycerol ethers in cardiac muscle, cod liver oil, and beef heart lipid, as well as dodecyl α-glycerol ether, chymyl alcohol and batyl alcohol, were assayed by the following procedure. Characterization of individual ethers was accomplished with TLC and GLC.

Determination of alkyl α-glycerol ethers.[6] Place duplicate aliquots of the test solution (estimated to contain 0·01–0·60 μmole of the ether) in 50 ml ground-glass stoppered centrifuge tubes. Remove solvent under a stream of nitrogen.

I

Treat a standard and a blank similarly. Add 1 ml of alcoholic periodic acid (5 mg/ml), swirl mixture and let stand for 15 min. Add, in sequence, 2 ml water, 0·7 ml of 1·2 N sodium arsenite, and 0·5 ml of 5N H_2SO_4. Swirl the mixture and let stand until the brown colour disappears. When the solution is clear, add 1 ml of 0·026 M p-nitrophenylhydrazine and 9 ml of 95% ethanol. Heat the mixture at 70°C for 20 min. Then cool in ice for 10 minutes. Add 10 ml of water followed by 10 ml of n-heptane. Shake the tubes for 30 sec, clarify the phases by centrifugation, and discard the bottom layer. Wash the upper layer twice with 10 ml of water. Remove an 8 ml aliquot of the heptane phase and dry under nitrogen at 70°. Dissolve the residue in 5 ml of 95% ethanol. Read the absorbance at 380 nm against the blank.

REFERENCES

1. M. L. Karnovsky and W. S. Rapson. *J. Soc. Chem. Ind.* **65**, 425 (1946).
2. J. R. Gilbertson and M. L. Karnovsky. *J. Biol. Chem.* **238**, 893 (1963).
3. H. E. Carter, D. B. Smith and D. N. Jones. *J. Biol. Chem.* **232**, 681 (1958).
4. M. M. Rapport, B. Lerner, N. Alonzo and R. E. Franzl. *J. Biol. Chem.* **225**, 859 (1957).
5. V. Ulbrich and J. Markes. *J. Chromatog.* **15**, 371 (1964).
6. R. A. Gelman and J. R. Gilbertson. *Anal. Biochem.* **31**, 463 (1969).
7. V. Ulbrich, J. Markes and M. Jurecek. *Coll. Czech. Chem. Commun.* **29**, 1466. (1964).
8. M. L. Karnovsky and A. F. Brumm. *J. Biol. Chem.* **216**, 289 (1955).

17. N-ALKYLPYRROLE-2-CARBOXALDEHYDES, PRECURSORS

These aldehydes are formed in the browning reaction of D-xylose (or 3-deoxy-D-pentosone) with alkylamines.[1] The yield of 2,4-dinitrophenylhydrazone was 225 mg from 12 g of D-xylose. These aldehydes were characterized through their dinitrophenylhydrazones, I, through comparison of their absorption spectra with the known compounds.

R	λ_{max}	mε
CH_3-	218,308,407	21·8, 10·3, 27·1
$CH_3(CH_2)_3-$	224,309,407	16·8, 9·8, 26·5

REFERENCE

1. H. Kato. *Agr. Biol. Chem.* **30,** 822 (1966).

18. 2-AMINOADIPALDEHYDIC ACID, PRECURSORS (2-AMINOADIPATE δ-SEMIALDEHYDE OR ALLYSINE)

The aldehyde, **I**, can be in equilibrium with Δ^1-piperideine-6-carboxylate, **II**. The relative proportions of **I** and **II** probably depend on pH and the composition of the mixture in which the aldehyde is present.

It has long been known that the leucofuchsin reagent of Schiff can colour elastic fibres or membranes.[1] The identity of the aldehyde precursor in this reaction has been stated to be plasmalogens, pseudoplasmalogens or unsaturated fatty acids oxidized by fixatives[2,3] and recently 2-aminoadipaldehydic acid or its precursor.[4] A vivid purple-red colour is obtained in the reaction of Schiff's reagent (conventional pH 2·5 or pH 6·7) with rat aortic elastin of animals 20 and 40d old. The elastin from 18-month old animals and the elastin from young animals (when subjected to aldehyde blockage prior to periodate oxidation) were not stained. Similarly this reaction is positive with human elastin from many different organs up to 20 years of age thereafter being unreactive.[5] Other analogous reports have been the intense periodic acid—Schiff (probably just Schiff's reagent) reactivity with neonatal rat aortic elastin[6] and with human aortic elastin until the later half of the first decade.[7] During the very active period of elastinogenesis larger amounts of semialdehydes are present[8] and the Schiff or MBTH tests would give their most intense reactions. Evidence has been presented indicating that the Schiff and periodic acid–Schiff reactivity with elastin is due to an intermediate compound, 2–aminoadipaldehydic acid, formed during the conversion of lysine to one of several cross-linking amino acids found in elastin.[4] There is a direct correlation between the formation of 2-aminoadipaldehydic acid and Schiff's reagent reactivity with elastin.[9] In addition, the addition of the lathyrogen, β-aminopropionitrile, which blocks the conversion of lysine to the semialdehyde,[10] results in a marked reduction in Schiff staining of chick aortic elastin. It has been suggested that the inability of Schiff's reagent to react with elastin from older animals and humans can be explained on the basis of elastin having been synthesized and cross-linked, the semialdehydes are present in, at most, minimal amounts.[4]

The initial reaction in the formation of intra- or intermolecular bonds in collagen or elastin is the oxidative deamination of the ε-amino groups of lysyl residues, forming 2-aminoadipaldehydic acid.[11,12] Subsequently these aldehydes react with adjacent lysyl ε-amino groups by a Schiff base reaction, or by aldol condensation with adjacent 2-aminoadipaldehydic acid groups.[13] These are predominant linkages in collagen and elastin. The ring structures of desmosine and isodesmosine are derived from the latter in elastin.[14,15] A lysyl oxidase obtained from embryonic chick cartilage catalyses the formation of 2-aminoadipaldehydic acid[16,17] from many lysyl residues in elastin[6] and from some lysyl and hydroxylysyl residues in collagen.[18] Once the aldehydes are available cross-linkages can then take place through aldol condensations and Schiff base formations in the collagen or elastin fibres.[19]

With the recent finding that lysyl oxidase from chick cartilage and aortic tissue has an enhanced stability in buffers containing urea and can be purified and recovered in high yield from DEAE–cellulose and collagen-derivatized sepharose,[17,20] the nature of this key enzymatic reaction can now be unravelled.

When collagen is incubated with preparations of lysyl oxidase, 2-amino-adipaldehydic acid[18] and the cross-linking compound, hydroxylysinonor-leucine[21] are formed. Hydroxylysine-derived aldehydes are also found in these preparations (discussed in the α-amino-δ-hydroxyadipic-δ-semi-aldehyde precursor section).

The various properties and reactions attributed to lysyl oxidase could be derived from a single enzyme but most probably represents several enzymes. Copper (II) appears to be an integral part of the enzyme.[22] Enzyme activity requires oxygen.[17,22] Pyridoxal may be a cofactor.[23] Oxygen is a reactant in the formation of the aldehyde and is a source of the aldehydic oxygen.

In addition to the aldehydes which participate in the cross-linking process, additional aldehyde groups are synthesized from lysine.[24-27] Incubation of neutral salt-soluble collagen from rat skin at 37° is accompanied by a conversion of some lysine residues into peptide-bound 2-aminoadipalde-hydic acid[13] as determined by the MBTH method[28] described in the aliphatic aldehydes section. Neutral salt-soluble chromogen incubated with lysyl oxidase forms the aldehyde which is determined with MBTH.[29]

The collagen defects in homocystinuria are attributed to blockage of the aldehyde by homocysteine, Fig. 67,[13] thus inhibiting cross-linkage of the protocollagen to form stable collagen. It is possible for D-penicillamine to block the linkage also,[13, 29, 30] Fig. 67.

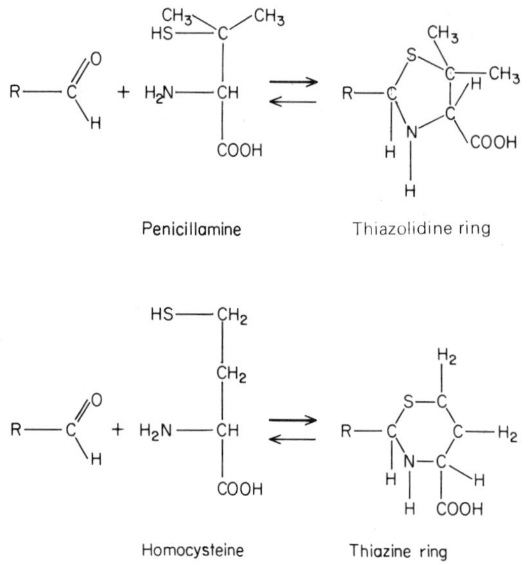

Penicillamine   Thiazolidine ring

Homocysteine   Thiozine ring

FIG. 67.   The reaction of an aldehyde with amino–thiol compounds.

Feulgen and Voit [31] described a Schiff-positive native aldehyde in elastic tissue, insoluble in fat tissues, requiring no acid hydrolysis and blocked by bisulphite or phenylhydrazine. The MBTH reagent has been used in its detection,[32, 33] but has been called very sensitive but unstable.[34] A review of the literature[5] states that the Schiff reaction is positive in most laboratory animal arterial elastin, and in young children, variable at 10–20 years and in some older animals and negative in adult human arteries. In the light of these studies Labella's[3] pungent, aldehyde–positive oil extracted by chloroform from an elastase digest and his "pseudoplasmalogen" are probably 2-aminoadipaldehydic acid.[34] In the staining of elastin with mono and diamino monoazo and other dyes, the reactive aldehyde appears to be 2-aminoadipaldehydic acid.[34]

See the peptide aldehyde precursors and protein aldehydes sections for further details.

The aldehyde can also be derived from lysine with the help of the enzyme L-lysine-6-aminotransferase (L-lysine: 2-oxoglutarate 6-aminotransferase, EC 2.6.1.36).[35, 36] e.g.

L-Lysine + 2-Oxoglutarate = 2-Aminoadipate δ-semialdehyde + L-Glutamate

The enzyme is a pyridoxal phosphate protein.

On the basis of the work summarized here and in other sections of these volumes, it would appear that Schiff's reagent, MBTH, and some of the other reagents described in the volumes could be of value in studying elastin biosynthesis *in situ*, especially when used in conjunction with other techniques such as autoradiography and microcolorimetry.

REFERENCES

1. A. G. E. Pearse, "Histochemistry," Vol. I, Little, Brown and Co., Boston, 1968.
2. R. E. Flygare, H. S. Broderson and E. R. Hayes. *Stain Technol.* **45**, 149 (1970).
3. F. S. Labella. *J. Histochem. Cytochem.* **6**, 260 (1958).
4. D. K. MacCallum. *Stain Technology* **48**, 117 (1973).
5. P. Pizzolato and R. D. Lillie. *Arch. Path.* **88**, 581 (1969).
6. W. J. Paule. *J. Ultrastruct. Res.* **8**, 219 (1963).
7. S. Bertelson in M. Sandler and G. H. Bourne, Eds "Atherosclerosis and its Origin," Academic Press, New York, 1963.
8. S. M. Partridge. *Gerontologia (Basel)* **15**, 85 (1969).
9. E. J. Miller and H. M. Fullmer. *J. Exp. Med.* **123**, 1097 (1966).
10. S. R. Pinnell, G. R. Martin and E. J. Miller. *Science* **161**, 475 (1968).
11. P. Bornstein, A. H. Kang and K. A. Piez. *Proc. Natl. Acad. Sci. U.S.* **55**, 417 (1966).
12. P. Bornstein and K. A. Piez. *Biochemistry* **5**, 3460 (1966).
13. S. H. Jackson. *Clin. Chim. Acta* **45**, 215 (1973).
14. A. J. Bailey and C. M. Peach. *Biochem. J.* **121**, 257 (1971).
15. J. Thomas, D. F. Elsden and S. M. Partridge. *Nature* **200**, 651 (1963).
16. S. R. Pinnell and G. R. Martin. *Proc. Nat. Acad. Sci. U.S.* **61**, 708 (1968).
17. A. S. Narayanan, R. C. Siegel and G. R. Martin. *Arch. Biochem. Biophys.* **162**, 231 (1974).
18. R. C. Siegel and G. R. Martin. *J. Biol. Chem.* **245**, 1653 (1970).
19. K. A. Piez. *Ann. Rev. Biochem.* **35**, 547 (1968).
20. E. D. Harris, W. A. Gonrerman and B. L. O'Dell. *Fed. Proc.* **32**, 594 (1973).
21. A. J. Bailey and L. J. Fowler. *Biochem. Biophys. Res. Commun.* **35**, 672 (1969).
22. R. C. Siegel, S. R. Pinnell and G. R. Martin. *Biochemistry* **9**, 4486 (1970).
23. W. S. Chou, R. B. Rucker, J. E. Savage and B. L. O'Dell. *Proc. Soc. Exp. Biol. Med.* **134**, 1078 (1970).
24. A. D. Desmukh and M. E. Nimni. *Biochem. Biophys. Res. Commun.* **35**, 485 (1969).
25. K. Desmukh and M. E. Nimni. *Biochim. Biophys. Acta* **154**, 258 (1968).
26. K. Desmukh and M. E. Mimni. *Biochem. J.* **112**, 397 (1969).
27. K. Desmukh and M. E. Nimni. *Biochemistry* **10**, 1640 (1971).
28. M. A. Paz, O. O. Blumenfeld, M. Rojkind, E. Henson, C. Furfine and P. M. Gallop. *Arch. Biochem. Biophys.* **109**, 548 (1965).
29. A. D. Desmukh, K. Desmukh and M. E. Nimmi, *Biochemistry* **10**, 2337 (1971).
30. K. Desmukh and M. E. Nimni. *J. Biol. Chem.* **244**, 1781 (1969).

31. R. Feulgen and K. Voit. *Arch. Physiol.* **206,** 389 (1924).
32. P. Ganter and G. Jolles, Histochemie Normale et Pathologique, Gauthier-Villars, Paris, 1970.
33. K. Nakao and A. A. Angrist, *J. Clin. Path.* **49,** 65 (1968).
34. R. D. Lillie, P. Pizzolato and P. T. Donaldson. *Acta Histochem.* **44,** 215 (1972).
35. K. Soda, H. Misono and T. Yamamoto. *Biochemistry* **7,** 4102 (1968).
36. K. Soda and H. Misono. *Biochemistry* **7,** 4110 (1968).

19. α-AMINOALDEHYDES, PRECURSORS

Covalently-bound aldehydes are present in collagen.[1-10] They appear to be bound to tropocollagen through their amino groups as α-acylated amino aldehydes, e.g. as shown for glycinal in **I**.

$$\text{Protein-C}\overset{\overset{\displaystyle O}{\|}}{}\text{—NHCH}_2\text{CHO}$$

I

The covalent attachment of the aldehyde group is still undefined.

This group may function in covalent attachments of the carbohydrate of ground substance to the collagen fibre during the maturation process.[1] It appears certain that tropocollagens contain a variety of biosynthetic aldehyde intermediates, derived from some of their constituent amino acids in pathways leading to the maturation of connective tissue. Six α-amino-aldehydes, namely glycinal, α-alaninal, α-aspartal, lysinal, serinal and threoninal, have been shown to be present as components of various tropocollagens.[1] Some of these aldehyde precursors may be intermediates on the way to final cross-linking compounds. There are at least 12 bound aldehydes per tropocollagen molecule, one-fifth of which react readily and the remainder react slowly. These latter are mainly the α-amino aldehydes which require either strong acid dinitrophenylhydrazine treatment, de-esterification by hydrazine, or mild saponification to release them from their covalent attachment to the protein. Sodium tetrahydroborane also facilitates this release and immediately reduces the free aldehydes thus formed. The quantitation of total aldehydes as derivatives of DNPH is approximate since the reaction does not go to completion and several types of derivatives are formed. The analytical aspects of this work are more fully discussed in the glyoxals precursors section.

REFERENCES

1. P. M. Gallop, O. O. Blumenfeld, E. Henson and A. L. Schneider. *Biochemistry* **7**, 2409 (1968).

I*

2. O. O. Blumenfeld and P. M. Gallop. *Proc. Natl. Acad. Sci. U.S.* **56,** 1260 (1966).
3. P. Bornstein, A. H. Kang and K. A. Piez. *Proc. Natl. Acad. Sci. U.S.* **55,** 417 (1966).
4. P. Bornstein and K. A. Piez. *Biochem.* **5,** 3460 (1966).
5. P. M. Gallop. *Biophys. J.* **4,** Part 2, 79 (1964).
6. K. A. Piez, G. R. Martin, A. H. Kang and P. Bornstein. *Biochem.* **5,** 3813 (1966).
7. M. Rojkind, O. O. Blumenfeld and P. M. Gallop. *Biochem. Biophys. Res. Commun.* **17,** 320 (1964).
8. M. Rojkind, O. O. Blumenfeld and P. M. Gallop. *J. Biol. Chem.* **241,** 1530 (1966).
9. A. Schneider, E. Henson, O. O. Blumenfeld and P. M. Gallop. *Biochem. Biophys. Res. Commun.* **27,** 546 (1967).
10. M. L. Tanzer, D. Monroe and J. Gross. *Biochem.* **5,** 1919 (1966).

20. ω-AMINOALDEHYDES, PRECURSORS

The final stages in the formation of collagen have been thoroughly discussed.
[1,2] It is believed that procollagen molecules acquire aldehydic and carbohydrate groups during their parallel packing.[2] But even prior to and after
this stage, aldehydes play an important role in collagen cross-linkings and
reactions, as has been described in other sections of this and other volumes.
A variety of ω-aminoaldehydes, or most likely their easily hydrolysed per-
cursors, appear to be present in collagens.[3,4] Some of these appear to be
related to lysine.

Another important group of precursors of the ω-aminoaldehydes are the
polyamines, putrescine, **I**, spermidine, **II**, and spermine, **III**.

$$H_2N—CH_2—CH_2—CH_2—CH_2—NH_2$$
$$\mathbf{I}$$

$$H_2N—(CH_2)_4—NH—(CH_2)_3—NH_2$$
$$\mathbf{II}$$

$$H_2N—(CH_2)_3—NH—(CH_2)_4—NH—(CH_2)_3NH_2$$
$$\mathbf{III}$$

The biosynthesis and accumulation of these polyamines appear to be a
universal prerequisite for growth.[5,6] They play an important role in the
control of cellular growth, as well as in protein synthesis. They are found in
every nucleated cell and increased concentrations of polyamines have been
reported in rapidly growing tissues such as embryonic tissue,[7] regenerating
liver,[8] regenerating rat and mouse liver,[6] hormone-stimulated tissues[6]
and rapidly growing neoplastic tissue.[9] This is in line with the report that
tumor cells accumulate high polyamine concentrations, particularly spermidine, so that they exhibit a relatively high ratio of spermidine to spermine.[10]
Treatment of a rapidly growing rat hepatoma with 5-fluorouracil results in a
rapid elevation of serum spermidine which correlates with the rapid diminu-
tion of tumor spermidine.[11] Putrescine, spermidine, and sometimes spermine, are usually elevated in the urine of diagnosed cancer patients;[11-13]
cancer patients may also have elevated serum levels of spermidine and
putrescine.[14] Data indicates that the polyamines found in the urine of
cancer patients come from the tumor tissue. It is possible that biochemical

markers like the polyamines, carcinoembryonic antigen and the α-feto-proteins may prove to be of value in the earlier detection of cancers and in following cancer chemotherapy.

Various α,ω-diaminoalkanes can be oxidized by air in the presence of diamine oxidase [diamine: oxygen oxidoreductase (deaminating), 1.4.3.6] to ω-aminoaldehydes, Table 52.[15] The following reaction takes place ($n = 4$)

$$H_2N—(CH_2)_nNH_2 + H_2O + O_2 \xrightarrow{\text{diamine oxidase}} H_2N—(CH_2)_{n-1}CHO + NH_3 + H_2O_2$$

The reaction has been used to determine diamine oxidase activity.[16, 17] With putrescine (1,4-diaminobutane) as the substrate, γ-aminobutyralde-hyde is formed. The aldehyde is ring-closed to 1-pyrroline; with o-amino-benzaldehyde as the reagent the pyrroline gives a yellow chromogen absorbing at 430 nm. The diethylacetal of γ-aminobutyraldehyde is used as the standard. Thus, γ-aminobutyraldehyde and its precursors could be determined in this fashion. MBTH or one of the other appropriate aldehyde reagents could also be used here for the determination of these aldehydes and their precursors.

Table 52. Oxidation of amines to aldehydes with diamino oxidase[15]

Substrate[a]	pH	Relative velocity
1,4-Diaminobutane	7·0	1·0
1,5-Diaminopentane	7·0	1·0
Spermidine	7·0	0·35
Agmatine	7·0	0·35
2-Phenylethylamine	8·5	0·28
1,6-Diaminohexane	8·0	0·25
1,10-Diaminodecane	8·0	0·19
Tyramine	8·5	0·18

[a] Negative results with 1,2-diaminoethane, 1,3-diaminopropane, diethylamine and L-adrenaline.

The bacterium, *Serratia marcescens*, contains a spermidine oxidase which catalyses the atmospheric oxidation of spermidine in the following fashion.[18]

$$H_2N(CH_2)_3NH(CH_2)_4NH_2 + H_2O + O_2 \rightleftharpoons H_2N(CH_2)_3CHO + H_2N(CH_2)_3NH_2 + H_2O_2$$

The above reagents could be used in the analysis of this aldehyde. Spermi-dine can be determined in the presence of spermine with this enzyme system.[17, 19, 20]

Spermidine oxidase determination of spermidine. Add 0·1–0·3 ml of the aq test solution to 50 μmoles of sodium phosphate buffer, pH 6·5 (0·5 ml), plus 0·1 ml freeze-dried, spermidine-adapted *S. marcescens* cell suspension (5 mg of dry weight of cells freshly suspended in 1 ml of 0·85% sodium chloride). Add 0·85% sodium chloride to a final volume of 0·9 ml. Incubate the suspension at 37° for 30 min, and add 0·1 ml of 0·1% o-aminobenzaldehyde solution. Incubate at 37° for another 30 min and read the absorbance at 435 nm.

The Schiff base formed from lysine and pyridoxal can undergo a decarboxylation followed by hydrolysis to 5-aminopentanal, the open chain form of Δ^1-piperideine.[21] N-Methylputrescine oxidase catalyses the oxidative deamination of the primary amino group of N-methylputrescine to give 4-methylaminobutanal.[22]

The ubiquitous polyamines,[23, 24] spermidine, $H_2N(CH_2)_3NH(CH_2)_4NH_2$, and spermine $H_2N(CH_2)_3NH(CH_2)_4NH(CH_2)_3NH_2$, have been shown to stimulate growth in several animals, microorganisms and plants. A polyamine oxidase found in the serum of ruminants oxidizes the primary amino groups of spermidine and spermine to the corresponding aldehydes.[25]

The oxidation of polyamines in higher plants has been discussed.[26] In *Pseudomonas aeruginosa* spermine is oxidized to spermidine and 3-aminopropionaldehyde. Spermidine is further oxidized to 1,3-diaminopropane and 1-pyrroline.[27] In another *Pseudomonas* (unspecified) an enzyme has been found which oxidizes spermidine to putrescine (1,4-diaminobutane) and 3-aminopropionaldehyde.[28] In *Serratia marcescens* a spermidine-specific oxidase oxidizes this polyamine to 1,3-diaminopropane and 1-pyrroline.[18,29] In *Neisseria perflava* and *Hemophilus parainfluenzae* spermidine and spermine are enzymically oxidized to 1-pyrroline and 1(3-aminopropyl) pyrroline, respectively, plus 1,3-diaminopropane in both cases.[30]

A highly selective spot test for lysine has been described which involves the oxidation of lysine to 5-aminopentanal,[31] e.g.

$$H_2N(CH_2)_4\text{—}CH(NH_2)COOH \xrightarrow[\Delta]{NaOBr} CO_2 + NH_3 + NaBr + H_2N(CH_2)_4CHO$$

In the test, volatile 5-aminopentanal is detected by the formation of a red precipitate on the addition of a Ni-dimethylglyoxime complex and heating to ca. 120°. Neither arginine nor histidine interfere. The test is applicable to mixtures of amino acids, e.g. protein hydrolysates, after evaporation of the solution to dryness and heating the residue at 120° with ammonium carbonate. In this way other amino acids give negative results. This formation of volatile 5-aminopentanal could be used in the photometric analysis of lysine by some of the many methods described for aldehydes.

A carboxyl-substituted ω-aminoaldehyde, such as L-aspartate β-semialdehyde can be formed from L-2,4-diaminobutyrate with the help of the enzyme, diaminobutyrate-pyruvate aminotransferase (L-2,4-diaminobuty-rate: pyruvate aminotransferase, EC 2.6.1.46),[52] e.g.

$$H_3\overset{+}{N}—CH_2—CH_2CH(\overset{+}{N}H_3)COO^- + CH_3COCOO^-$$
$$OHC—CH_2CH(\overset{+}{N}H_3)COO^- + CH_3CH(\overset{+}{N}H_3)COO^-$$

REFERENCES

1. E. J. Miller and V. J. Matukas. *Fed. Proc.* **33,** 1197 (1974).
2. M. Weinstock and C. P. Leblond. *Fed. Proc.* **33,** 1205 (1974).
3. P. M. Gallop, O. O. Blumenfeld, E. Henson and A. L. Schneider. *Biochemistry* **7,** 2409 (1968).
4. O. O. Blumenfeld and P. M. Gallop. *Proc. Natl. Acad. Sci. V.S.* **56,** 1260 (1966).
5. S. S. Cohen. "Introduction to the Polyamines," Prentice-Hall, New Jersey, 1971, pp. 1–179.
6. D. H. Russell, Ed., "Polyamines in Normal and Neoplastic Growth," Raven Press, New York, 1973, pp. 1–429.
7. S. H. Snyder and D. H. Russell. *Fed. Proc.* **29,** 1575 (1970).
8. A. Raina and J. Janne. *Fed. Proc.* **29,** 1568 (1970).
9. H. G. Williams-Aehman, G. L. Cappoc and G. Weber. *Cancer Res.* **32,** 1924 (1972).
10. D. H. Russell and C. C. Levy. *Cancer Res.* **31,** 248 (1971).
11. D. H. Russell. *Life Sciences* **13,** 1635 (1973).
12. D. H. Russell. *Nature* **233,** 144 (1971).
13. D. H. Russell, C. C. Levy, S. C. Schimpff and I. A. Hawk. *Cancer Res.* **31,** 1555 (1971).
14. L. J. Marton, J. G. Vaughn, I. A. Hawk, C. C. Levy and D. H. Russell, in D. H. Russell, Ed. "Polyamines in Normal and Neoplastic Growth," Raven Press, New York, 1973, pp. 289–298.
15. J. M. Hill and P. J. G. Mann. *Biochem. J.* **91,** 171 (1964).
16. J. Kusche, H. Richter, R. Hesterberg, J. Schmidt and W. Lorenz. *Agents and Actions* **3,** 148 (1973).
17. B. Holmstedt, L. Larsson and R. Tham. *Biochem. Biophys. Acta* **48,** 182 (1961).
18. U. Bachrach. *J. Biol. Chem.* **237,** 3443 (1962).
19. U. Bachrach and B. Reches. *Anal. Biochem.* **17,** 38 (1966).
20. U. Bachrach and I. S. Oser. *J. Biol. Chem.* **238,** 2098 (1963).
21. E. Leete and M. R. Chedekel, *Phytochemistry* **11,** 2751 (1972).
22. S. Mizusaki, Y. Tanabe, M. Noguchi and E. Tamaki. *Phytochemistry* **11,** 2757 (1972).
23. T. A. Smith. *Biol. Rev.* **46,** 201 (1971).
24. H. Tabor and C. W. Tabor. *Pharmacol. Nev.* **16,** 245 (1964).
25. C. W. Tabor, H. Tabor and U. Bachrach. *J. Biol. Chem.* **239,** 2194 (1964).
26. T. A. Smith. *Xenobiotica* **1,** 449 (1971).
27. S. Razin, I. Gery and U. Bachrach. *Biochem. J.* **71,** 551 (1959).
28. R. Padmanabhan and K. Kim. *Biochem. Biophys. Res. Commun.* **19,** 1 (1965).
29. C. W. Tabor and P. D. Kellogg, *J. Biol. Chem.* **245,** 5424 (1970).
30. R. H. Weaver and E. J. Herbst. *J. Biol. Chem.* **231,** 647 (1958).
31. A. K. Saund and N. K. Mathur. *Microchem. J.* **18,** 300 (1973).
32. D. R. Rao, K. Hariharan and K. R. Vijayalakshmi. *Biochem. J.* **114,** 107 (1969).

21. (POLY)-AMINOALDEHYDES, PRECURSORS

Monoamine oxidase [Monoamine: oxygen oxidoreductase (deaminating), 1.4.3.4] exhibits low specificity.[1, 2] In its presence amines are oxidatively deaminated to aldehydes. Beef serum amine oxidase has been used in the determination of polyamines[3, 4] and in the estimation of amine oxidase activity in beef serum.[5] The aldehydes obtained from polyamines can be reacted with resorcinol to give fluorogens which can then be measured.[4]

The oxidative determination of spermine and spermidine with amine oxidase and MBTH is depicted in Fig. 68.[3] The millimolar absorptivities obtained at 660 nm for spermine and spermidine were 12·5 and 6·25, respectively. Theoretical results would be about ten times higher. So the methods could stand considerable improvement. The method is still more sensitive than the resorcinol[4] or the dinitrofluorobenzene[6] methods. Crude bovine serum can be used in place of purified amine oxidase in the MBTH procedure. Beer's law is obeyed from 0·008–0·06 μmoles of spermine and 0·016–0·06 μmol of spermidine. In some mixtures it may be necessary to separate interfering aldehydes from the polyamines by absorption on Dowex 50H$^+$.[7]

The MBTH enzymatic method has been applied to extracts from bacteria, yeast and mouse liver.[3]

MBTH determination of some polyamine aldehyde precursors.[3] To 0·01–0·06 ml of aq test solution add 0·1 ml of 0·2 M tris-HCl buffer (pH 7·4), 0·02 ml of serum amine oxidase (200 units/ml), and 0·85% sodium chloride to a final volume of 0·2 ml. Incubate this mixture at 37° for 4 h, then add 0·5 ml, 0·4% aq MBTH·HCl. After incubation at 25° for 30 min, add 2·5 ml of 0·2% ferric chloride solution. Incubate at 25° for another 15 min and then read the absorbance at 660 nm.

Spermine oxidase [Spermine: oxygen oxidoreductase (donor-cleaving), 1.5.3.3] obtained from *Neisseria perflava* is highly specific[8] and catalyses the following reaction

$$\text{Spermine} + H_2O + O_2 = H_2N(CH_2)_3NH(CH_2)_3CHO + H_2N(CH_2)_3NH_2 + H_2O_2$$

Negative results are given by aliphatic amines, ranging in size from methylamine to amylamine, benzylamine, diamines from ethylenediamine to hexamethylenediamine, N-(3-aminopropyl)-1,3-propanediamine, N-(3-

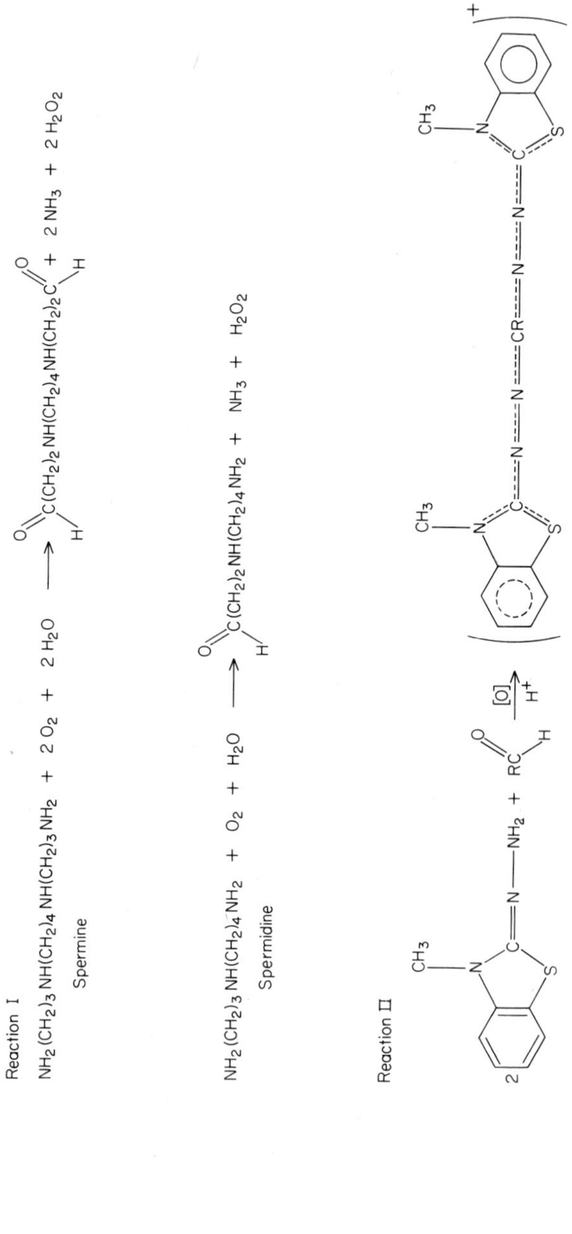

Reaction I

$$NH_2(CH_2)_3 NH(CH_2)_4 NH(CH_2)_3 NH_2 + 2 O_2 + 2 H_2O \longrightarrow \underset{H}{\overset{O}{\parallel}} C(CH_2)_2 NH(CH_2)_4 NH(CH_2)_2 \underset{H}{\overset{O}{C}} + 2 NH_3 + 2 H_2O_2$$

Spermine

$$NH_2(CH_2)_3 NH(CH_2)_4 NH_2 + O_2 + H_2O \longrightarrow \underset{H}{\overset{O}{\parallel}} C(CH_2)_2 NH(CH_2)_4 NH_2 + NH_3 + H_2O_2$$

Spermidine

Reaction II

Blue cation

Fig. 68. Determination of spermine and/or spermidine with MBTH.

aminopropyl)-1,5-pentanediamine, putrescine, N-butylputrescine, and several N-aminoalkylputrescines. Of the polyamines tested only spermine, spermidine and N-(4-aminobutyl)-1,4-butanediamine are oxidized. These compounds could thus be determined with one of the aldehyde reagents.

REFERENCES

1. C. M. McEwen. *J. Biol. Chem.* **240,** 2003, 2011 (1965).
2. H. Yamada and K. T. Yasunobu. *J. Biol. Chem.* **237,** 1511 (1962).
3. U. Bachrach and B. Reches. *Anal. Biochem.* **17,** 38 (1966).
4. T. Unemoto, K. Ikeda, M. Hayashi and K. Miyaki. *Chem. Pharm. Bull., Tokyo* **11,** 148 (1963).
5. T. Unemoto. *Chem. Pharm. Bull. Japan* **12,** 65 (1964).
6. D. T. Dubin. *J. Biol. Chem.* **235,** 783 (1960).
7. B. M. Guirard and E. E. Snell. *J. Bact.* **88,** 72 (1964).
8. R. H. Weaver and E. J. Herbst. *J. Biol. Chem.* **231,** 647 (1958).

22. *o*-AMINOBENZALDEHYDES, PRECURSORS

Quaternary salts of 2,1-benzisothiazoles are rapidly decomposed by aqueous acid or base yielding *o*-aminobenzaldehydes,[1,2] Fig. 69. The precursor benzisothiazolium salts are readily made by alkylation of 2,1-benzisothiazoles. Some of these 1-alkyl salts readily form the aldehyde when their aqueous solutions are warmed, e.g. the 1-methyl-5-nitro derivative. In most cases the aldehydes are best formed by the base-catalysed procedure.

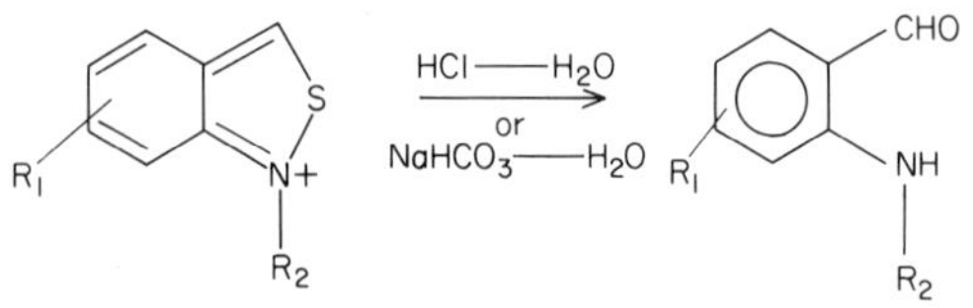

Fig. 69. Ring-opening of 1-alkyl-2,1-benzisothiazolium salts.

REFERENCES

1. O. Aki, Y. Nakagawa and K. Sirakawa. *Chem. Pharm. Bull. (Japan)* **20,** 2372 (1972).
2. M. Davis, E. Homfeld and K. S. L. Srivastava. *J. Chem. Soc.* 1863 (1973).

23. α-(2-AMINOBENZOYL) ACETALDEHYDE, PRECURSORS

This aldehyde is formed during the fluorimetric determination of mono-amine oxidase.[1] Kynuramine is oxidized to the aldehyde, which then ring-closes to the 4-hydroxyquinoline anion which is measured at $F315/380$. Fig. 70. This method is a modification of the method of Krajl[2] used for determination of monoamine oxidase in various tissues.

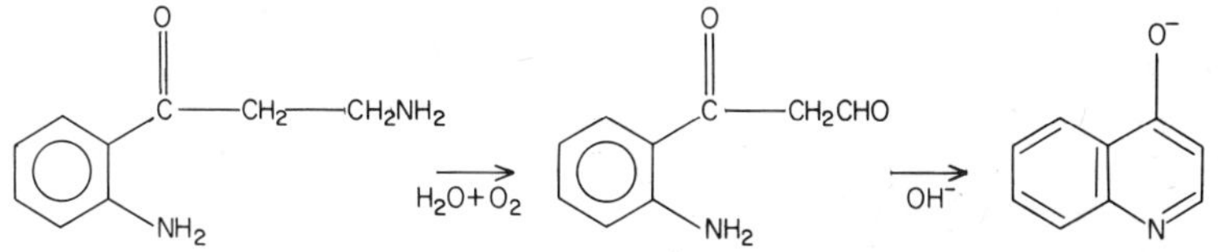

FIG. 70. Formation of the aldehyde and the derived 4-hydroxyquinoline from kynuramine.

REFERENCES

1. G. Tufvesson. *Scand. J. Clin. Lab. Invest.* **26,** 151 (1970).
2. M. Krajl. *Biochem. Pharmacol.* **14,** 1684 (1965).

24. 2-AMINO-3-CARBOXYMUCONATE SEMIALDEHYDE, PRECURSORS

Through the catalytic effect of 3-hydroxyanthranilate oxygenase (3-hydroxy-anthranilate : oxygen oxidoreductase, 1.13.1.6) 3-hydroxanthranilate can be oxidized by oxygen to 2-amino-3-carboxymuconate semialdehyde,[1, 2] e.g.

This aminoaldehyde and its precursor could be determined by one of the acrolein or α, β-unsaturated aldehyde methods or by one of the aliphatic aldehyde methods. On the other hand an aminoaldehyde of this type would be expected to absorb near 340–350 nm with a millimolar absorptivity of about 40–50. One could analyse the aldehyde directly at its long wavelength band.

REFERENCES

1. N. Ogasawara, J. E. Gander and L. M. Henderson. *J. Biol. Chem.* **241,** 613 (1966).
2. A. Vescia and G. di Prisco. *J. Biol. Chem.* **237,** 2318 (1962).

25. 2-AMINOGLUTARALDEHYDIC ACID, PRECURSORS

This aldehyde is formed by the periodate oxidation of δ-hydroxylysine (5-hydroxy-2,6-diaminohexanoic acid), as shown in the following equation.[1-3]

$$CH_2(NH_2)CH(OH)CH_2CH_2CH(NH_2)CO_2H \xrightarrow{\quad HIO_4 \quad}$$

$$CH_2O + NH_3 + HIO_3 + OCH-CH_2CH_2CH(NH_2)CO_2H$$

The MBTH test can be used to determine the two aldehydes. The larger of the aldehydes could be determined by one of the methods more selective for RCH_2CHO compounds, e.g. o-aminobenzaldehyde or 3,5-diaminobenzoic acid.

An alternative method of analysis for hydroxylysine also involves the oxidation of this amino acid by periodate to 2-aminoglutaraldehydic acid and the condensation product of the aldehyde, 1-pyrroline-5-carboxylic acid.[4] These products are further oxidized to a pyrrole which is then determined with 4-dimethylaminobenzaldehyde in isobutanol-perchloric acid. The chromogen is extracted into toluene-isobutanol-propanol, 5:5:2, and the absorbance is measured at 565 nm. Proline interferes and must be removed by silica gel TLC with propanol-water (7:3) as solvent. As little as 2 μg of hydroxylysine can be determined. Albumin, trypsin, hydroxyglutamic acid, serine, or threonine show no interference.

REFERENCES

1. D. D. Van Slyke, A. Hiller and D. A. MacFadyen. *J. Biol. Chem.* **141,** 681 (1941).
2. M. W. Rees. *Biochem. J.* **40,** 632 (1946).
3. P. Desnuelle and S. Antonin. *Biochim. Biophys. Acta* **1,** 50 (1947).
4. N. Blumenkrantz and D. J. Prockop. *Anal. Biochem.* **39,** 59 (1971).

26. 2-AMINO-δ-HYDROXYADIPIC-δ-SEMIALDEHYDE (HYDROXYLYSINE ALDEHYDE), PRECURSORS

The integrity and stability of the fibrillar macromolecular matrix of collagenous tissue depend on covalent crosslinks between collagen molecules.[1] Δ^6-Dehydro-5′-dihydroxylysinonorleucine, I, a Schiff base involving the aldehyde group of α-amino-δ-hydroxyadipic-δ-semialdehyde, II, and the ε-amino group of hydroxylysine, III.[2]

This crosslink is the most abundant $NaBH_4$-reducible compound[1] in mature bovine tendon,[2] embryonic skin[3, 4] foetal bovine tendon,[1] foetal bovine dentine, mature dentine and foetal bovine bone[5] and granulation tissue.[6, 7]

Collagen is synthesized more rapidly in inflamed tissue and accumulates in granuloma to a higher concentration than in normal tissue.[8−10] It possesses the stable **I** crosslink which is not present to any significant extent in normal subcutaneous skin collagen.[6] **I** probably exists as its keto-imino form 5-keto-5′-hydroxylysinonorleucine in bone[11] and in cartilage.[12] Once the inflamed tissue starts to heal, the collagen of the granuloma is progressively resorbed and the repaired tissue returns to the normal composition which is stabilized, at least in part, by the presence of two aldimine crosslinks, hydroxylysinonorleucine and histidinohydroxymerodesmosine[13] derived from lysine aldehyde residues in the non-helical region of the collagen molecule.[14] Although I in mature tendon and scar collagen is stable to heat and mild acid conditions, the two crosslinks of normal skin collagen are labile.[15]

Much more needs to be known about the formation of hydroxylysine aldehyde from hydroxylysine. The derivatives formed from this aldehyde could probably be analysed through the aldehyde by many of the methods described in these volumes.

REFERENCES

1. G. L. Mechanic. *Biochem. Biophys. Res. Commun.* **56,** 923 (1974).
2. G. L. Mechanic and M. L. Tanzer. *Biochem. Biophys. Res. Commun.* **41,** 1597 (1970).
3. S. P. Robins, M. Shimokamaki and A. J. Bailey. *Biochem. J.* **131,** 771 (1973).
4. A. J. Bailey and S. P. Robins. *FEBS Lett.* **21,** 330 (1972).
5. G. L. Mechanic, P. M. Gallop and M. L. Tanzer. *Biochem. Biophys. Res. Commun.* **45,** 644 (1971).
6. A. J. Bailey, S. Bazin and A. Delaunay. *Biochim. Biophys. Acta* **328,** 383 (1973).
7. J. Forrest, A. Shuttleworth, D. S. Jackson and G. L. Mechanic. *Biochem. Biophys. Res. Commun.* **46,** 1776 (1972).
8. S. Bazin and A. Delaunay. *Ann. Inst. Pasteur* **107,** 163 (1964).
9. J. W. Bothwell. *Nature* **201,** 825 (1964).
10. R. J. Adamson, F. Musco and I. F. Enquist. *Surgery Gynecol. Obstet.* **123,** 515 (1966).
11. D. R. Eyre and M. J. Glimcher. *Biochem. Biophys. Res. Commun.* **52,** 663 (1973).
12. E. J. Miller and P. B. Robertson. *Biochem. Biophys. Res. Commun.* **54,** 432 (1973).
13. A. J. Bailey, C. M. Peach and L. J. Fowler. *Biochem. J.* **117,** 819 (1970).
14. W. Traub and K. A. Piez. *Adv. Prot. Chem.* **25,** 243 (1971).
15. D. S. Jackson, S. Ayad and G. L. Mechanic. *Biochim. Biophys. Acta* **336,** 100 (1974).

27. 5-AMINO-6-HYDROXYHEXANAL, PRECURSORS

$$HOCH_2CHCH_2CH_2CH_2CHO$$
$$|$$
$$NH_2$$

This aldehyde is formed from the oxidation of 2-hydroxymethylpiperidine, **I**, with chloramine T.[1]

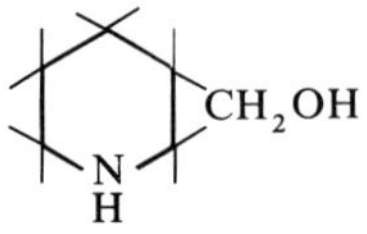

I

REFERENCE

1. P. M. Gallop, O. O. Blumenfeld, E. Henson and A. L. Schneider. *Biochemistry* **7,** 2409 (1968).

28. o-AMINOPHENYLACETALDEHYDE, PRECURSORS

o-Aminophenethylamine is a precursor of this aldehyde. It has been used as a substrate for the assay of monoamine oxidase (monoamine: oxygen oxidoreductase, EC 1.4.3.4).[1] The enzyme oxidatively deaminates the substrate to the aldehyde which in turn undergoes internal cyclization to form indole. The latter is measured using a p-dimethylaminocinnamaldehyde procedure.[2] p-Dimethylaminobenzaldehyde[3-5] or MBTH[6, 7] can also be used for the determination of the indole. o-Aminophenethylamine forms the basis of a sensitive (down to about 1 μg per sample) assay for the effect of monoamine oxidase-inhibitors, such as anti-depressant drugs, on the enzyme.

REFERENCES

1. E. A. Zeller, B. H. Babu, N. J. Cavanaugh and G. J. Stanich. *Pharmacol. Res. Commun.* **1**, 20 (1969).
2. J. M. Turner. *Biochem. J.* **78**, 790 (1961).
3. P. Byrom and J. H. Turnbull. *Talanta* **10**, 1217 (1963).
4. M. A. Muhs and F. T. Weiss. *Anal. Chem.* **30**, 259 (158).
5. C. R. Pasqualucci, P. Radaelli and A. Vigevani. *Farmaco, Ed. Prat.* **24**, 571 (1969).
6. E. Sawicki, T. W. Stanley, T. R. Hauser, W. C. Elbert and J. L. Noe. *Anal. Chem.* **33**, 722 (1961).
7. E. Sawicki, T. R. Hauser, T. W. Stanley, W. C. Elbert and F. T. Fox. *Anal. Chem.* **33**, 1574 (1961).

29. β-AMINOPROPIONALDEHYDE, PRECURSORS

Polyamines, some of which are precursors of β-aminopropionaldehyde, are important to the growth of microorganisms, plants and animal cells undergoing regeneration.[1] See also β-aminoaldehydes section. One mechanism which explains the involvement of the polyamines in growth regulation is the inhibitory action of their metabolic breakdown products—the aldehydes. This mechanism has been studied by assaying the aldehydes released by treating human serum with arsenious oxide. Bound serum aldehydes were found to be released with this type of treatment.[2] With the help of thin layer chromatography of the 2,4-dinitrophenylhydrazones it was found that, of the 2 components which increased on arsenious oxide treatment, β-aminopropionaldehyde increased about 200% and the other component about 74%.[3]

One pathway through which β-aminopropionaldehyde can arise is through 1,3-diaminopropane. It has been shown that this diamine can arise from spermidine in spermidine-adapted *Serratia marcescens*[4] as follows

$$NH_2(CH_2)_3NH(CH_2)_4NH_2 \longrightarrow NH_2(CH_2)_3NH_2 \ + \ $$

Hog kidney diamine oxidase[5] converts 1,3-diaminopropane to the aldehyde[3] as follows

$$NH_2(CH_2)_3NH_2 \rightarrow NH_2(CH_2)_2CHO$$

This aldehyde can arise in hog kidney, as in *Pseudomonas* sp.[6] from the enzymatic breakdown of spermidine as follows

$$NH_2(CH_2)_4NH(CH_2)_3NH_2 \rightarrow NH_2(CH_2)_4NH_2(I) + NH_2(CH_2)_2CHO$$

In line with this reaction it has been shown that labelled putrescine (I) is formed from spermidine labelled with ^{14}C in the $(CH_2)_4$ portion of the molecule.[7]

As β-aminopropionaldehyde comprises more than 70% of the aldehydes released by arsenious oxide treatment, it could also account for the majority of the aldehyde measured by the following procedure.

MBTH estimation of liberated serum aldehydes.[1] To 10 mg of As_2O_3 add 0·2 ml serum and 0·9 ml of 50% methanol. The control consists of 0·2 ml serum and 0·9 ml of 50% methanol. Mix on a Vortex mixer, heat at 70° for 30 min and then cool to room temp. To each tube add 0·5 ml of 0·4% MBTH·HCl. Incubate at room temp for 30 min and then add 2·5 ml of 0·2% $FeCl_3$ to each tube, followed by a further incubation at room temp for 15 minutes. Centrifuge the tubes at 3000 rev min^{-1} for 15 min in a refrigerated centrifuge. Read the absorbance of the supernatant at 660 nm.

Maximum release of aldehydes occurs on heating the serum at 70° for 30 min in the presence of 10 ml of As_2O_3.

REFERENCES

1. G. Quash and K. Maharaj. *Clin. Chim. Acta* **29,** 13 (1970).
2. L. Egyud, J. McLaughlin and A. Szent-Gyorgi. *Proc. Natl. Acad. Sci. V.S.* **57,** 1422 (1967).
3. G. Quash and D. R. Taylor. *Clin. Chem. Acta* **30,** 17 (1970).
4. U. Bachrach. *J. Biol. Chem.* **194,** 377 (1962a).
5. H. Tabor. *J. Biol. Chem.* **188,** 125 (1951).
6. R. Padmanabhan and K. Kim. *Biochem. Biophys. Res. Commun.* **19,** 1 (1965).
7. M. Siimes. *Acta Physiol. Scand., Suppl.* **298,** 44 (1967).

30. 2,5-ANHYDROHEXOSES, PRECURSORS

$$\text{HOH}_2\text{C} \quad \text{O} \quad \text{CHO}$$
$$\text{HO}$$
$$\text{OH}$$

Hexosamines can be deaminated by nitrous acid to 2,5-anhydrohexoses which when heated in the presence of strong acid can dehydrate to 5-hydroxy-methylfurfural or δ-hydroxylevulinaldehyde which can then be determined with indole,[1] pyrrole,[2] phenol,[3] orcinol[4] and anthrone.[5] Since these reaction conditions are drastic, the reaction suffers interference from neutral sugars and amino sugars.[2, 4, 6]

In the use of indole to determine hexosamines, glucosamine and galactosamine gave mε of 15·5 and 13·3, respectively, by the following procedure.

Indole determination of hexosamines.[1] To 0·5 ml of aq test solution add 0·5 ml of 5% sodium nitrite and 0·5 ml of 33% aq acetic acid. Mix, let stand for 10 min, add 0·5 ml of 12.5% aq ammonium sulphamate and then mix occasionally during the next 30 minutes. Add 2 ml of 1·5 N HCl followed by 0·2 ml of 1% ethanolic indole. Heat for 5 min at 100°, cool and add 2 ml of ethanol. Cool at 0° for 5 min and read the absorbance at 492 and 520 nm. The concentration is furnished by the difference between the two absorbances.

In a somewhat similar reaction glucosamine, galactosamine, 2-amino-2-deoxyglucuronic acid and 2-amino-2-deoxygalacturonic acid can be detected and differentiated by deamination, paper electrophoresis, and spraying with an indole solution.[7]

Recently a method was developed whereby the 2,5-anhydrohexose reacts directly with MBTH at room temp in a mildly acidic solution to give a formazan, Fig. 71.[8, 9]

Neutral sugars, N-acylglucosamines, ascorbic acid and glucuronic acid yield no colour. Most amino acids give, at most, a faint colour in the reaction. Tryptophan, threonine and methionine react somewhat but the colour intensities are far lower than those of hexosamines. Tryptophan gives 15·9% of the chromogenicity obtained with glucosamine. After hydrolysis

274

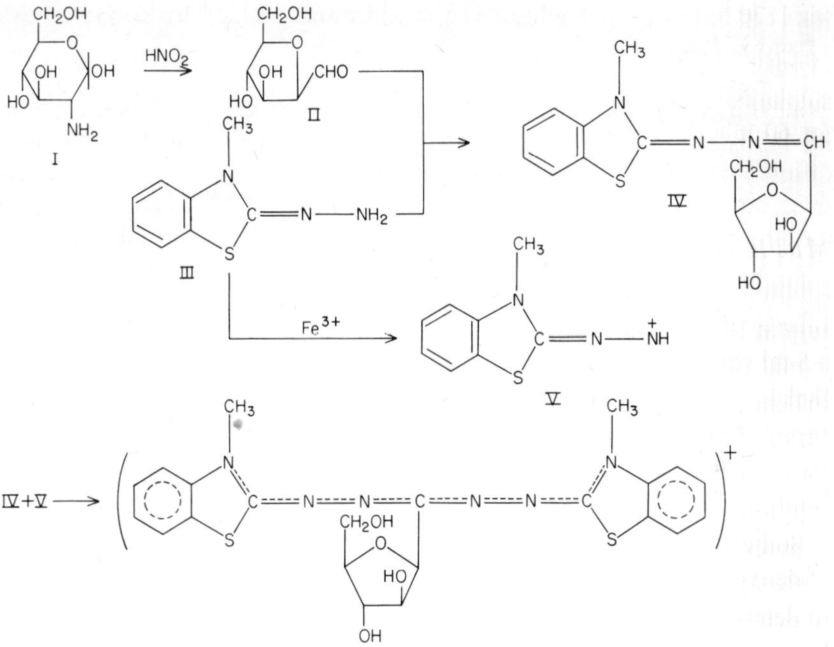

FIG. 71. Determination of hexosamines with MBTH.

with 2 N HCl for 2 h at 100° N-acetylglucosamine, chondroitin sulphate A, chondroitin sulphate C and hyaluronic acid can be assayed.[9] Free hexosamine can be determined in the presence of N-acylglucosamines. In addition, with the present method hydrolysis in 2 N HCl at 100° for only 2 h is required for the mucopolysaccharide, whereas the Elson–Morgan method[10] or the Dische–Borenfreund method[1] requires hydrolysis for 16 h under the same conditions.

The various 2,5-anhydrohexose precursors give one band in the visible with MBTH at 652 ± 5 nm, as shown in Table 53. These results are obtained

Table 53. Spectral data from the determination of 2,5-anhydrohexose precursors with MBTH[9]

Compound	λ_{max}	mε
D-Glucosamine	653	38·6
D-Galactosamine	653	36·2
D-Mannosamine	657	8·0
Methyl α-D-glucosaminide	651	38·9

with the following procedure. The chondroitin sulphate hydrolysates give a band at 648 ± 1 nm.

MBTH determination of hexosamines.[8] To 1 ml of aq test solution containing 1–30 µg of hexosamine add 1 ml of 5% $KHSO_4$ and 1 ml of 5% $NaNO_2$. Occasionally shake during 15 minutes. Add 1 ml of 12·5% aq ammonium sulphamate. Shake for 5 minutes. Add 1 ml of 0·5% MBTH·HCl. Let stand for 60 minutes. Add 1 ml of 0·5% $FeCl_3$. After a further 30 min, read the absorbance at 650 nm.

MBTH determination of hexosamines in mucopolysaccharides.[8, 9] Heat a solution of a mucopolysaccharide (about 0·3 mg/ml) in 2N HCl in a sealed tube at 100° for 2 h and then cool under tap water. Pipette a 1 ml aliquot into a 5-ml volumetric flask. Add 1 drop of 0·5% alcoholic solution of phenolphthalein and then 1N NaOH carefully until the solution turns pink. Back-titrate dropwise with 1% $KHSO_4$ until the colour just disappears. Dilute the resultant colourless mixture to 5 ml with water. With a 1 ml aliquot of this solution use the above procedure to estimate the hexosamine content.

Some methods have been described for the determination of 2-sulphoamino-2-deoxy-D-glucose and 2-acetamido-2-deoxy-D-glucose.[11] MBTH is used to determine the sulphoamino derivative in heparin and to determine total hexosamines in an acid hydrolysate of heparin, the content of 2-acetamido-2-deoxy-D-glucose being found by difference. Undesirable side-reactions are minimized, as MBTH reacts under mild conditions with the 2,5-anhydroglucose produced by deamination of the hexosamine. The method is also useful in determining the degree of deacetylation of chitosan.

REFERENCES

1. Z. Dische and E. Borenfreund. *J. Biol. Chem.* **184,** 517 (1950).
2. D. Exley, *Biochem. J.* **67,** 52 (1957).
3. Y. C. Lee and R. Montgomery. *Arch. Biochem. Biophys.* **93,** 292 (1961).
4. M. V. Tracey. *Biochem. J.* **52,** 265 (1952).
5. S. T. Horowitz, S. Roseman and H. J. Blumenthal. *J. Am. Chem. Soc.* **79,** 5046 (1957).
6. J. F. McCrea. *Biochem. J.* **48,** XLIX (1951).
7. A. R. Williamson and S. Zamenhof. *Anal. Biochem.* **5,** 47 (1963).
8. A. Tsuji, T. Kinoshita and M. Hoshino. *Chem. Pharm. Bull.* **17,** 217 (1969).
9. A. Tsuji, T. Kinoshita and M. Hoshino. *Chem. Pharm. Bull.* **17,** 1505 (1969).
10. L. A. Elson and W. T. J. Morgan. *Biochem. J.,* **26,** 1824 (1933).
11. A. Tsuji, T. Kinoshita, M. Hoshino and M. Takeda. *Chem. Pharm. Bull.* **18,** 2544 (1970).

31. p-ANISALDEHYDE, PRECURSORS

This compound can be derived from thonzylamine through oxidation, Fig. 72.[1] With the following procedure 0·1–10 µg of thonzylamine hydrochloride per ml can be determined. The ultraviolet absorption spectra of the oxidation product is closely similar to p-anisaldehyde, both in n-butanol.

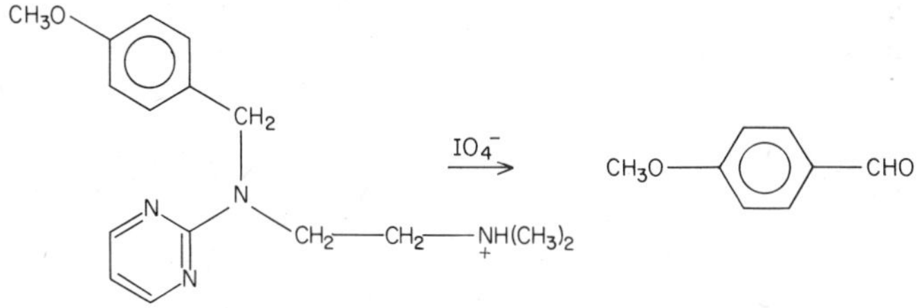

FIG. 72. Periodate oxidation of thonzylamine to p-anisaldehyde.

The absorption spectra of the chromogen, I, formed from p-anisaldehyde and from thonzylamine in alcohol and in solutions of varying pH are shown in Fig. 73.

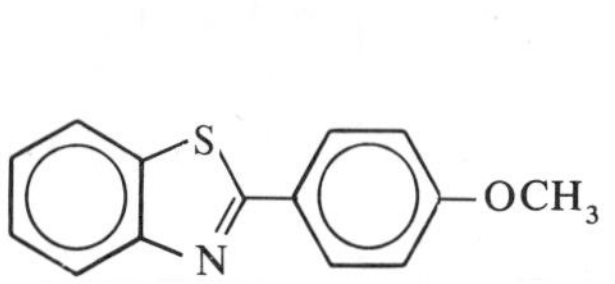

I

o-*Aminothiophenol determination of thonzylamine.*[1] To 5 ml of test solution containing 0·5–50 µg of thonzylamine, add 5 ml of 10% sodium carbonate and 0·5 ml of 0·1% sodium periodate. Heat for 15 min at 100°, cool, then extract with 10 ml of ether. Wash the ether layer twice with 5 ml of water. Add 1 ml of 0·5% o-aminothiophenol HCl, evaporate the ether, and add 5ml of 30% (w/v) H_2SO_4 to the residue. Heat the mixture for 1 h at 100°, cool, and dilute with 20 ml of water. Measure the fluorescence intensity at $F357/412$.

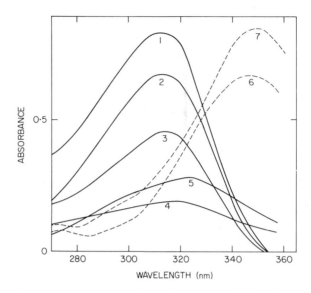

FIG. 73. Absorption spectra of chromogen formed in analysis and 2-(4-methoxyphenyl)-benzothiazole (I).[1] ———1: chromogen derived from *p*-anisaldehyde in ethanol, ——— 2: chromogen derived from thonzylamine HCl in ethanol, ——— 3: 2.5×10^{-5} M I in ethanol, ——— 4: 2.5×10^{-5} M I (pH 9), ——— 5: 2.5×10^{-5} M I (pH 1.8), ––––– 6: 2.5×10^{-5} M I (pH 0.8), ––––– 7: 2.5×10^{-5} M I (pH 0.3).

p-Anisaldehyde precursors could also be determined by procedures presented in the aromatic aldehydes and oxybenzaldehyde sections.

The spectra obtained at pH 0.8 and 0.3 are derived from the cationic salt, **II**, which would be expected to absorb at longer wavelength and with greater intensity than **I**.

$$\left[\underset{\underset{\text{H}}{\text{N}}}{\overset{\text{S}}{\bigcirc}} \text{=} \bigcirc \text{=} OCH_3 \right]^{+}$$

II

REFERENCE

1. S. Nakano, H. Taniguchi and T. Furuhashi. *Yakugaku Zasshi* **92**, 411 (1972).

AUTHOR INDEX

Numbers in italics refer to the pages where references are listed; numbers in parentheses are reference numbers and are included to assist location in the text.

279

K

Bacon, R. G. R.   71(44), 83(44), *113*, 126(67), *138*
Badin, E. J.   122(14), *137*
Baer, E.   88(224), 98(242), *117*, *118*, 136(134). *140*, 208(16), *240*
Baghos, V. B.   71(68), 85(68), *113*
Bailey, A. J.   251(14, 21), *254*, 267(3, 4, 6), 268(13), *268*
Bailey, P. S.   103(254), *118*, 134(109), *139*
Bailey, R. W.   72(121), 95(121), *115*
Baillod, C. R.   141(21), 152(21), *174*
Bakos, G.   182(43), *192*
Baltes, M.   126(68), *138*
Bandi, Z. I.   71(36), *112*
Banks, Jr., W. L.   141(55), 151(55), *175*
Barakat, M. E.   213(71), *242*
Baraud, M. J.   71(73), 85(73), *113*
Barham, D.   143(104), 159(104), 160(104), *176*
Barker, R.   207(4), *240*
Barker, S. A.   72(122), 95(122), *115*
Barker, S. B.   1(106), 3(106), 10(106), 13(106), 18(106), *28*
Barnes, D.   218(117), *243*
Barnes, I. C.   209(41), *241*
Barthelmai, W.   141(70), 164(70), *175*
Bartlett, P. B.   129(88), *139*
Bartlett, P. D.   72(95), 90(95), *114*
Barton, D. H. R.   125(46), *138*
Barton, E. C.   182(15), 187(15), *191*
Bartos, J.   1(63), 3(63), 10(63), *27*, 71(9, 11), 72(88), 73(11), 77(9, 11), 78(9, 11), 87(88), *112*, *114*, 170(165), *177*, 237(192), *244*
Basilio, M.   71(39), *113*
Bassette, R.   129(96), *139*
Batt, D. B.   145(106), *176*
Baum, E. J.   1(2), 2(2), *25*
Baumann, K.   141(76), 164(76), 165(76), *175*
Baumann, M. L.   1(94), 3(94), 13(94), *27*
Baumann, W. J.   71(28), 72(135), 96(135), *114*, *115*
Baumel, I. M.   1(120), 4(120), 5(120), *28*
Baumgardt, F.   73(176), 100(176), *116*
Baumgarten, R. J.   71(45), *113*, 126(75), *138*
Bazin, S.   267(6, 8), *268*
Beach, E. F.   141(8), 151(8), 152(8), *174*
Behnke, V.   168(142), *177*
Beljean, M.   159(135), *177*
Bell, D. J.   213(95), 223(95), *242*
Bellar, T. A.   54(6), 55(6), *52*, 72(158), 97(158), *116*, 134(127), *140*
Belmaker, R.   128(86), *139*
Belt, W. D.   73(209), 108(209), *117*
Belzecki, Cz.   134(110), *139*
Bemiller, J. N.   72(139), 95(139), *115*
Bemm, H.   181(24), 182(24), *192*
Benckhuysen, L.   55(9), 56(9), 57(9), *62*

Bender, D. F.   163(138), *177*
Bendich, A.   47(81), *53*
Benedict, S. R.   209(22, 23, 28, 30, 32), 212(23), 226(153, 154), *240*, *241*, *243*
Bennett, D. A. M.   168(155), *177*
Bentley, R.   141(18), 143(99), *174*, *176*
Bergelson, L. D.   110(263), *118*
Berger, M. G.   73(187), 103(187), *116*, 134(112, 116), *139*
Bergmeyer, H. U.   1(51), 3(51), 10(51), 13(51), *26*, 141(7, 69, 89), 143(7), 152(7), 156(69), 164(69), 165(69), 168(156, 158, 160), *174*, *175*, *177*, 186(61), *192*
Bergsavel, D. E.   203(8), *204*
Bergstrom, J.   183(58), *192*
Berkowitz, L. M.   67(1), *67*
Bernard, B. de.   1(124), 4(124), 23(124), *28*
Bernard, C.   168(149), *177*
Berndt, W.   143(113), *176*
Bernt, E.   141(7), 143(7), 152(7), *174*, 213(79), 221(79), *242*
Beroza, M.   1(24, 26), 2(24,26), 14(24), *26*, 72(102), 73(188), 75(102), 76, 102(102), (188), 103(188), 110(267), *114*, *116*, *118*
Berrens, L.   208(11), 228(159, 160, 161), *240* *244*
Berry, J. F.   92(229), *117*
Bertelson, S.   250(7), *252*
Berther, C.   71(46), 83(46), 84(46), *113*
Bertram, C.   203(3), *204*
Bertrand, P.   213(107), *242*
Bestvater, G.   182(37, 42), 183(37), *192*
Beynon, P. J.   72(141), 95(141), *115*
Beyrich, T.   104(255), *118*
Beyrich, V. T.   1(126), 4(126), 23(126), *28*
Bharucha, K. E.   68(3), *69*
Bhate, D. S.   143(99), *176*
Bhattacharya, A. K.   1(40), 2(40), 3(40), 4(40), 10(40), 17(40), *26*
Bickel, M.   212(51), *241*
Bierens de Haan, J.   172(178), *178*, 182(25), 185(25), *192*
Bierl, B. A.   1(24), 2(24), 14(24), *26*, 72(102), 73(188), 75(102), 76(102), 102(188), 103(188), 110(267), *114*, *116*, *118*
Biltcliffe, D. O.   228(162, 163, 164), *244*
Biltner, D.   150(123), *176*
Bilton, R.   55(10), 57(10), *62*
Birkofer, L.   30(1), 31(1, 11, 37), *51*, *52*
Bittner, D. L.   156(132), *176*
Blakely, R. L.   31(36), 38(36), 39(36, 39), 40(36), *52*, *53*
Blank, M. L.   71(34), 73(191), 81(34), 104(191), *112*, *116*
Blanquet, P.   31(31), *52*
Blaschko, H.   71(51), *113*, 128(80, 81, 82), *139*

K*

Viel, C.   30(2, 53), 31(2, 8, 9), 33(2), 34(2), 35(8), *51, 52*
Vigevani, A.   270(5), *270*
Vijayalakshmi, K. R.   260(32), *260*
Virtanen, A. I.   1(9), 2(9), *26*, 71(70, 76, 79), 85(70, 76, 79), *113, 114*
Visser, J.   230(173), 231(173), *244*
Viswanathan, C. V.   71(32, 39, 40), 82(32), *112, 113*
Vit, J.   134(106), *139*
Voit, K.   251(32), *254*
Volger, H. C.   96(214), *117*
Von Kreybig, T.   203(2), *204*
Von Rudloff, E.   110(266), *118*
Voronkova, V. V.   110(263), *118*

Wade, C. W. R.   208(7), *240*
Wager, H. G.   211(47), *241*
Wagner, E.   71(78), 85(78), *114*
Wagner, W.   195(10, 12), 196(10, 12), 199(10), *200*
Waibel, P. E.   71(63), 86(63), *113*
Walborsky, H. W.   72(109), 91(109), *114*
Walden, C. C.   168(159), *177*
Wallace, D. M.   64(1), *66*
Wallenfels, A.   213(79), 221(79), *242*
Wallenfels, K.   213(85), *242*
Wallen-Lawrence,   1(85), 3(85), *27*
Wallis, A. F. A.   72(107), 90(107), *114*
Walsh, M. J.   1(156), 4(146), 8(156), *29*
Wander, J. D.   207(6), *240*
Wardi, A. M.   1(71), 3(71), 7(71), *27*
Ware, A. G.   141(67), *175*
Wark, S.   1(94), 3(94), 13(94), *27*
Warner, H. R.   31(33), 32(33), *52*, 71(25, 26), 80(25), 81(26), 82(26), *112*
Warner, K.   72(111), 94(111), *114*
Warner-Lambert, C. O.   141(83), 164(83), *175*
Wartburg, A. F.   134(124), *140*
Wartburg, Jr., A. F.   54(28), *62*
Washko, M. E.   141(27, 28), 143(27, 28), *174*
Wass, G.   222(144), *243*
Wassmundt, F. W.   73(212), 106(212), *117*
Watanabe, F.   172(172), 173(172), *177*
Watanabe, M.   213(102), 223(102, 147), 226 (102, 147), 227(102), *242, 243*
Watanabe, S.   213(65), 214(65), 215(65), *241*
Waters, W. A.   72(137), *115*
Watson, D.   182(47), 190(47), *192*
Wearer, W. M.   125(52), *138*
Weaver, R. M.   259(30), *260*, 262(8), *262*
Webb, E. C.   145(107), *176*
Webb, J. M.   31(40), 33(40), 43(40), 44(40), 47(40), *52*
Webb, M.   1(16), 2(16), *26*

Weber, G.   257(9), *260*
Webster, W. W.   172(184), *178*, 182(8), *191*
Weed, J. C.   213(66), 215(66), *241*
Weglein, R. C.   126(69), *138*
Weicker, H.   221(136), *243*
Weigert, E.   195(17), *200*
Weihrauch, J. L.   72(98), 74(203), 75(98, 203), 76(98, 203), 83(218), 95(98), 110(203), *114*, 117, 129(99), 131(99), 132(99), 136(139), 137 (99), *139, 140*
Weiland, J. F. S.   96(215), *117*
Weinhouse, S.   1(100), 3(100), 13(100), *28*
Weinstock, M.   257(2), *260*
Weis, C.   88(225), 106(225), *117*
Weiss, F. T.   270(4), *270*
Weiss, L.   149(121), 153(121), *176*
Welti, D.   54(20), 55(20), 60(20), *62*
Wendel, W. B.   1(86, 127), 4(86, 127), 7(127), *27, 28*
Wenk, R. E.   182(26), 187(26), *192*
Wenzel, E. J.   141(26), 143(26), *174*
Werle, E.   71(48), 83(48), *113*
Werner, W.   143(105), 148(119), 149(119, 120), 153(105, 119, 120), *176*
Wersuhn, H.   168(142), *177*
Wertheim, E.   122(8), *137*
Wesson, T. C.   134(125), *140*
West, B. L.   123(34), *138*
West, C.   245(5), *246*
West, C. A.   245(4), *246*
Westerfeld, W. W.   1(115), 3(115), 22(115), 23(115), *28*
Westgard, J. O.   155(131), 156(131), *176*
Westphal, O.   31(7), 43(7), *51*
Westra, J. G.   55(9), 56(9), 57(9), *62*
Weygand, C.   122(16), *137*
Wheeler, D. H.   72(115), 94(115), *114*
Wheeler, J.   218(118), *243*
Whelan, W. J.   141(40), 143(40), 147(40), 168 (156), *174, 177*
Whistler, R. L.   72(139), 95(139), *115*, 141(15), 152(15), *174*
White, A.   245(1), *246*
White, J. M.   71(32), 82(32), *112*
Whited, E. A.   1(67), 3(67), 18(67), 19(67), *27*
Whittaker, D.   54(20), 55(20), 60(20), *62*
Wibault, J. P.   73(193), 104(193), *117*
Wiberg, K. B.   120(4), *137*
Wickers, P. L. M.   182(10), 187(10), 188(10), 189(10), *191*
Wickroshi, A. F.   168(161), *177*
Wickstrom A.   1(46, 47), 2(46, 47), 10(47), *26*
Widish, J. R.   156(133), *176*, 182(28), 187(28), *192*
Widstrom, G.   35(64), *53*
Wieland, O.   149(121), 153(121), *176*

SUBJECT INDEX

Since practically every chapter contains data on the absorption spectra of the aldehyde concerned, these spectra are not referenced in the subject index. The Table of Contents and the Subject Index complement each other.

AAD, detn of ethanol, 3
Acetaldehyde, DNPH, abs. spectrum, 97, 132
    acetaldehyde precursor, 129
    detn with MBTH, 79
    formation from, acetaldehyde DNPH, 129
    acetoin, 76
    alanine, 86
    crotonaldehyde, 75
    trans-2,3-epoxydecane, 75
    ethanol, 121, 122
    ethylamine, 127
    ethylene glycol, 96
    cis-5-heptenal, 75
    lactic acid, 76, 136
    2-methylthiazolidine, 109
    trans-7-nonenal, 75
    2-phosphonoacetaldehyde, 73, 104
    1,2-propanediol, 76, 132
    N,N,N',N'-tetramethyl-4,4'-diaminoazobenzene, 84
    1,2,2-trimethylpropanol, 79
    unsaturated acids, 110
    industrial usage, 70
    3-methyl-2-benzothiazolinone azine, detn of H_2O_2, 155
    physiological properties, 70
    precursors, 1–29
    structures, 6
    reagent in detn of DNA, 36, 37, 41
    semicarbazone, abs. spectrum, 11
Acetals, 2, 6
    detn with, MBTH, 10, 12, 13
    4-phenylphenol, 14
    formation, plasmalogens, 82
Acetaldiacetates, formation from 2-alkyl-1,3-dithianes, 130
2-Acetamido-2-deoxy-D-glucose, detn with MBTH, 275
Acetate buffer, 164, 169, 190, 196, 200

Acetic acid, 24, 36, 38, 39, 41, 49, 59, 68, 72, 77, 82, 88, 94, 103, 108, 122, 134, 146, 155, 180–189, 200, 223, 236, 273
    drawbacks in *o*-toluidine method, 181
Acetic anhydride, 84, 125, 136
Acetoacetaldehyde acetal, detn of, aldose precursors, 231
    ammonia, 231
    cyanohydrins, 231
    dimethyl, detn of glucose, 168
Acetoin, acetaldehyde precursor, 2, 76
Acetone, 120, 197, 235, 247
    DNPH, abs. spectrum, 132
    extractant, 3, 36
    fluor. enhancement, 61
    formation from, 2-hydroxy-2-methyl-3-butanone, 132
    2-methyl-2-heptene, 103
    pinacol, 132
    interference in ethanol detn, 9
    interference removal, 77, 103, 129
    reductant, 226
Acetophenone, 163
    formation from, 1-methylbenzylamine, 121
    1-phenylethanol, 121
3-Acetoxy-4,4-diethoxybutanal, 130
7-Acetoxyheptanal, formation from, *cis*-7,8-epoxydecyl acetate, 75
    cis-7,8-epoxyhexadecyl acetate, 75
9-Acetoxynonanal, formation from *cis*-9,10-epoxytetradecyl acetate, 75
β-Acetylacrolein, *p*-nitrophenylhydrazone, absorption spectrum in butanol, 48
    formation from, 2-deoxyribose, 44
    2,5-dimethoxy-2-methyl-2,5-dihydrofuran, 44
    DNA, 43, 44
    furfuryl alcohol, 44
    precursors, 30–53

L